PIECEWISE LINEAR TOPOLOGY

MATHEMATICS LECTURE NOTE SERIES

E. Artin and J. Tate	CLASS FIELD THEORY
Michael Atiyah	K-THEORY
Hyman Bass	ALGEBRAIC K-THEORY
Melvyn S. Berger Marion S. Berger	PERSPECTIVES IN NONLINEARITY
Paul J. Cohen	SET THEORY AND THE CONTINUUM HYPOTHESIS
Walter Feit	CHARACTERS OF FINITE GROUPS
William Fulton	ALGEBRAIC CURVES
Marvin J. Greenberg	LECTURES ON ALGEBRAIC TOPOLOGY
Marvin J. Greenberg	LECTURES ON FORMS IN MANY VARIABLES
Robin Hartshorne	FOUNDATIONS OF PROJECTIVE GEOMETRY
J. F. P. Hudson	PIECEWISE LINEAR TOPOLOGY
Irving Kaplansky	RINGS OF OPERATORS
K. Kapp and H. Schneider	COMPLETELY O-SIMPLE SEMIGROUPS
Serge Lang	ALGEBRAIC FUNCTIONS
Serge Lang	RAPPORT SUR LA COHOMOLOGIE DES GROUPES
Ottmar Loos	SYMMETRIC SPACES I: GENERAL THEORY II: COMPACT SPACES AND CLASSIFICATION
I. G. Macdonald	ALGEBRAIC GEOMETRY: INTRODUCTION TO SCHEMES

George Mackey	INDUCED REPRESENTATIONS OF GROUPS AND QUANTUM MECHANICS
Andrew Ogg	MODULAR FORMS AND DIRICHLET SERIES
Richard Palais	FOUNDATIONS OF GLOBAL NON-LINEAR ANALYSIS
William Parry	ENTROPY AND GENERATORS IN ERGODIC THEORY
D. S. Passman	PERMUTATION GROUPS
Walter Rudin	FUNCTION THEORY IN POLYDISCS
Jean-Pierre Serre	ABELIAN l-ADIC REPRESENTATIONS AND ELLIPTIC CURVES
Jean-Pierre Serre	ALGEBRES DE LIE SEMI-SIMPLE COMPLEXES
Jean-Pierre Serre	LIE ALGEBRAS AND LIE GROUPS
Shlomo Sternberg	CELESTIAL MECHANICS

PIECEWISE LINEAR TOPOLOGY

J. F. P. HUDSON

University of Durham

University of Chicago Lecture Notes prepared
with the assistance of
J. L. Shaneson and J. Lees

W. A. BENJAMIN, INC.

New York 1969 Amsterdam

PIECEWISE LINEAR TOPOLOGY

Library of Congress Catalog Card Number 72-75219
Manufactured in the United States of America
12345 S 2109

*The manuscript was put into production on December 7, 1968;
this volume was published on March 1, 1969*

W. A. BENJAMIN, INC.
New York, New York 10016

PREFACE

This book consists of notes on lectures given at the University of Chicago in the academic year 1966-67. My aim in these lectures was to develop PL theory from basic principles and cover most of that part of the theory which does not require the use of bundles. Thus the book is complete in itself, apart from a very little algebraic topology. It covers subdivision, regular neighbourhoods, general position, engulfing, embeddings, isotopies and handle-body theory, including a complete proof of the s-cobordism theorem.

Fortunately there have been considerable simplifications in the basic theory, in particular in the proof of Newman's theorem that the closed complement of an n-ball in an n-sphere is an n-ball. The original proof required a considerable study of 'stellar theory'. This was first rendered unnecessary by Zeeman's proof, using a large induction including regular neighbourhood theory. M. Cohen's short proof simplified things further. I heard of Cohen's proof just in time to put a version of it into the lectures.

A certain amount of new material is included, notably the proof that concordance implies isotopy for embeddings in codimension ≤ 3. I have drawn heavily on E. C. Zeeman's seminar notes on Combinatorial Topology (IHES, Paris, 1963), for much of the basic theory, though my treatment of general position and engulfing is somewhat different. The section on

Whitehead torsion is lifted direct from J. Milnor's paper in the Bulletin of the A. M. S., 1966.

I am very grateful to the Mathematics Department at the University of Chicago for inviting me there to give these lectures. I also wish to thank J. Lees and J. L. Shaneson for the considerable amount of time and effort they spent helping me with the preparation of these notes.

My thanks also to R. Lashof and M. A. Armstrong for many discussions during the course, and to E. C. Zeeman for introducing me to PL topology and for all his help and encouragement since.

November, 1968 JOHN F. P. HUDSON

CONTENTS

Part 1

Part 2

A Note from the Publisher

This volume was printed directly from a typescript prepared by the author, who takes full responsibility for its content and appearance. The Publisher has not performed his usual functions of reviewing, editing, typesetting, and proofreading the material prior to publication.

The Publisher fully endorses this informal and quick method of publishing lecture notes at a moderate price, and he wishes to thank the author for preparing the material for publication.

Chapter I - Basic Definitions and Subdivision Theorems

1. Basic Definitions

If $x_0, \ldots, x_r$ are points in n-dimensional Euclidean space, E^n, we say that $x_0, \ldots, x_r$ are linearly dependent (in the affine sense) if there exist real numbers $\lambda_0, \ldots, \lambda_r$, not all zero, such that $\sum_{i=1}^{r} \lambda_i x_i = 0$ and $\sum_{i=1}^{r} \lambda_i = 0$. We say that y is linearly dependent on $x_0, \ldots, x_r$ if there exists $\lambda_0, \ldots, \lambda_r$, with $\sum_{i=0}^{r} \lambda_i = 1$, such that $y = \sum_{i=0}^{r} \lambda_i x_i$.

If S is a subset of E^n, then the convex hull (or span) of S is the set of all finite linear combinations of elements of S with positive coefficients whose sum is one.

A convex cell A in E^n is a compact, non-empty subset of E^n which is the solution set of a finite number of linear equations $f_i(x) = 0$ and linear inequalities $g_i(x) \geq 0$. (That is, the f_i and g_i are functions of the form $(x_1, \ldots, x_n) \longrightarrow \lambda_0 + \lambda_1 x_1 + \ldots + \lambda_n x_n$.) A face of A is cell obtained by changing some of the inequalities $g_i \geq 0$ to equalities. A vertex is a face consisting of one point. We also consider A to be a face of itself. A face of A not equal to A is called a proper face. We say that a cell A has dimension n if it contains $(n+1)$ linearly independent points but no more.

Note that the faces of A are determined by A itself and not by the particular choice of equations and inequalities representing it. For a cell B is a face of A if and only if

1) If P is the hyperplane spanned by B, $P \cap A = B$

and

2) No point of P lies directly between two points of $A - B$.

This characterization of faces follows from the definition. The details appear in the appendex at the end of this chapter. Note that this characterization implies that the dimension of a proper face of a cell is strictly lower than the dimension of the cell itself.

The proofs of the following elementary results are left to the reader:

(1) A cell is convex. Moreover, it is the convex hull of its vertices.

(2) The intersection and product of cells are cells. (We identify $E^p \times E^q = E^{p+q}$.)

(3) The convex hull of a finite set is a cell.

(4) Let $A \subseteq E^p$ be a cell. Let $f\colon E^p \to E^q$ be (affine) linear. Then $f(A)$ is a cell.

(Note that by (4), it suffices to prove (3) for the subset $\{(1,0,\ldots,0),\ldots,(0,\ldots,0,1)\}$ of E^n, each n, a triviality.)

A Euclidean Polyhedron in E^h is any finite union of cells. We have the following elementary properties:

(1) The intersection, union, and product of Euclidean polyhedra are Euclidean polyhedra.

(2) The linear image of a polyhedron is a polyhedron.

If $f\colon P \to Q$ is a map, P and Q polyhedra, then we say that f is piecewise linear provided that

(1) f is continuous; and

(2) $\Gamma_f = \{(x, f(x)) \mid x \in P\}$ is a polyhedron.

(Note: if $P \quad E^p$ and $Q \quad E^q$, $\Gamma_f \quad E^p \times E^q = E^{p+q}$.)

<u>Lemma 1.1</u> a) If P_1 and P_2 are polyhedra, and $f: P_1 \quad P_2 \to Q$, Q another polydron, then f is piecewise linear if and only if $f|P_1$ and $f|P_2$ are piecewise linear.

b) $1: P \to P$ is p.l. (= piecewise linear), P any polyhedron.

c) The composite of p.l. maps is a p.l. map.

<u>Proof.</u> a) $\Leftarrow$ Since P_1 and P_2 are closed, f is continuous if $f|P_i$, $i = 1, 2$, are. $\Gamma_f = \Gamma_{f|P_1} \cup \Gamma_{f|P_2}$.

$\Rightarrow$ $\Gamma_{f|P_1} = \{(x, f(x)) | x \in P_1\} = \Gamma_f \cap (P_1 \times Q)$.

b) If A is a cell then $\Gamma_{1_A} = \{(x, x) | x \in A\} = \{(x, y) \in A \times A | x = y\} = \{z \in A \times A | \text{ for all } i, 1 \leq i \leq m, g_i(z) = 0\}$, where if $z = (x, y)$, $g_1(z) = x_i - y_i$. Here m is the dim. of the Euclidean space containing A and $x = (x_1, \ldots, x_m)$, $y = (y_1, \ldots, y_m)$.

c) Let $P \subseteq E^p$, $Q \subseteq E^q$, $R \subseteq E^r$ be polyhedra, and let $f: P \to Q$ and $g: Q \to R$ be p.l. maps. Let $\Gamma = \{(x, f(x), gf(x)) | x \in P\} \subseteq E^{p+q+r}$. Then

$\Gamma = \{(x, f(x), z) | x \in P, z \in R\} \cap \{(x, y, gy) | x \in P, y \in Q\} = (\Gamma_f \times R) \cap (P \times \Gamma_g)$.

Hence Γ is a polyhedron. The map $\pi: E^p \times E^q \times E^r \to E^p \times E^r$, projection on the first and third factors, is linear. Hence $\pi(\Gamma) = \Gamma_{g \circ f}$ is a polyhedron.

We now make a definition which will not be used for at least the rest of the chapter, but will be referred to eventually. Let X be a topological space. A <u>co-ordinate map</u> of X is a map $f: P \to X$, P a polyhedron, which is an embedding [i.e., a homeomorphism onto its image]. We usually write (f, P) to denote such a map. Two co-ordinate maps (f, P) and $(g; Q)$ are said to be <u>compatible</u> if either $f(P) \cap g(Q) = \emptyset$ or there exists a co-ordinate map $(h; R)$ such that the following hold:

(1) $h(R) = f(P) \cap g(Q)$

(2) $f^{-1}h$ and $g^{-1}h$ are piecewise linear.

A <u>P.L. structure</u> on X is a family $\mathfrak{F}$ of co-ordinate maps satisfying the following:

(1) Any two elements of $\mathfrak{F}$ are compatible.

(2) If $x \in X$, there exists $(f, P) \in \mathfrak{F}$ such that $f(P)$ is a neighborhood of x in X.

(3) $\mathfrak{F}$ is maximal; i.e., if (f, P) is compatible with every map in $\mathfrak{F}$, then $(f, P) \in \mathfrak{F}$.

If $\mathfrak{F}$ satisfies (1) and (2), it is called a <u>basis for a P.L. structure on X.</u>

<u>Examples:</u> 1) If P is a polyhedron, $1_P : P \to P$ forms a basis for a P.L. structure.

2) If $U \subseteq E^n$, $\mathfrak{F} = \{(i, P) \mid P$ a polyhedron, $P \subseteq U$, $i : P \to U$ the inclusion map$\}$ is a basis for a P.L. structure.

2. Cell Complexes, Simplicial Complexes, and Subdivision

A convex linear cell complex in E^n is a finite set of cells in E^n, K such that

1) If $A \in K$, every face of A is in K.

2) If A and $B \in K$, then $A \cap B = \emptyset$ or $A \cap B$ = common face of A and B.

An n-simplex in E^N is the convex hull of (n+1) linearly independent points, called its vertices. Each face of an n-simplex is the convex span of some of the vertices and therefore is an m-simplex, $m \leq n$. We write $\sigma < \tau$ for "σ is a face of τ".

A simplicial complex is a cell complex whose cells are all simplices. If K is any complex, by $|K|$ we denote the union of all the cells in K. We call $|K|$ the underlying polyhedron of K.

If K and L are cell complexes, K is called a subdivision of L if the following hold.

1) $|K| = |L|$.

2) Every cell of K is a subset of some cell of L.

Lemma 1.2. If K is a subdivision of L, then every cell of L is the union of cells of K.

Proof. Since $|K| = |L|$, it suffices to show that if A is a cell of L and $x \in A$, then there is a cell B of K, $x \in B$, with $B \subseteq A$. There is a cell B' of K such that $x \in B'$ and there is a cell A' of L such that $B' \subseteq A'$. But

$A \cap A'$ is a common face A_1, say. $B' \subseteq A'$ are convex linear cells, so $B' \cap A_1$ is a face, B say, of B', and $x \in B \subseteq A$.

A subdivision K of L is said to be simplicial if it is a simplicial complex.

One of the most important types of subdivision of a simplicial complex is stellar subdivision. In order to define stellar subdivision, we must first introduce the notions of joins, stars, and links; however these notions (let the reader be forewarned!!) also are important in themselves.

Let A and B be two simplices in E^n. If the set consisting of all the vertices of A and of B form a linearly independent set, then we say that A and B are joinable. By A.B we denote the simplex whose vertices are those of A and B. The simplex A.B is called the join of A and B.*

If K and L are two simplicial complexes in E^n, we say that K and L are joinable if the following hold:

(1) If $A \in K$ and $B \in L$, A and B are joinable.

(2) If $A' \in K$ and $B' \in L$, also, then either $A.B \cap A'.B' = \emptyset$ or $A.B \cap A'.B'$ is a face of $A.B$ and of $A'.B'$.

If K and L are joinable simplicial complexes, we define $K.L = K \cup L \cup \{AB \mid A \in K, B \in L\}$, called the join of K and L. K.L is clearly a simplicial complex.

---

*By convention, we allow A or B = $\emptyset$ and write $A.\emptyset = \emptyset.A = A$.

Example: Let A and B be joinable simplices. By $\overline{A}$ we denote the complex whose elements are A and all its faces. Then $\overline{A}$ and $\overline{B}$ are joinable complexes, and $\overline{A}.\overline{B} = \overline{(A.B)}$.

Now let K be a simplicial complex. If $A \in K$, then we make the following definitions:

$\text{star}(A;K) = \{B \in K \mid B \geq A\}$.

$\overline{\text{star}}(A;K) = \{B \in K \mid B$ is a face of an element of $\text{star}(A;K)\}$.

$\text{link}(A;K) = \{B \in K \mid B$ and A are joinable and $A.B \in K\}$.

The reader can easily verify that $\overline{\text{star}}(A;K)$ and $\text{link}(A;K)$ are complexes, that $\overline{A}$ and $\text{link}(A;K)$ are joinable, and that the following equality holds:

$$\overline{\text{star}}(A;K) = \overline{A}.\,\text{link}(A;K).$$

Remark. In general, if L is a convex linear cell complex and K is a subset of L, then if $\overline{K}$ is the set of all cells of K and their faces, $\overline{K}$ is a subcomplex of L; i.e., $\overline{K}$ is a subset of L which is a complex. Clearly, this notation is consistent with the definitions of star and $\overline{\text{star}}$.

Notation. If A is a simplex, $\mathring{A}$ = points of A not contained in any face. $\dot{A}$ = subcomplex of A consisting of the proper faces. (If A = point, we put $\dot{A} = \emptyset$.)

Definition of Stellar Subdivision. Let K be a simplicial complex, $A \in K$ a simplex. Let $a \in \mathring{A}$. Then define:

$$L = \{K - \overline{\text{star}}(A;K)\} \cup (a.\dot{A}.\,\text{link}(A;K))$$

$$= [K - A.\,\text{link}(A;K)] \cup [a.\dot{A}.\,\text{link}(A;K)].$$

(The reader will note that in general if K, L, and M are three complexes each joinable to the join of the other two, then the following equality is both meaningful and true: $(K.L).M = K.(L.M)$

L is called the <u>complex obtained from K by starring A at a.</u> The reader can easily verify that L is indeed a complex and that it is a subdivision of K.

The complex L may also be obtained from K as follows. Write $K = K_o \cup A.P$, with $A \notin K_o$. Then set $L = K_o \cup a.\dot{A}.P$.

We say that the complex L is a <u>stellar</u> subdivision of K if there exists a series $K = K_o, K_1, \ldots, K_r = L$ such that K_r is obtained from K_{r-1} by starring a simplex at some interior point.

<u>Picture:</u>

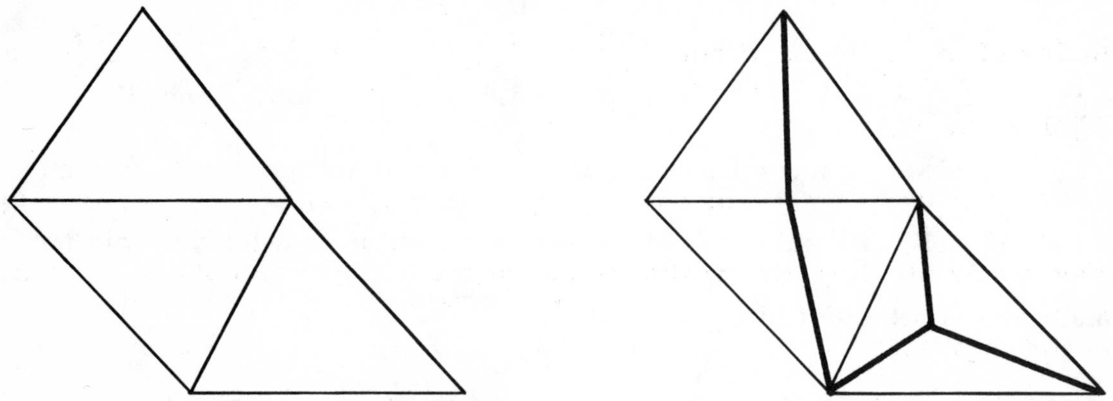

<u>Example of a non-stellar subdivision:</u>

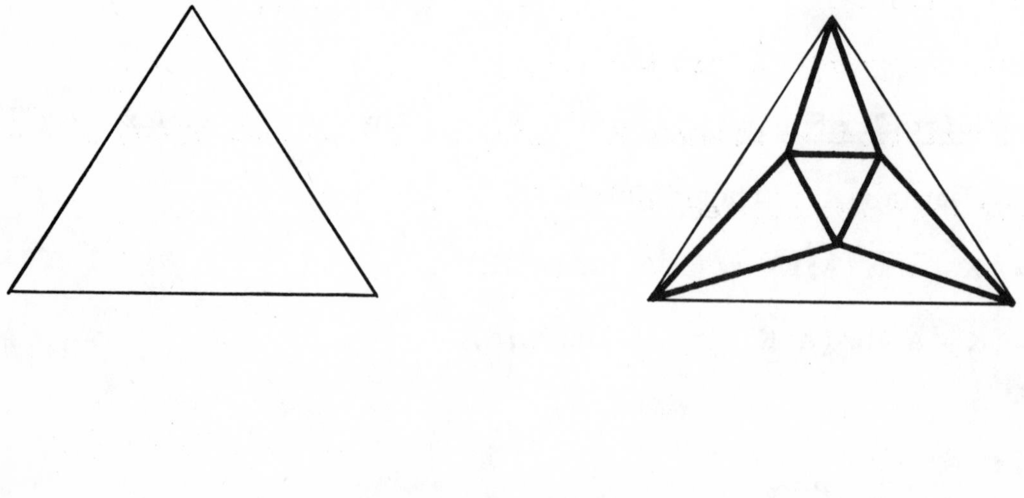

The complex K' is called a first derived of the simplicial complex K if it is obtained as a stellar subdivision from K as follows: For each simplex $A \in K$, choose $\hat{A} \in \mathring{A}$. Star each simplex A at $\hat{A}$ in order of decreasing dimension. This construction makes sense because if we star A at $\hat{A}$ and if $B \in K$, and $\dim B \leq \dim A$, then B will be a simplex of the resulting subdivision.

Note that if $\mathring{A}'$ denotes the first derived subdivision of $\mathring{A}$ obtained by using, for $\dot{A}$, the same starring points, and $\overline{A}'$ denotes the subdivision of $\overline{A}$ obtained similarly, then

$$\overline{A}' = \hat{A}.\mathring{A}'.$$

From this formula it follows by induction on dimension that the general simplex of K' is of the form $\hat{A}_1\hat{A}_2\ldots\hat{A}_r$, where $A_1 \lneqq A_2 \lneqq \ldots \lneqq A_r$ are simplices in K.

After reading the definition of simplicial map, the reader will be able to prove easily that any two first deriveds of the same complex are simplicially homeomorphic.

If A is a simplex with vertices $\{a_o, \ldots, a_n\}$, $\frac{1}{n+1} a_o + \ldots + \frac{1}{n+1} a_n$ is called the <u>barycenter</u> of A. K' is called a <u>barycentric</u> first derived of K if all the starring points $\hat{A}$ are barycenters.

An rth derived subdivision $K^{(r)}$ of K is defined inductively to be a first derived of an $(r-1)$th derived, $K^{(r-1)}$.

3. Basic Lemmas on Subdivision

Lemma 1.3. Let K_o be a subcomplex of the simplicial complex K. Then 1) If K' is a subdivision of K, it contains a subdivision of K_o; and 2) If K'_o is a subdivision of K_o, there exists a subdivision of K containing K'_o.

Proof. 1) Put $K'_o = \{$simplices of K' contained in $|K_o|\}$. If $A \in K'_o$, then A is contained in a simplex of K_o. For $A \subseteq B$, some $B \in K$. Hence $A \subsetneq B \cap |K_o|$, a union of faces of B. Since A is a simplex, it lies in one of these faces; in a simplex of K_o. So K'_o is a subcomplex of K' and $|K'_o| \subsetneq |K_o|$. By Proposition 1.2, every simplex of K_o is a union of simplices which are in K' and so also in K'_o; therefore $|K_o| \subsetneq |K'_o|$.

2) By induction on the number of simplices in $K - K_o$. If none, there is nothing to prove. So suppose $A_1, \ldots, A_n \in K - K_o$, with $i \le j \Longrightarrow \dim i \le \dim j$.

Let $K_1 = K_o \cup \{A_1, \ldots, A_{n-1}\}$, a subcomplex. By induction, we may suppose that K'_1 is a subdivision of K_1 such that K'_o is a subcomplex of K'_1. By 1), K'_1 contains a subdivision $(\dot{A}_n)'$ of $\dot{A}_n$. Let $a \in \mathring{A}_n$. Define

$$K' = K'_1 \cup a.(\dot{A})'.$$

Notation. If we write K' or $\sigma(K)$ to denote a subdivision of K and if L is a subcomplex of K, by $\sigma(L)$ or L' we mean the subdivision of L as in 1); it is called the induced subdivision of L and is the unique subdivision of L which is a subcomplex of K'.

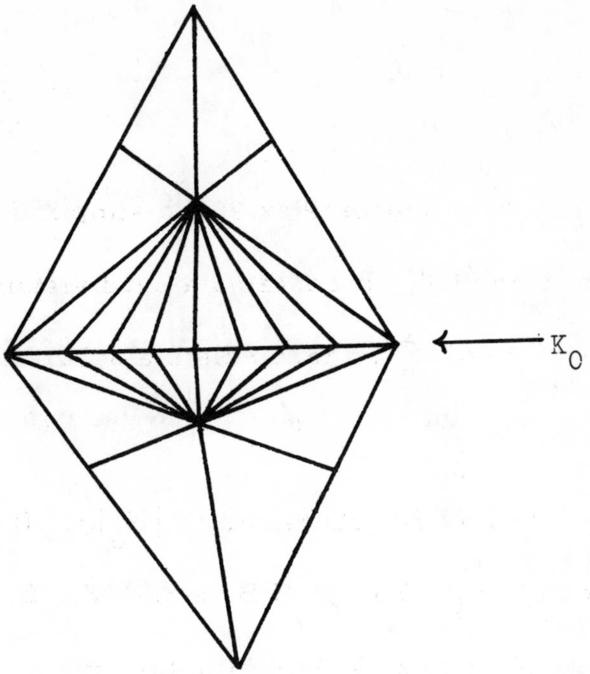

Figure for Lemma 1.3, Part 2.

Remark. Lemma 1.3 holds equally well for cell-complexes.

Lemma 1.4. If K is a cell complex, then K has a simplicial subdivision with no extra vertices.

Proof. Order the vertices of K. If $A \in K$, write $A = |aB|$, a the first vertex of A, B = all faces of A not containing a. Define subdivision of cells in order of increasing dimension by the rule:

$$A' = a.B',$$

where B' is the subdivision of B determined by the (simplicial) subdivision of cells of lower dimension. (If A = a, set A' = a). The construction is self-consistent because if C is a face of A containing a, then a is the first vertex of C.

<u>Lemma 1.5.</u> Let $A_1, \ldots, A_n$ be convex linear cells. Let K be a simplicial complex in E^N with $A_1 \cup \ldots \cup A_n \subseteq |K|$. Then K has an rth derived $K^{(r)}$ containing subdivisions of $A_1, \ldots, A_n$.

<u>Proof.</u> Let $c_1, \ldots, c_k$ be $A_1, \ldots, A_n$ and their faces, in order of increasing dimension. Then c_1 is a point, and there is obviously a first derived $K^{(1)}$ of K in which c_1 is a vertex. Suppose there exists an (r-1)-st derived $K^{(r-1)}$ of K containing subdivisions of $c_1, \ldots, c_{r-1}$.

For each simplex $\sigma \in K^{(r-1)}$, let $\hat{\sigma} \in \sigma \cap c_r$, provided that this interesection is non-empty. Otherwise, choose any point $\hat{\sigma} \in \mathring{\sigma}$. Let $K^{(r)}$ be the rth derived obtained from $K^{(r-1)}$ by starring each simplex of $K^{(r-1)}$, σ, at $\hat{\sigma}$, in order of decreasing dimension. We are going to show that $K^{(r)}$ contains a subdivision of $\sigma \cap c_r$ for all $\sigma \in K^{(r-1)}$ such that $\sigma \cap c_r \neq \emptyset$. This clearly implies that $K^{(r)}$ contains a subdivision of c_r.

Consider $c_r \cap \sigma \neq \emptyset$. We may assume that $c_r \cap \sigma \neq \emptyset$, since otherwise the there is nothing to prove, by the inductive hypothesis. Let H = hyperplane of lowest dimension containing c_r; i.e., H is the unique hyperplane, containing c_r, with respect to which c_r has interior points. Then $c_r \cap \sigma = H \cap \sigma$. For $\dot{c}_r$ = proper faces of c_r is subdivided as a subcomplex of $K^{(r-1)}$, and so its intersection with σ is a union of faces of σ. So $\dot{c}_r$ meets $\mathring{\sigma}$ only if $\sigma \subseteq \dot{c}_r$, and so $c_r \cap \sigma = H \cap \sigma$.

Now we prove by induction on the dimension of σ that for any $\sigma \in K^{(r-1)}$ with $\sigma \cap c_r \neq \emptyset$, $K^{(r)}$ contains a subdivision of $\sigma \cap c_t$. If $\sigma = \{\hat{\sigma}\}$, thi[illegible] clear. By induction, $K^{(r)}$ contains a subdivision L of $c_r \cap \dot{\sigma}$, if $c_r \cap \sigma \neq \emptyset$. We may assume that $\mathring{c}_r \cap \sigma \neq \emptyset$. If $\sigma \cap c_r \subset \dot{\sigma}$, it is already a subcomplex, so suppose that $\mathring{\sigma} \cap c_r \neq \emptyset$. Hence we have:

$$\sigma \cap c_r = \sigma \cap H = \hat{\sigma}.|\dot{\sigma} \cap H| = \hat{\sigma}.|\dot{\sigma} \cap c_r| = \hat{\sigma}.|L|.$$

Hence $\hat{\sigma}.L$, a subcomplex of $K^{(r)}$, is a subdivision of $\sigma \cap c_r$.

Note. By $\hat{\sigma}.|L|$, for example, we mean the join of $\{\hat{\sigma}\}$ and $|L|$. Clearly, $|\hat{\sigma}.L| = \hat{\sigma}.|L|$.

Picture:

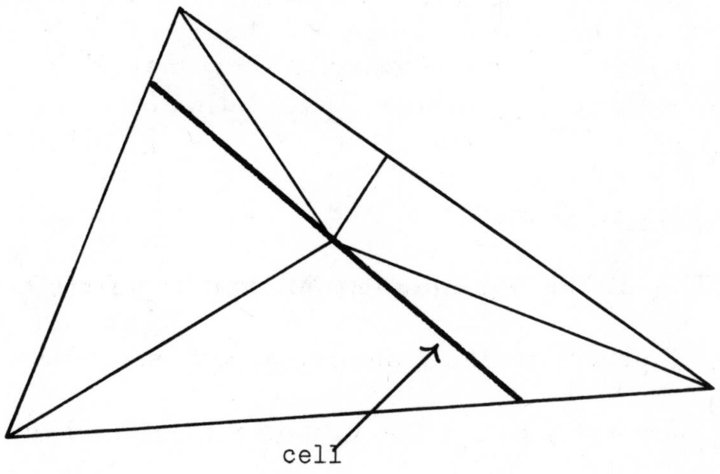

Corollary 1.6. If $|K| \subseteq |L|$, K and L simplicial complexes, then there exists an rth derived subdivision $L^{(r)}$ of L which contains a subdivision of K.

Proof. By Lemma 1.5, subdivide L to get an rth derived $L^{(r)}$ which contains a subdivision of each of the simplices of K. Let K' be the union of these subcomplexes. Then K' is a subcomplex of $L^{(r)}$ and a subdivision of K.

Corollary 1.7. Every Euclidean Polyhedron is the underlying set of a simplicial complex.

Proof. Let Δ^N be an N-simplex containing the compact subset P of E^N, where $P = A_1 \cup \ldots \cup A_r$, each A_i a convex linear cell. Apply Lemma 1.5 to find a subdivision of $\overline{\Delta^N}$ which contains a subdivision of each A_i, and take the union of these subcomplexes to get a complex whose underlying set is P.

Definition. If P is a Euclidean Polyhedron and K is a simplicial complex with $|K| = P$, K is called a triangulation of P.

Unsolved Problem: Suppose K and L are simplicial complexes, and $|K| = |L|$. Then is there a complex M which is a stellar subdivision of both K and L?

4. Piecewise Linear Maps, Simplicial Maps, and Subdivisions.

In this section we study the relation between piecewise linear maps and simplicial maps. If K and L are simplicial complexes, a simplicial map $f: K \longrightarrow L$ is a continuous map $f: |K| \longrightarrow |L|$ which maps vertices of K to vertices of L and simplicies of K linearly into (and hence onto) simplices of L.

Remarks: 1) Although we write $f: K \longrightarrow L$, f is not really a function from the set K to the set L; but it may be though of as a collection of linear maps of simplices of K onto simplices of L.

2) Any simplicial map is piecewise linear. (Use Lemma 1.1.)

3) A simplicial map f is determined by its values on vertices. Conversely, given a function g which assigns to each vertex of K a vertex of K' in such a way that if $v_1, \ldots, v_n$ are in a simplex of K, $g(v_1), \ldots, g(v_n)$ are in a simplex of L, there exists a unique simplicial map $f: K \longrightarrow L$ which extends g. Namely, if

$$\sum_{i=1}^{n} \lambda_i = 1, \quad \lambda_i \geq 0 \text{ all } i, \quad \text{set} \quad f\left(\sum_{i=1}^{n} \lambda_i v_i\right) = \sum_{i=1}^{n} \lambda_i g(v_i)$$

Lemma 1.8. Let $f: K \longrightarrow L$ be simplicial. Given any subdivision L' of L, there exists a subdivision K' of K such that $f: K' \longrightarrow L'$ is simplicial.

Proof. If A is a simplex of K, $f(A)$ is a simplex of L. We also write $f(A)$ for the subcomplex consisting of $f(A)$ and its faces, and $f(A)'$ for the induced subdivision.

Let $K_1 = \{A \cap f^{-1}(\sigma) | A \in K$ and $\sigma \in L'\}$. Then K_1 is a convex linear cell complex (together with the empty set). For $A \cap f^{-1}(\sigma)$ is a convex linear cell (or empty). A typical face is of the form $B \cap f^{-1}(\tau)$, where B and τ are (not necessarily proper) faces of A and σ, respectively. (The reader may verify the last statement by consideration of the appropriate linear inequalities.) Hence faces of cells of K_1 and in K_1. Moreover, $(A \cap f^{-1}(\sigma)) \cap (C \cap f^{-1}(\eta)) = (A \cap C) \cap (f^{-1}(\sigma) \cap f^{-1}(\eta)) = (A \cap C) \cap (f^{-1}(\sigma \cap \eta))$, which is a common face if $A \cap f^{-1}(\sigma)$ and $C \cap f^{-1}(\eta)$.

Obviously, $|K_1| = |K|$. Also, f is linear on each cell of K_1 and maps vertices of K_1 to vertices of L'. Let K' = a simplicial subdivision of K_1 with no extra vertices, by Lemma 1.4.

Lemma 1.9. Let K and L be simplicial complexes, with $|L| \subseteq E^N$. Let $f: |K| \rightarrow |L|$ be a map whose restriction to each cell of K is linear. Then there exists subdivisions K' and L' of K and L respectively, such that $f: K' \rightarrow L'$ is simplicial. Moreover, we may insist that L' be stellar.

Proof. If $A \in K$, f(A) is a convex linear cell; hence there exists an rth derived $L^{(r)}$ of L in which all the cells f(A), $A \in K$, are subdivided as subcomplexes. Consider $K_1 = \{A \cap f^{-1}(B) | A \in K, B \in L^{(r)}\}$. Then as in Lemma 1.8, K_1 is a cellular subdivision of K, f is linear on cells of A, and maps vertices onto vertices. Subdivide K_1 with no extra vertices.

<u>Lemma 1.10.</u> Let $f: |K| \to |L|$ be a piecewise linear map of simplicial complexes. Then there exist subdivisions K' and L' of K and L respectively, so that $f: K' \to L'$ is simplicial. We may insist that L' be stellar.

<u>Proof.</u> Say $|K| \subseteq E^p$, $|L| \subseteq E^q$. $\Gamma_f \subseteq E^{p+q}$, the graph of f, is a polyhedron. Let M be a simplicial subdivision of Γ_f, by Corollary 1.7. If $\pi_1: F^p \times E^q \to E^p$ is projection on the first factor, then by Lemma 1.9 there exist subdivisions M_1 and K_1 of M and K respectively, such that $\pi_1 | \, |M| : M_1 \to K_1$ is simplicial. $\pi_1 | \, |M_1|$ is a bijection; hence it is a homeomorphism. Moreover, if π_2 is projection on the second factor, $f = \pi_2 \circ (\pi_1 | \, |M|)^{-1}: K_1 \to L$. But π_2 is a linear map, and so we may apply Lemma 1.9 to the map $f = \pi_2 \circ (\pi_1 | M)^{-1}: K_1 \to L$.

Now consider the following diagram:

$$\begin{array}{ccc} K & \xrightarrow{f} & L \\ \downarrow{\scriptstyle g} & & \\ M & & \end{array}$$

In general we cannot find subdivisions of K, L, and M with respect to which f and g are simultaneously simplicial, as the following example shows.

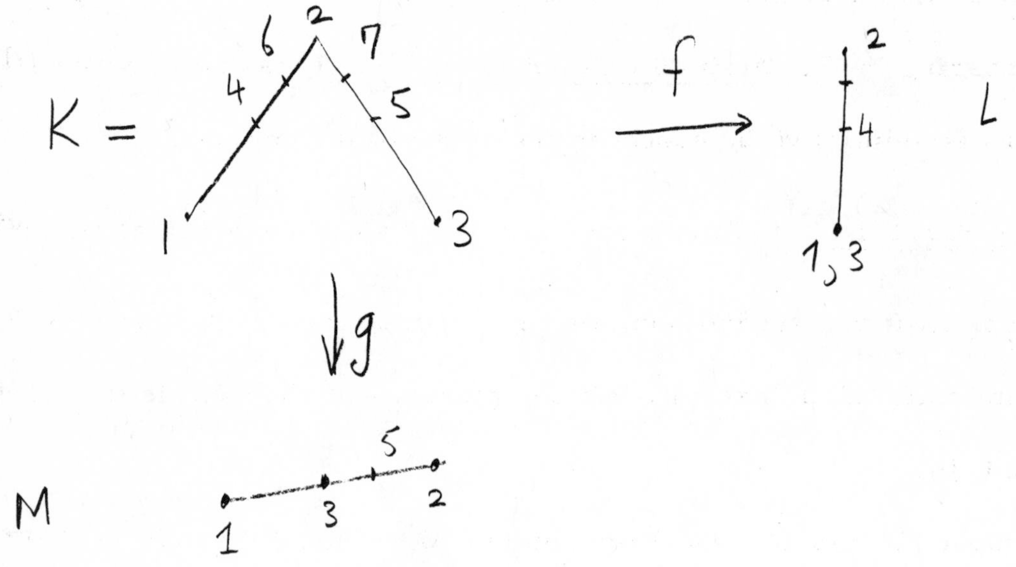

Here f and g map vertices 1, 2, and 3 as shown and are linear. To make g simplicial (3 in M is not a given vertex), we must introduce vertec 4 in K. Then keeping f simplicial requires the introduction of vertices 4 and 5 in L and K respectively. Then keeping g simplicial requires 5 in M and 6 in K; and then we must add 6 in L and 7 in K. Continuing in this way we find it necessary to add infinitely many vertices between 1 and 2 in K, for example. This cannot be done by subdivision.

However, there are some types of diagrams in which it is always possible to subdivide all the complexes so that all the maps are simultaneously simplicial.

Definition. A finite diagram of cell complexes and piecewise linear maps is called a one-way tree if

1) The corresponding complex is one-connected; i.e., the diagram has no loops; and

2) Each complex is the domain of at most one map.

A subdivision of a diagram T is a diagram obtained by subdividing each complex appearing in T. A simplicial subdivision of T is one in which all the maps are simplicial with respect to the subdivided complexes.

Theorem 1.11. If T is a one-way tree, it has a simplicial subdivision.

Proof. After a subdivision, we may assume that all the complexes of T are simplicial. If T has only two complexes, this theorem is then just Lemma 1.10.

Suppose T has at least three complexes. There is a map $f: K \rightarrow L$ in T such that K is not the range of any map in T. Let K' and L' be subdivisions of K and L such that $f: K' \rightarrow L'$ is simplicial. Let T^* be the tree obtained from T by deleting $f: K \rightarrow L$ and replacing L by L'. By induction there is a subdivision T^{**} of T^* which is simplicial. Let L" be the corresponding subdivision of L'. Apply Lemma 1.8 to find K", a subdivision of K', such that $f: K'' \rightarrow L''$ is simplicial.

5. Piecewise Linear Manifolds

Definition. A piecewise linear m-ball is a polyhedron which is piecewise homeomorphic to an m-simplex. A piecewise linear m-sphere is a polyhedron which is p.l. homeomorphic to the boundary on an (m+1)-simplex. A p.l. manifold of dimension m, M^m, is a Euclidean polyhedron in which every point has a (closed) neighborhood which is a p.l. m-ball.

Remark. One can show by topological arguments that given an m-manifold M, m is uniquely determined by M. However, this result will also follow from the results of this section.

Lemma 1.12. If A is a convex linear cell of dimension m, then A is a p.l. m-ball.

Proof. Let Δ be an m-simplex containing A; i.e., let Δ be a simplex containing A and contained in the unique hyperplane containing A with respect to which A has an interior. Choose $a \in \mathring{A} \subseteq \mathring{\Delta}$. Then let $p: \dot{A} \longrightarrow \dot{\Delta}$ be radial projection from a. It is easy to verify that p is a homeomorphism. Unfortunately, p is not piecewise linear.

We are going to alter p to get a p.l. map. Consider $\sigma \in \dot{\Delta}$, Then a is joinable to σ. $\dot{A} \cap a.\sigma$ is a union of cells, and $p(\dot{A} \cap a.\sigma) = \sigma$. Let $\dot{A}'$ be a subdivision of $\dot{A}$ which contains subdivisions of the polyhedra $p^{-1}(\sigma) = \dot{A} \cap a.\sigma$, $\sigma < \Delta$.

Let τ be a simplex of $\dot{A}'$. Then $p(\tau)$ is a simplex contained in a face of Δ. Define $p': \dot{A}' \longrightarrow \dot{\Delta}$, by letting $p'(\xi) = p(\xi)$ if ξ is a vertex of $\dot{A}'$, and extending linearly. Then p' is a well-defined p.l. map, and $p'\tau = p\tau$. So p' is p.l. homeomorphism $\dot{A} \longrightarrow \dot{\Delta}$.

Finally, to define a p.l. homeomorphism $f: A \longrightarrow \Delta$, we just set $f = p'$ on $\dot{A}$, $f(a) = a$, and then extend f linearly to A. Then f is a p.l. homeomorphism; in fact $f: |a.\dot{A}'| \longrightarrow |a\dot{\Delta}|$ maps simplices linearly onto simplices.

Picture:

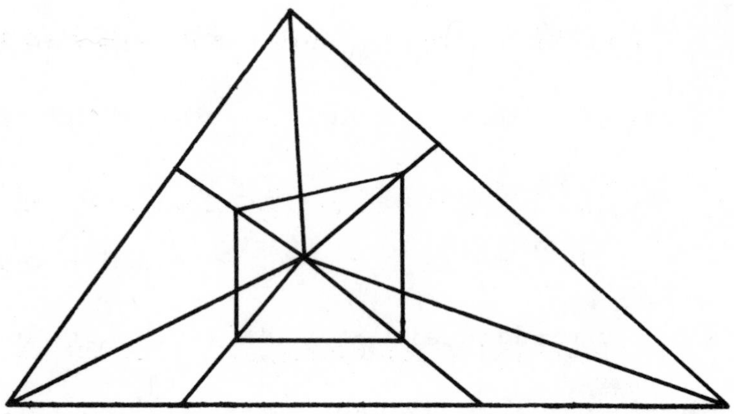

Remark. The map p' constructed in the proof of Lemma 1.12 is called a pseudo-radial projection. It is obtained from an ordinary radial projection by an adjustment which insures piecewise linearity. In the sequel, we shall construct pseudo-radial projections with impunity and without the detailed discussion of the last proof.

<u>Lemma 1.13</u>. 1) Let B^m and B^q be joinable simplicial complexes whose underlying polyhedra are an m-ball and a q-ball, respectively. Then $|B^m . B^q|$ is an m+q+1 ball.

2) Let B^m and S^q be joinable simplicial complexes, with $|B^m|$ and m-ball, $|S^q|$ a q-sphere. Then $|B^m . S^q|$ is an m+q+1 ball.

3) Let S^m and S^q be joinable simplicial complexes, $|S^m|$ an m-sphere and $|S^q|$ a q-sphere. Then $|S^m . S^q|$ is an m+q+1 sphere.

<u>Proof.</u> 1) Let Δ^m and Δ^q be an m-simplex and a q-simplex which are non-intersecting faces of another simplex (of suitably high dimension). Let h: $B^m \longrightarrow \Delta^m$ be a p.l. homeomorphism, and let k: $B^q \longrightarrow \Delta^q$ be a p.l. homeomorphism. Let B_1^m, B_1^q, Δ_1^m, and Δ_1^q be subdivisions such that h and k are simplicial. The reader may verify that if two complexes are joinable, so are any subdivisions of these two complexes. Moreover, the vertices of $B_1^m . B_q^m$ are just the vertices of B_1^m and B_q^m. Hence h and k determine, by their values on vertices, a unique simplicial isomorphism

h.k: $B_1^m . B_1^q \longrightarrow \Delta_1^m . \Delta_1^q$. But $|\Delta_1^m . \Delta_1^q| = |\Delta^m . \Delta^q|$, an m+q+1 simplex.

2) As in 1), it suffices to show that if Δ^m and Δ^{q+1} are joinable, then $|\Delta^m . \dot{\Delta}^{q+1}|$ is an m+q+1 ball. Let $\Delta^m = v.\Delta^{m-1}$, v a vertex of Δ^m. Then consider the map $\Delta^m . \dot{\Delta}^{q+1} \xrightarrow{f} \Delta^{m-1} . \Delta^{q+1}$ defined as follows. Let f(v) be the barycenter of Δ^{q+1}. Let f(x) = x if x is a vertex of Δ^{q+1} or a vertex of Δ^{m-1}. Extend f linearly over simplices of $\Delta^m . \dot{\Delta}^{q+1}$. It is not hard to check that f defines a p.l. homeomorphism. Now apply 1).

3) In 2), replace m by m+1. Then f: $\Delta^{m+1} . \dot{\Delta}^{q+1} \rightarrow \Delta^{m} . \Delta^{q+1}$.
Moreover, $f(|\dot{\Delta}^{m+1} . \dot{\Delta}^{q+1}|) = |\dot{\Delta}^{m+q+2}|$ where $\Delta^{m+q+2} = |\Delta^{m} . \Delta^{q+1}|$.
So $\dot{\Delta}^{m+1} . \dot{\Delta}^{q+1}$ is an m+q+1 sphere. As in 1), this suffices to prove 3).

Lemma 1.14. If K' is a subdivision of K, K and K' simplicial, then link(a; K) $\cong$ link(a; K').

Note: $\cong$ means p.l. homeomorphic.

Proof. If B' $\in$ link(a; K'), then aB' $\in$ K'. Hence there exists B $\in$ K such that aB $\in$ K, and aB' $\subset$ aB, since a is also a vertex of K. Hence we may define a radial projection p: link(a; K') $\longrightarrow$ link(a; K). The map p is a topological homeomorphism. In addition, p(B) is a simplex which lies in B and is spanned by the images of the vertices of B'. Hence, using the technique of Lemma 1.12, we may find a pseudo-radial projection p': link|a; K| $\cong$ link(a; K'). [Note: In this case it is unnecessary to subdivide link(a; K') in order to define the pseudo-radial projection.]

Corollary 1.15. If h: |K| $\rightarrow$ |L| is a p.l. homeomorphism, K and L simplicial complexes, then link(a; K) $\cong$ link(ha; L), provided ha is a vertex of L.

Proof. Let K' and L' be subdivisions so that h: K' $\rightarrow$ L' is simplicial. Then h: link(a; K') $\longrightarrow$ link(ha; L') is a p.l. homeomorphism. Apply Lemma 1.14.

Picture for 1.14:

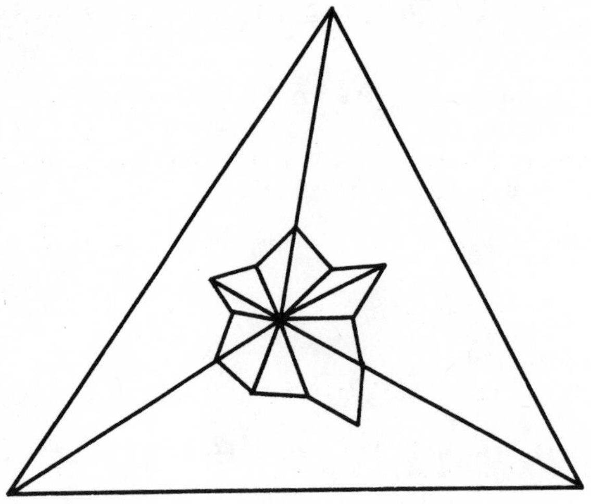

Corollary 1.16. If $|K|$ is a p.l. n-manifold, K a simplicial complex, then if $A \in K$, link(A, K) is an (n-r-1) sphere or ball, where r = dimension A.

Proof. First consider the case $A = a$ is a vertex. Let $B \subset |K|$ be a neighborhood of A which is p.l. homeomorphic to Δ^n, an n- simplex. Then let K' be a subdivision of K which contains a triangulation of B, K_o, as a subcomplex. Let $h: |K_o| \to \Delta^n$ be a p.l. homeomorphism.

By 1.14, it suffices, in this case, to show that link(a; K') is an (n-1) sphere or ball. But link(a; K') = link(a; K_o), since $|K_o|$ is a neighborhood of a in $|K'|$. Let Δ' = stellar subdivision of Δ^n obtained by starring at ha. Then by 1.15, link(a; K_o) $\cong$ link(ha; Δ'). So it suffices to prove that link(ha; Δ') is an (n-1) sphere or ball.

Case 1: $ha = b \in \mathring{\Delta}$. Then $\Delta' = ha.\dot{\Delta}$. So link(ha; Δ') = $\dot{\Delta}$, an (n-1) sphere.

Case 2: $b \in \mathring{A}$, A a proper face of Δ. Say $A = A^s$; i.e., A is an s-simplex.

Then $\Delta^n = A^s . B^{n-s-1}$, where B is the convex hull of the vertices not in A. Star at b to get $\Delta' = b\dot{A}B$; hence $\text{link}(b; \Delta') = \dot{A}.B$, an $(s-1) + (n-s-1) + 1 = (n-1)$-ball.

Now we consider the general simplex $A \in K$ and proceed by induction on the dimension of A; i.e., we assume that if B has lower dimension, link(B; K) is a ball or sphere of dimension n - dim B - 1.

Write $A = a.A_1$, where a is a vertex of A and A_1 a face. Let $L = \text{Link}(A_1; K)$, an n-r sphere or ball, r = dim A. Then a is a vertex of L, since $aA_1 \in K$. Moreover, $B \in \text{link}(a; L) \Longleftrightarrow a.B.A_1 \in K \Longleftrightarrow B.(a.A_1) \in K \Longleftrightarrow B \in \text{link}(A; K)$. That is,

$$\text{link}(a; L) = \text{link}(A; K).$$

Thus to complete the proof, it suffices to show only that $L = \text{link}(A_1; K)$ is an (n-r) manifold. This will be the case if, for <u>any</u> r, Δ^r is an r-manifold and $\dot{\Delta}^{r+1}$ is also an r-manifold, Δ^r and Δ^{r+1} being r- and (r+1)-simplices, respectively.

It is clear that Δ^r is an r-manifold. Consider $\dot{\Delta}^{r+1}$. Let $\xi \in \dot{\Delta}^{r+1}$ be a given point. Let σ be an r-simplex of $\dot{\Delta}^{r+1}$ with $\xi \notin \sigma$. Let x be the vertex not in σ. Now, $\text{cl}(\dot{\Delta}^{r+1} - \sigma) = \bigcup_{\substack{\tau < \Delta^{r+1} \\ \tau \neq \sigma}} \tau$ is a neighborhood of ξ in $\dot{\Delta}^{r+1}$ (cl = topological closure.). But $\text{cl}(\dot{\Delta}^{r+1} - \sigma) = |x.\dot{\sigma}|$. This is an r-ball. Namely, map $\dot{\sigma} \longrightarrow \dot{\sigma}$ by the identity, let x be mapped to a point in $\overset{\circ}{\sigma}$, and extend linearly to get a p.l. homeomorphism $x.\dot{\sigma} \longrightarrow \sigma$.

Definition. The complex K is called a combinatorial n-manifold if for all $A \in K$, $link(A; K)$ is a sphere or ball of dimension $n - \dim A - 1$. (Note: We have been writing $link(A; K) = |link(A; K)|$.)

Remark. Corollary 1.16 asserts that if $|K|$ is a p.l. n-manifold, then K is a combinatorial n-manifold. Conversely, if K is a combinatorial n-manifold, let $x \in |K|$. Say $x \in \mathring{A}$, $A \in K$. Let K' be obtained from K by starring A at x. Then $|\overline{star}(a; K')| = |a.\dot{A}.link(A; K)|$, an n-ball containing x in its interior (w.r.t. $|K|$). Hence K a combinatorial n-manifold implies $|K|$ is a p.l. n-manifold.

Definition. Let P be an n-manifold. Let $x \in P$. We say $x \in \mathring{P}$ if given any triangulation of P having x as a vertex, K, $link(x; K)$ is a sphere. We say $x \in \dot{P}$ (or $x \in \partial P$) if for $|K| = P$ a triangulation of P, with x a vertex, $link(x; K)$ is a ball. $\mathring{P}$ is called the interior of P, and $\dot{P} = \partial P$ is called the boundary of P. If $\dot{P} = \emptyset$, we say that P is a manifold without boundary.

Remarks: 1) To determine whether or not $x \in P$ is in the boundary or interior it suffices to consider only one triangulation of P having x as a vertex. For 1_P is a p.l. homeomorphism and so if K and K_1 are two such triangulations, then there is a p.l. homeomorphism $link(x; K) \cong |k(x; K')$, by Corollary 1.15. In particular, $P = \mathring{P} \cup \dot{P}$.

2) $\mathring{P} \cap \partial P = \emptyset$, since a ball is not homeomorphic to a sphere. This is true for purely topological reasons. However, the non-existence of a p.l. homeomorphism of a ball with a sphere also follows from the facts that a simplex Δ is

a p.l. manifold with boundary $|\dot{\Delta}|$, a p.l. homeomorphism preserves boundary, and the following lemma:

Lemma 1.17. An n-sphere is an n-manifold without boundary.

Proof. Let Δ be an (n+1) simplex. Assume $a \in \mathring{A}$, A a proper face. Star A at a to get $\Delta' = a.\dot{A}.B$, where $\Delta = A.B$, $\dot{\Delta} = A.\dot{B} \cup \dot{A}.B$, so $\dot{\Delta}' = a.\dot{A}.\dot{B} \cup \dot{A}.B$. Hence $\text{link}(a;\dot{\Delta}') = \dot{A}.\dot{B}$, an (n-1) sphere.

The next lemma tells us how to find the boundary of a m-manifold M using only one triangulation.

Lemma 1.18. If $|K| = M$ is a triangulation of the m-manifold M, define $\dot{K} = \{A \in K \mid \text{link}(A;K) \text{ is a ball}\}$. Then $\dot{K}$ is a subcomplex of K, $|\dot{K}| = \dot{M}$, and $|\dot{K}|$ is an (m-1) manifold without boundary.

Proof. Let $A \in \dot{K}$. Let B be a face of A of one less dimension. Then $A = x.B$, x the remaining vertex. Then $\text{link}(A;K) = \text{link}(x;\text{link}(B;K))$, so by Lemma 1.17, link(B; K) must be a ball. Hence $\dot{K}$ is a subcomplex.

Suppose $a \in |K|$. Let $a \in \mathring{A}$, $A \in K$, and star A at a to obtain K'. Then

$$\text{link}(a;K') = \dot{A}.\text{link}(A;K).$$

Therefore, $A \in \dot{K}$ implies $a \in \dot{M}$; $A \notin \dot{K} \Rightarrow \text{link}(A,K)$ is a sphere $\Rightarrow a \notin \dot{M}$.

To show that $|\dot{K}|$ is an (m-1) manifold without boundary, let $A \in \dot{K}$. Then $B \in \text{link}(A;\dot{K}) \Longleftrightarrow A.B \in \dot{K} \Leftrightarrow AB \in K$ and $\text{link}(A.B;K)$ is a ball. But $\text{link}(AB;K) = \text{link}(B;\text{link}(A;K))$, so link(AB; K) is a ball $\Leftrightarrow$ B is contained in the boundary of $|\text{link}(A;K)|$. So $\text{link}(A,\dot{K})$ = the boundary of $|\text{link}(A;K)|$, which is an (n - dim A - 2)-sphere; thus $\dot{K}$ is a combinatorial (n-1) manifold and by what we already proved, $|\dot{K}|$ has no boundary.

Note: In view of 1.18, if K is a combinatorial manifold, we refer to $\dot{K} = \{A \in K \mid \text{link}(A;K) \text{ is a ball}\}$ as the boundary of K.

6. Dual Cells

The main aim of the next three sections is to prove that if S is a p.l. sphere and $B \subseteq S$ is a p.l. ball of the same dimension, then $\overline{S - B}$ is a p.l. ball of the same dimension. In this section we define and study dual cells, in the next we prove some lemmas, and in Section 8 we prove this assertion and derive some corollaries.

Let K be a simplicial complex and K' its barycentric first derived. If $A \in K$, we define A^*, the dual cell of A, to be the following subcomplex:

$$A^* = \bigcap_{v \text{ a vertex of } A} \overline{\text{star}}(v; K').$$

Picture:

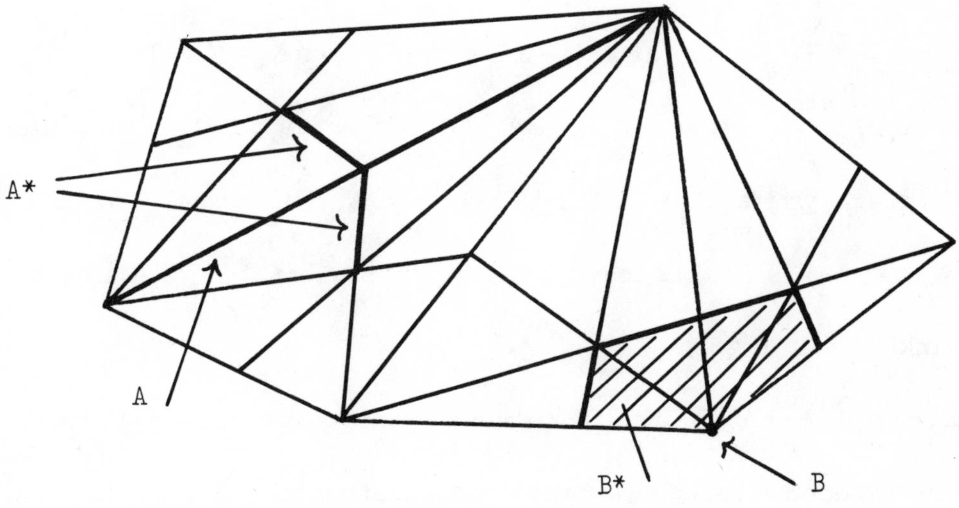

The reader will observe that in general the underlying polyhedron of A^* is not a convex linear cell.

Suppose $\sigma \in K'$. Then $\sigma = \hat{A}_1 \ldots \hat{A}_s$ say, where $A_1 < \ldots < A_s \in K$, and A_i is the barycenter of $\hat{A}_i$. Now $\sigma \in A^*$ if and only if $\sigma \in \text{star}(v; K')$ for each vertex v of A. But $\sigma \in \text{star}(v; K')$ if and only if $v \leq A_1$. So $\sigma \in A^*$ if and only if $A \leq A_1$. So

$$A^* = \{\hat{A}_1 \ldots \hat{A}_s \mid A \leq A_1 < A_2 < \ldots < A_s\} .$$

<u>Definition.</u> If B is a p.l. ball of dim n, a <u>combinatorial face</u> of B is a p.l. ball of dimension $(n-1)$ lying in $\dot{B}$.

When there is no danger of confusion, a combinatorial face of B will be referred to simply as a <u>face</u> of B.

<u>Lemma 1.19.</u> Let K be a combinatorial m-manifold. Let $A \in K$, $\dim A = r$. Then $|A^*|$ is an $(m-r)$ ball. Furthermore, if $A \in \mathring{K}$ and if $A^\#$ is the dual cell of A in $\dot{K}$ then $A^\#$ and $\text{cl}\{|\partial(A^*)| - |A^\#|\}$ are faces of $|A^*|$.

<u>Proof.</u> To prove the first assertion, let $A \in K$. Then $A^* = \{\hat{A}_1 \ldots \hat{A}_s \mid A \leq A_1 < \ldots < A_s\}$. If $\sigma = \hat{A}_1 \ldots \hat{A}_s \in A^*$, then for each j with $A < A_j$, write $A_j = AB_j$. Then $\sigma = \hat{A}.\widehat{AB}_2 \ldots \widehat{AB}_s$ or $\sigma = \widehat{AB}_1 \ldots \widehat{AB}_s$. Every $\sigma \in A^*$ is of this form, where $B_i < \ldots < B_s$, $i = 1$ or 2, and $B_j \in \text{link}(A; K)$, $i \leq j \leq s$.

Let $\text{link}(A;K)'$ be the first barycentric subdivision of $\text{link}(A;K)$, which is also the induced subdivision from K'. Define $h: A^* \longrightarrow \hat{A}.\text{link}(A;K)'$ by mapping $\hat{A}$ to $\hat{A}$ and $\widehat{AB}$ to $\hat{B}$, $B \in \text{link}(A;K)$, and extending linearly over simplices. Then by the last paragraph, h is a simplicial isomorphism. But $|A.\text{link}(A;K)'|$ is an $(n-r)$ ball, since $\text{link}(A;K)$ is an $(n-r-1)$ sphere or ball.

Suppose $A \in \dot{K}$. Then the restriction of h to $A^{\#}$ is a simplicial isomorphism of $A^{\#}$ onto $\hat{A}.\text{link}(A;\dot{K})'$. But $|k(A;K)$ is a p.l. ball with boundary $\text{link}(A;\dot{K})$. (This was shown in the proof of Lemma 1.18.) So A^*, $A^{\#}$, and $\overline{\partial A^* - A^{\#}}$ are p.l. homeomorphic to $\hat{A}.\Delta$, $\hat{A}.\dot{\Delta}$ and Δ, respectively, where Δ is a simplex, (via the same homeomorphism). So $A^{\#}$ and $\overline{\partial A^* - A^{\#}}$ are faces of A^*.

<u>Lemma 1.20</u>. Let K be a combinatorial manifold. Let $\{B_i \mid i = 1,\ldots,r\}$ be the dual cells in K and $\dot{K}$. Then the following hold:

1) $|K| = \bigcup_{i=1}^{r} B_i$

2) $\mathring{B}_i \cap \mathring{B}_j = \emptyset$, if $i \neq j$.

3) $\dot{B}_i$ is a union of dual cells of lower dimension than the dimension of B_i.

<u>Note</u>: In 2), $\mathring{B}_i$ denotes the set $|B_i| - |\partial B_i|$.

<u>Proof</u>. 1) Let K' = barycentric first derived of K. If $x \in |K|$, $x \in \sigma$, some $\sigma \in K'$. Let $\sigma = \hat{A}_1 \ldots \hat{A}_s$, $A_1 < \ldots < A_s$. Then $\sigma \in A_1^*$.

2) Every point of $|K'|$ is contained in the interior of a (unique) simplex of K'. Hence it suffices to show that if $\sigma \in K'$, then σ is contained in at most one $\mathring{B}_i$.

So let $\sigma = \hat{A}_1, \ldots, \hat{A}_s$, $A_1 < \ldots < A_s$, be in K'. Then $\sigma \in A_1^*$. Suppose $\sigma \in A^*$. Then $A \leq A_1$. If $A \neq A_1$, then $\sigma \subseteq |\partial A^*|$. For let $h: A^* \Longrightarrow \hat{A}.\text{link}(A;K)$ be the p.l. homeomorphism defined in the proof of Lemma 1.19. Then $h(\sigma) \subseteq |\text{link}(A;K)|$. Similarly, if $\sigma \in \dot{K}$, then $\sigma \in A^{\#} \Longrightarrow A \leq A_1$; and if $A \neq A_1$, then $\sigma \subseteq |\partial A^{\#}|$.

Hence we have only the possibilities $\mathring{\sigma} \subseteq (A^*)^\circ$ and, if $A_i \in \dot{K}$, $1 \leq i \leq s$, $\mathring{\sigma} \subseteq (A_1^{\#})^\circ$. In case $\sigma \notin (\dot{K})'$, we thus have nothing more to prove. So assume that $\sigma \in (\dot{K})'$; i.e., $A_s \in \dot{K}$. Then $\mathring{\sigma} \subseteq |A_1^{\#}|$, a face of A_1^*. So $\mathring{\sigma} \subseteq |\partial(A_1^*)|$, and thus $A_1^{\#}$ is the unique dual cell which contains $\mathring{\sigma}$.

3) Consider again the map $h: A^* \longrightarrow \hat{A}\,|k(A;K)$, defined as in Lemma 1.19 (proof). Using this homeomorphism, it is easy to see that if $\sigma = \hat{A}_1 \ldots \hat{A}_s$, $A_1 < \ldots < A_s$, then $\sigma \in \partial(A^*)$ if and only if $A \not\leq A_1$ or $\sigma \in A^{\#}$. Since $A < A_1$ implies $A_1^* \subseteq A^*$ and has lower dimension by 1.19, and since $|A^{\#}|$ is a face of $|A^*|$, this shows that $|\partial A^*|$ is the union of dual cells of lower dimension.

7. More Lemmas

Lemma 1.21. If B_1^m and B_2^m are p.l. balls, $n > m$, and if $h: \dot{B}_1 \to \dot{B}_2$ is a p.l. embedding (or homeomorphism), then there exists a p.l. embedding (homeomorphism) $h': B_1 \to B_2$ extending h.

Proof. $\Delta^m = |x.\dot{\Delta}^m|$. $\Delta^n = |y.\dot{\Delta}^n|$, x and y in the interior of Δ^m and Δ^n, respectively. We may view h as a map $h: \dot{\Delta}^m \to \dot{\Delta}^n$. Set $h'(x) = y$ and join up linearly. This is a p.l. map, because it is simply the map obtained by subdividing $\dot{\Delta}^m$ and $\dot{\Delta}^n$ to make h simplicial, defining $h'(x) = y$, and extending linearly over simplices to get $h': x.(\dot{\Delta}^m)' \to y.(\dot{\Delta}^n)'$. It is clearly an embedding.

Lemma 1.22. Let K be a simplicial complex and let V be a point which is joinable to K. Let L be a subdivision of $v.K$. Then if $|K| \cap |\overline{\text{star}}(v;L)| = \emptyset$, then $\text{cl.}(|v.K| - |\overline{\text{star}}(v;L)|)$ is p.l. homeomorphic to $K \times I$, $I = [0,1]$. (K' = induced subdivision of K.)

Proof. Let $R = \text{link}(v;L)$. Let $p: R \to K = \text{link}(v; rK)$ be radial projection. Then p is not a p.l. map. However, p carries simplices of R onto simplices contained in $|K|$. Hence we may find a subdivision K' of K which contains a triangulation of $p(A)$ for each simplex A of K'.

For each $A \in K'$, let $\overline{A} = \text{cl.}(|v.A| - |v.A| \cap |v.R|) = \text{cl.}(|v.A) - |v.p^{-1}(A)|)$. $\overline{A}$ is a convex linear cell (in fact, a "truncated simplex"). The faces of $\overline{A}$ are the simplex $p^{-1}(A)$ and its faces, A and its faces, and the cells $\overline{B}$, where $B < A$. Moreover, $\overline{A} \cap \overline{B} = \overline{A \cap B}$, a common face of $\overline{A}$ and $\overline{B}$. Let $\overline{K} = \{\overline{A}$ and its faces $| A \in K'\}$. Then $\overline{K}$ is a cell complex and $|\overline{K}| = \text{cl.}(|v.K| - |\overline{\text{star}}(v;L)|)$.

Let K^* be a simplicial subdivision of $\overline{K}$ with no extra vertices. Then each vertex of K^* is either a vertex of K' or the image of a vertex of K' under p^{-1}. Define h: $K^* \to K \times I$ by sending a vertex x in K' to h(x) = (x, 0), a vertex y in |R| to h(y) = (py, 1), and extending linearly. This definition makes sense because $|R| \cap |K| = \emptyset$ and because h maps all the vertices of any simplex in K^* into the same convex subset of $K \times I$. It is clear that h is a homeomorphism; in fact, h maps $\overline{A}$ homeomorphically onto $A \times I$.

Lemma 1.22. If P and Q are n-balls, $P \cap Q = F$ is a common face, and cl.($\dot{P}$-F) and cl.($\dot{Q}$-F) are faces of P and Q respectively, then $P \cup Q$ is an n-ball.

Proof. Triangulate and let $A \in$ cl.(P-F). Link(A; $\overline{P\text{-}F}$) fails to be a sphere if and only if link(A; F) is non-empty. Similarly, link(A; F) fails to be a sphere if and only if link(A; $\overline{P\text{-}F}$) $\neq \emptyset$, if $A \in F$. So

$$\partial F = F \cap \overline{P\text{-}F} = \partial(\overline{P\text{-}F}).$$

Similarly, $\partial F = \partial(\overline{Q\text{-}F})$. Now the identity $\dot{F} \to \dot{F}$ extends (by Lemma 1.21) to p.l. homeomorphisms:

$$h_1: \overline{P\text{-}F} \longrightarrow a.\dot{F}$$

$$h_2: F \longrightarrow b.\dot{F}$$

$$h_3: \overline{Q\text{-}F} \longrightarrow c.\dot{F}.$$

(Here a, b, c, and $\dot{F}$ are assumed joinable in some Euclidean space.) Again we may extend h_1, h_2, and h_3 to get h_4: $P \to ab\dot{F}$ and $h_5: Q \to bc\dot{F}$, giving a p.l. homeomorphism

$$P \cup Q \cong ab\dot{F} \cup bc\dot{F} \cong ac\dot{F} = \text{a p.l. ball.}$$

<u>Lemma 1.23.</u> Let K be a combinatorial n-manifold. Let $K^+ = (K \times 0) \cup (\dot{K} \times I)$. Then $K^+ \cong K$ via a p.l. homeomorphism sending $(x, 1)$ to x if $x \in \dot{K}$.

<u>Proof.</u> Let $\{A_i \mid i = 1, \ldots, N\}$ be the simplices of $\dot{K}$ in order of decreasing dimension. Let $B_i = |A_i^*|$, $F_i = |A_i^{\#}|$; the p.l. balls are ordered in order of increasing dimension. Let $D_i = (B_i \times 0) \cup (F_i \times I)$. Let $V_o = \text{cl.}(K - \bigcup_{i=1}^{N} B_i)$. Let $U_o = V_o \times 0$. Let $U_i = U_o \cup \bigcup_{j=1}^{i} D_j$. Let $V_i = V_o \cup \bigcup_{j=1}^{i} B_j$. We define inductively a sequence of p.l. homeomorphisms

$h_i \colon U_i \longrightarrow V_i$ such that

1) $h_i(D_j) = B_j$, $j \leq i$

2) $h_i | U_o$ is given by $h_i(x, 0) = x$.

3) $h_i(x, 1) = x$ for all $x \in K$

Then the map h_N proves the lemma.

2) defines h_o. Assume h_{i-1} defined.

Now, $D_i = (B_i \times 0) \cup (F_i \times I)$.

$(B_i \times 0) \cap (F_i \times I)$, a face of $B_i \times 0$ by 1.19 and clearly a face of $F_i \times I$.

By 1.19, $\text{cl.}(\dot{B}_i - F_i)$ is a face of $\dot{B}_i$. Also $(F_i \times 1) \cup (\dot{F}_i \times I)$ is a face of $F_i \times I$. For let Δ be a simplex and linearly embed $\Delta \times I$ in $v\Delta$ with $\Delta \times 0 \subseteq \Delta$. Pseudo-radial projection from a point in $\mathring{\Delta} \times 0$ gives a p.l. homeomorphism $(\Delta \times 1) \cup (\dot{\Delta} \times I) \longrightarrow v\mathring{\Delta}$. Hence D_i is a ball.

Now, $\text{cl.}(\dot{D}_i - F_i \times 1) \subseteq U_{i-1}$. h_{i-1} maps $\text{cl.}(\dot{D}_i - F_i \times 1)$ homeomorphically to $\text{cl.}(\dot{B}_i - F_i)$. Define $h_i | F_i \times$) by $h_i(x, 1) = x$. This together with h_{i-1} defines a p.l. homeomorphism $\mathring{D}_i \longrightarrow \mathring{B}_i$, which may be extended to a p.l. homeomorphism $D_i \longrightarrow B_i$. Combine this last map with h_{i-1} to get h_i.

Corollary 1.24. There exists a neighborhood of $\dot{K}$ in K which is p.l. homeomorphic to $\mathring{K} \times I$. In fact, there exists an imbedding $c: \dot{K} \times I \longrightarrow K$, with $c(x, 0) = x$, whose image is a neighborhood of $\mathring{K}$. (The map c is called a boundary collar.)

Lemma 1.25. If S is a sphere and x and y are points of S, then there exists a p.l. homeomorphism $S \longrightarrow S$ sending x to y.

Proof. Exercise. (Hint: Use pseudo-radial projection.)

8. Removing Balls from Spheres.

Theorem 1.26. If B is an m-ball contained in the m-sphere S, then cl.$(S-B)$ is an m-ball.

Proof. By induction. For $m = 0$, this theorem is trivial. Assume the theorem for $(m-1)$.

1) $\overline{S-B}$ is a manifold with boundary $\dot{B}$. For there exist simplicial complexes $K_o \subseteq K$ with $|K| = S$, $|K_o| = B$. Now $|\overline{K-K_o}| = \text{cl.}\ \{|K| - |K_o|\}$.
(Recall: $\overline{K-K_o}$ = simplices of $K-K_o$ and their faces.)

We show that $\overline{K-K_o}$ is a combinatorial manifold. If $A \in K-K_o$, then $\text{link}(A;K)=\text{link}(A;\overline{K-K_o})$. For if $B \in \text{link}(A;K)$, then $AB \in K$. Since $A \notin K_o$, $AB \notin K_o$. Hence $B \in \text{link}(A;\ \overline{K-K_o})$. Hence $\text{link}(A;\overline{K-K_o})$ is an $(n-r-1)$ sphere, $r = \dim A$.

Say $A \in (\overline{K-K_o}) \cap K_o$. Let $r = \dim A$.

Claim: $\text{link}(A;\ \overline{K-K_o}) = \{\overline{\text{link}(A;K) - \text{link}(A;K_o)}\}$.

For $B \in \text{link}(A;\overline{K-K_o}) \iff AB \in \overline{K-K_o} \iff AB < C$, some $C \in K-K_o \iff AB < AC_1$, some $AC_1 \in K-K_o \iff B < C_1$, some C_1 in $\text{link}(A;K) - \text{link}(A;K_o)$.

Now, $\text{link}(A;K)$ is an $(m-r-1)$ sphere, and $\text{link}(A;K_o)$ is an $(m-r-1)$ sphere or ball. Since $\text{link}(A;K_o) \subsetneqq \text{link}(A;K)$, it cannot be a sphere. Hence by induction.

$$|\text{link}(A;\overline{K-K_o})| = \text{cl}(|\text{link}(A;K)| - |\text{link}(A;K_o)|)$$
$$= |\{\overline{\text{link}(A;K) - \text{link}(A;K_o)}\}|$$

is an m-r-1 ball. Hence $\overline{K-K_o}$ is a combinatorial n-manifold with boundary $\overline{K-K_o} \cap K_o$ $(= \partial K_o)$.

2) Let $L = \overline{K-K_o} \cup v.\dot{K}_o$, v a joinable point. The identity map on $|\overline{K-K_o}|$ extends to a p.l. homeomorphism $|L| \longrightarrow |K|$. For $|\dot{K}_o|$ is a sphere, so the identity map on $|\dot{K}_o|$ extends to a p.l. homeomorphism $|v.\dot{K}_o| \longrightarrow |K_o|$, by Lemma 1.21. So $|L|$ is an m-sphere. By Lemma 1.25, let $k: |L| \longrightarrow |\dot{\Delta}^{m+1}|$ be a p.l. homeomorphism such that $v' = k(v)$ is a vertex of $\dot{\Delta}^{m+1}$.

Now take first derived subdivisions and follow by further subdivision to get $\alpha(L)$ and $\beta(\Delta)$ so that $k: \alpha(L) \longrightarrow \beta(\dot{\Delta})$ is simplicial. Then $\overline{star}(v; \alpha(L)) = \overline{star}(v; \alpha(v.\dot{K}_o))$ does not meet $\alpha(\dot{K}_o)$ and $\overline{star}(v'; \beta(\Delta))$ does not meet $\beta(\Delta_1)$, where $\Delta = v'\Delta_1$.

By Lemma 1.22, $cl(|v\dot{K}_o| - |\overline{star}(v; \alpha(L))|) \cong \dot{K}_o \times I$, and $cl.\{|v'.\dot{\Delta}_1| - |\overline{star}(v'; \beta(v'.\dot{\Delta}_1))|\} \cong \dot{\Delta}_1 \times I$. By Lemma 1.23, $|\overline{K-K_o}| \cong [(\overline{K-K_o}) \times \{0\}] \cup |\dot{K}_o \times I|$. This last polyhedron is p.l. homeomorphic to

$$|\overline{K-K_o}| \cup cl.\{|v.\dot{K}_o| - |\overline{star}(v; \alpha(L)|\}$$

$$= cl.\{|\alpha(L)| - |\overline{star}(v; \alpha(L))|\} \cong cl.\{|\beta\dot{\Delta}| - |star(v'; \beta\dot{\Delta})|\}.$$

This last isomorphism being the restriction of k. Now, $\overline{star}(v'; \beta\dot{\Delta}) = \overline{star}(v'; \beta(v'.\dot{\Delta}_1))$ and $\beta(\dot{\Delta}) = \beta(\Delta_1) \cup \beta(v.\dot{\Delta}_1)$. Hence the last polyhedron above is p.l. homeomorphic to $|\Delta_1| \cup |\dot{\Delta}_1 \times I| \cong |\Delta_1|$, this last homeomorphism being given by Lemma 1.23. So $|\overline{K-K_o}| \cong |\Delta_1|$ and so $cl.(S-B)$ is an m-ball.

Corollary 1.27. If A is an n-ball and F is a face of A, then any p.l. homeomorphism $h\colon F \longrightarrow \Delta^{n-1}$ extends to a p.l. homeomorphism $A \longrightarrow \Delta^n = v.\Delta^{n-1}$.

Proof. $\dot{F}$ is the boundary of the ball $cl.(\dot{A}-F)$; this was shown in 2) of the proof of 1.26. So $h|\dot{F}$ extends to a p.l. homeomorphism $h_1\colon cl.(\dot{A}-F) \longrightarrow v.\dot{\Delta}^{n-1}$. Now $h_1 \cup h\colon \dot{A} \longrightarrow \dot{\Delta}^n = v.\dot{\Delta}^{n-1} \cup \Delta^{n-1}$ is a p.l. homeomorphism, and so we may extend to a p.l. homeomorphism $h'\colon A \longrightarrow \Delta^n$.

Corollary 1.28. If A and B are n-balls and $A \cap B$ is a common face, then $A \cup B$ is an n-ball.

Proof. Immediate from 1.26 and 1.22.

Corollary 1.29. If M is an n-manifold, B an n-ball, and $B \cap M = F$ is a face of B which lies in ∂M, then $M \cup B \cong M$.

Proof. Let $c\colon \dot{M} \times I \longrightarrow M$ be a boundary collar. Let $A = c(F \times I)$. A is an n-ball. $A \cap B = \{c(x,0) | x \in F\} = c(F \times 0) = F$, a common face of A and of B. Hence $A \cup B$ is an n-ball.

Let $F_1 = c(\dot{F} \times I \cup F \times 1)$, a face of A. Let $h\colon F_1 \longrightarrow \Delta^{n-1}$ be a p.l. homeomorphism. By Corollary 1.27, let $h_1\colon A \longrightarrow v\Delta$, extending h, be a p.l. homeomorphism. F_1 is also a face of $A \cup B$, since $F_1 = cl.(\dot{A} - F)$. Let $h_2\colon A \cup B \longrightarrow v\Delta$ extend h. Then $h_1^{-1}h_2\colon A \cup B \longrightarrow A$ is a p.l. homeomorphism which is the identity on $c((\dot{F} \times I) \cup (F \times 1))$. Define $k\colon M \cup B \longrightarrow M$

by letting it be an extension of $h_1^{-1}h_2$ which is the identity whenever $h_1^{-1}h_2$ is not already defined. Then k is a p.l. homeomorphism.

APPENDIX TO CHAPTER I.

We want to show that if A is a convex linear cell, then a cell B is a face of A if and only if

1) If P is the hyperplane spanned by B, $P \cap A = B$;

and

2) No point of P lies between any two points of $A - B$.

Clearly any face satisfies these conditions. Conversely, let $\{f_i = 0,\ g_j \geq 0\}$ be a system of equations for A. Suppose $\{f_i = 0,\ g_1 = \dots = g_s = 0,\ g_{s+1} \geq 0, \dots, g_t \geq 0\}$ is the smallest face $\ulcorner B \urcorner$ of A containing B. Then given $j > s$, there exists $x_j \in B$ with $g_j(x_j) > 0$. Put

$$x = \frac{x_1 + \dots + x_j}{t-s} .$$

Then $g_j(x) > 0$ for all $j \geq s+1$. If $y \in \ulcorner B \urcorner$ and ℓ is the line segment from x to y, then from 1) there must exist $z \in \ell \cap \ulcorner B \urcorner$ with x between y and z. By 2), y and/or z is in B. So by 1), y <u>and</u> z are in B. So $x \in B$. Thus $B = \ulcorner B \urcorner$.

Chapter II - Regular Neighborhood Theory

1. Collapsing

Definition. Suppose $P_0 \subseteq P$ are Euclidean polyhedra, and suppose $B = cl_P(P - P_0)$ is a p.l. ball which has $B \cap P_0$ as a face. Then we say that P collapses to P_0 by an elementary collapse, and we write $P \overset{e}{\searrow} P_0$. We say that P collapses to the subpolyhedron P_0 and write $P \searrow P_0$ if there exists a finite sequence $P = P_r \overset{e}{\searrow} P_{r-1} \overset{e}{\searrow} \cdots \overset{e}{\searrow} P_0$.

Remark. If $P \searrow P_0$, then P_0 is a strong deformation retract of P. For suppose $P \overset{e}{\searrow} P_0$; then if $B = cl(P - P_0)$, $B \cap P_0$ is a strong deformation retract of B, being a face of B. If $\tilde{\varphi}_t$ is the deformation retraction, then setting $\varphi_t = 1_{P_0} \cup \tilde{\varphi}_t$ defines a strong deformation retraction of P to P_0.

Definition. P is said to be collapsible if P collapses to a singular point. If this is the case, we write $P \searrow 0$.

By the preceding remark, every collapsible polyhedron is contractible. The converse is false, however, as the following example shows.

Consider a two-simplex: 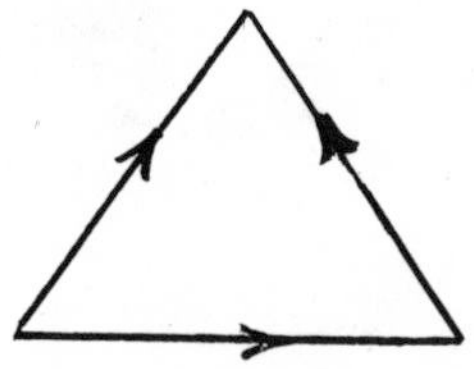 Let D be the quotient space obtained by making the identifications shown. Thesecond derived of this two-simplex is a triangulation consistent with the identifications, and so we may consider D to be a simplicial complex. Moreover, by a theorem of Whitehead,

D is contractible; for $\pi_1(D) = 0$, the obvious cell-decomposition shows $H_i(D) = 0$, $i > 0$, and so $\pi_i(D) = 0$, all i.

Now D is not collapsible. For suppose $D \overset{e}{\searrow} D_o$, $\overline{D - D_o} = B$. Let $x \in \partial B - B \cap D_o$. Then $\text{link}(x; D) = \text{link}(x, B)$ = a p.l. ball. But no point of D has a p.l. ball as a link. It turns out that $D \times I \searrow 0$, $I = [0, 1]$.

<u>Definition.</u> Let $K_o \subseteq K$ be simplicial complexes. Suppose A and aA are not in K_o but are simplices of K, where a is a vertex of K_o, and suppose that $K = K_o \cup \{A\} \cup \{aA\}$. (We also write this condition in the form $K = K_o + A + aA$.) Then we say that K collapses by an <u>elementary simplicial collapse</u> to K_o, and we write $K \overset{es}{\searrow} K_o$. We say that K <u>collapses simplicially</u> to K_o if there is a finite sequence $K = K_r \overset{es}{\searrow} K_{r-1} \overset{es}{\searrow} \cdots \overset{es}{\searrow} K_o$, and if this is the case, we write $K \overset{s}{\searrow} K_o$.

<u>Definition.</u> If K is a complex, $B \in K$ is called a <u>principal simplex</u> if B is not a proper face of any simplex of K. If the face A of B is the proper face of no other simplex of K, then A is called a <u>free face</u> of B in K.

<u>Remarks:</u> 1) An elementary simplicial collapse is an elementary collapse.
2) If $K \overset{es}{\searrow} K_o$ and $K = K_o + A + aA$, then aA is a principal simplex of K with free face A. On the other hand, if B is a principal simplex of K with free face A, then $B = aA$; and if $K_o = K - (\{A\} \cup \{B\})$, K_o is a subcomplex and $K \overset{es}{\searrow} K_o$.
3) It is false that $|K| \searrow |L|$, L a subcomplex of K, implies that $K \overset{s}{\searrow} L$.

Lemma 2.1. a) A cone collapses simplicially to a subcone. Precisely, if $K_o \subsetneq K$ are simplicial complexes, then $v.K \overset{s}{\searrow} v.K_o$, v a joinable point.

b) Say K_1, K_2 are subcomplexes of K, $K_1 \overset{s}{\searrow} K_3$, and $K_1 \cap K_2 \subseteq K_3$. Then $K_1 \cup K_2 \overset{s}{\searrow} K_3 \cup K_2$.

Proof. Let $A_1, \ldots, A_r$ be the simplices of $K - K_o$ in order of decreasing dimension. Then A_1 is a free face of the principal simplex $v.A_1$. Collapse out A_1 and $v.A_1$. Then A_2 is a free face of the principal simplex $v.A_2$, in what remains, etc. ...

b) It suffices to consider $K_1 \overset{es}{\searrow} K_3$, with $K_1 \cap K_2 \subseteq K_3$. Suppose $K_1 = K_3 + aA + A$. Then aA and A are not in K_2, since $K_1 \cap K_2 \subseteq K_3$. Hence $K_1 \cup K_2 = K_3 \cup K_2 + aA + A$ defines an elementary simplicial collapse $K_1 \cup K_2 \overset{es}{\searrow} K_3 \cup K_2$.

Lemma 2.2. If K collapses to K_o simplicially, and if $\sigma(K)$ is a stellar subdivision of K, then $\sigma(K) \overset{s}{\searrow} \sigma(K_o)$.

Unsolved Problem: Is this true for non-stellar subdivision? It is true for complexes of dimension ≤ 3.

Proof. In this proof we do not distinguish in the notation between a simplex and its associated simplicial complex. If A is a simplex, we write A for the complex $\overline{A}$.

It suffices to consider elementary simplicial collapses. It also suffices to consider only subdivisions obtained by starring at one simplex. So suppose $K = K_o + aA + A$, aA a principal simplex with free face A, and suppose that

$\sigma(K) = K - B.\mathrm{link}(B;k) + b\dot{B}\,\mathrm{link}(B;K), \quad b \in \mathring{B}, \quad B \in K.$

<u>Case 1:</u> B not a face of aA; then $\sigma(aA) = aA$, and

$\sigma(K) = \sigma(K_o) + aA + A.$

<u>Case 2:</u> $B \leq A$. Let $A = BA_1$ (with $A_1 = \emptyset$ a possibility). Then $\sigma(aA) = b.B.a.A_1$. We have:

$$a.A_1.b.\dot{B} \overset{s}{\searrow} a.A_1.\dot{B} + a\dot{A}_1.b.\dot{B},$$

since $A_1.\dot{B} + \dot{A}_1.b.\dot{B}$ is a subcomplex of $A_1.b.\dot{B}$, and by Lemma 2.1.

[Picture for Case 2]

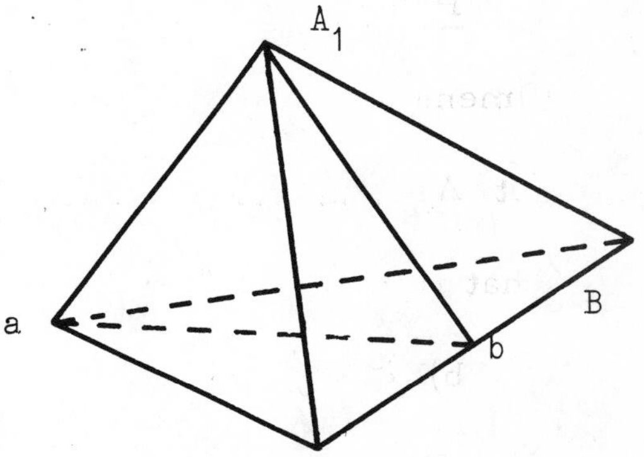

But $a\dot{A} = a.\dot{B}A_1 + aB\dot{A}_1$, so

$$\sigma(a\dot{A}) = a.\dot{B}.A_1 + a.b.\dot{B}\dot{A}_1.$$

So, $\sigma(aA) \overset{s}{\searrow} \sigma(a\dot{A})$. Let $K_1 = \sigma(aA)$, $K_3 = \sigma(a\dot{A})$, $K_2 = \sigma(K_o)$. Then $K_1 \cap K_2 = \sigma(a\dot{A}) \subseteq K_3$, so

$$K_1 \cup K_2 = \sigma(aA) \cup \sigma(K_o) \overset{s}{\searrow} K_2 \cup K_3 = \sigma(K_o) \cup \sigma(a\dot{A}) = \sigma(K_o).$$

That is, $\sigma(K) \overset{s}{\searrow} \sigma(K_o)$, by Lemma 2.1.

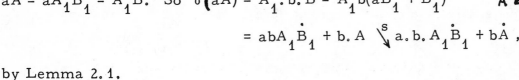

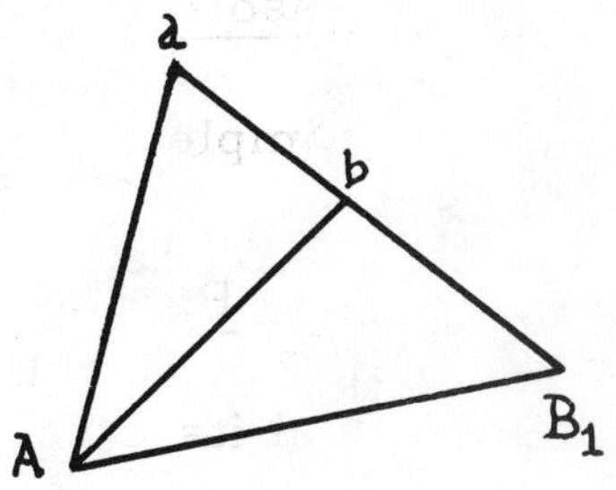

<u>Case 3:</u> $B \lneq aA$ but $B \nleq A$ ($\nleq$ = "not a face of"); that is, $B \subsetneq a\dot{A}$. Put $B = aB_1$, $A = A_1B_1$. Then $aA = aA_1B_1 = A_1B$. So $\sigma(aA) = A_1.b.\dot{B} = A_1b(a\dot{B}_1 + B_1)$

$$= abA_1\dot{B}_1 + b.A \overset{s}{\searrow} a.b.A_1\dot{B}_1 + b\dot{A},$$

by Lemma 2.1.

Now,

$$abA_1\dot{B}_1 + b\dot{A} = abA_1\dot{B}_1 + b(\dot{A}_1B_1 + A_1\dot{B}_1)$$

$$= abA_1\dot{B}_1 + b\dot{A}_1B_1 \overset{s}{\searrow} a(b\dot{A}_1\dot{B}_1 + A_1\dot{B}_1) + b\dot{A}_1B_1 ,$$

by Lemma 2.1 (both parts). Hence we have

$$\sigma(aA) \overset{s}{\searrow} a(b\dot{A}_1\dot{B}_1 + A_1\dot{B}_1) + b\dot{A}_1B_1 .$$

Now,

$$\sigma(a\dot{A}) = \sigma(a\dot{A}_1B_1 + aA_1\dot{B}_1) = \sigma(\dot{A}_1B + aA_1\dot{B}_1)$$

$$= aA_1\dot{B}_1 + b(a\dot{B}_1 + B_1)\dot{A}_1 = a(b\dot{A}_1\dot{B}_1 + A_1\dot{B}_1) + b\dot{A}_1B_1 .$$

That is, $\sigma(aA) \overset{s}{\searrow} \sigma(a\dot{A})$. Now continue as in Case 2).

<u>Case 4:</u> $B = aA$. Then $\sigma(B) = \sigma(aA) = b.\dot{B} = b(a\dot{A} + A)$. But $b(a\dot{A} + A) \overset{s}{\searrow} ba\dot{A}$ and $ab\dot{A} \searrow a\dot{A} = \sigma(a\dot{A})$. Thus $\sigma(aA) \overset{s}{\searrow} \sigma(a\dot{A})$. Now proceed as in Case 2).

<u>Lemma 2.3.</u> Let $|K| \overset{e}{\searrow} |L|$, L a subcomplex of the simplicial complex K. Then there exists a subdivision K' of K such that if L' is the induced subdivision of L, $K' \overset{s}{\searrow} L'$, and L' is stellar.

<u>Proof.</u> Let $B = cl(|K| - |L|) = |\overline{K-L}|$. $B \cap |L| = F$, a face of the ball B. By Corollary 1.27, there is a p.l. homeomorphism $h: (B, F) \longrightarrow (\Delta; \Delta_1)$, where Δ_1 is a free face of the simplex Δ (i.e., $\dim \Delta_1 = \dim \Delta - 1$).

Write B for the triangulalion $\overline{K - L}$ of B. Let B' and Δ' be subdivisions of B and Δ respectively, such that $h: B' \longrightarrow \Delta'$ is simplicial and B' is stellar; apply Lemma 1.10 to h^{-1}. Note that as $h(F) = \Delta_1$, B' contains a triangulation of F, say F'. Let K' be a stellar subdivision of K whose induced subdivision on B is B'.

Let $p: \Delta \longrightarrow \Delta_1$ be the linear map which is the identity on Δ_1 and sends the vertex v opposite Δ_1 to an interior point of Δ_1. Then there is a subdivision Δ'' of Δ' such that $p: \Delta'' \longrightarrow \Delta_1''$ is simplicial, and Δ_1'' is a stellar subdivision of Δ_1'.

Let B" be the subdivision of B' making $h: B'' \longrightarrow \Delta''$ simplicial. Since $h: B' \longrightarrow \Delta'$ was already simplicial, F" is a stellar subdivision of F', and extends to a stellar subdivision L" of L, Put $K'' = B'' \cup L''$. Since B" and L" meet in the common subcomplex F", K'' is a well defined subdivision of K, not necessarily stellar.

To prove this lemma, it suffices by Lemma 2.1 to prove that $B'' \overset{s}{\searrow} F''$, as $B'' \cap L'' = F''$. To prove that $B'' \overset{s}{\searrow} F''$, it suffices to prove that $\Delta'' \overset{s}{\searrow} \Delta_1''$, where $p: \Delta'' \longrightarrow \Delta_1''$ is simplicial. Now let $\{A_i\}$ be the simplices of Δ_1'' in order of decreasing dimension. $p^{-1}A_i \overset{s}{\searrow} p^{-1}\dot{A}_i \cup A_i$ by collapsing the principal simplexes of $p^{-1}A_i$ from their top faces in order. Doing this in turn gives the required simplicial collapse of Δ'' onto Δ_1''.

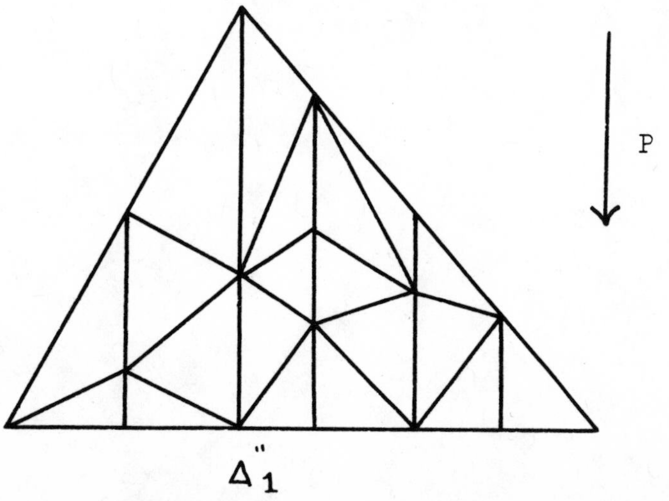

Theorem 2.4. If L and K are simplicial complexes, $|L| \subseteq |K|$, and if $|K| \searrow |L|$, then there exists subdivisions K' and L' with $L' \subset K'$ and $K' \overset{s}{\searrow} L'$.

Proof. By induction, assume the theorem for all collapses consisting of at most (n-1) elementary collapses. Suppose $|K| = P_n \overset{e}{\searrow} \cdots \overset{e}{\searrow} P_o = |L|$. There is a triangulation K_n of K containing as subcomplexes triangulations of P_i, say K_i. By induction, there is a subdivision K'_{n-1} of K_{n-1} with $K'_{n-1} \overset{s}{\searrow} K'_o$. Now, K'_{n-1} extends to a subdivision K'_n of K_n. By Lemma 2.3, there exist subdivisions K''_n and K''_{n-1} of K'_n and K'_{n-1} respectively, with K''_{n-1} stellar, such that $K''_n \overset{s}{\searrow} K''_{n-1}$.

By Lemma 2.2, $K''_{n-1} \overset{s}{\searrow} K''_o$ = induced subdivision of K'_o. Hence $K''_n \overset{s}{\searrow} K''_o$.

2. Full Subcomplexes and Derived Neighborhoods

Definition. If K_o is a subcomplex of the simplicial complex K, K_o is said to be full if any simplex in K all of whose vertices lie in K_o is a simplex of K_o; i.e., no simplex in $K - K_o$ has all its vertices in K_o.

Lemma 2.5. 1) If K_o is a subcomplex of K and $K'_o \subseteq K'$ are first deriveds, then K'_o is a full subcomplex of K_o.

2) If K_o is a full subcomplex of K and $K'_o \subseteq K'$ is any subdivision then K'_o is full in K'.

3) If K_o is full in K and $A \in K\text{-}K_o$, then $A \cap |K_o|$ is either empty or a single face of A. (And conversely.)

4) K_o is full in $K \iff$ there exists a linear map $f: K \longrightarrow R^+$ such that $f^{-1}(0) = K_o$. (Linear means linear on simplices $R^+ = [0, \infty)$.)

Proof. 1) If $\sigma \in K'$, let $\sigma = \hat{A}_1 \dots \hat{A}_s$, $A_1 < \dots < A_s \in K$. If $\hat{A}_i \in K'_o$, $1 \leq i \leq s$, then A_s has an interior point in K_o and hence $A_s \in K_o$. So $A_i \in K_o$, $i \leq s$, and $\sigma \in K'_o$.

3) If $A \in K\text{-}K_o$ meets $|K_o|$, let $(a_1, \dots, a_i)$ be the vertices of A in K_o. Let $A_1 = \text{span}\,\{a_1, \dots, a_i\}$. Then $A_1 \in K_o$ and $A_1 < A$. Since $A \cap |K_o|$ is always a union of faces of A, each of which is spanned by its vertices, $A_1 = A \cap |K_o|$.

2) Suppose $K_o \subseteq K$ is full. Let $\sigma \in K'$. Choose $A \in K$ such that the barycenter of σ is in $\mathring{A}$. Then $\mathring{\sigma} \subseteq \mathring{A}$. Moreover, $\sigma \cap |K_o| \subseteq A \cap |K_o| = A_1$, A_1 a face of A. Therefore $\sigma \cap |K_o| = \sigma \cap A_1$, which is either empty or a

face of σ. Thus, every simplex of K' which meets K'_o meets it in exactly one face. This means that K'_o is full in K'. (Converse of 3).)

4) If $K_o \subseteq K$ is a full subcomplex, let $f: K \to R^+$ be defined by setting $f(v) = 0$ if v is a vertex of K_o and $f(v) = 1$ if v is a vertex in $K-K_o$, and extending linearly over simplices. Clearly, $|K_o| = f^{-1}(0)$.

Conversely, if $f: K \to R^+$ is given and we set $K_o = f^{-1}(0)$, then K_o is a full subcomplex. It is a subcomplex because if $x \in \mathring{\sigma}$, $\sigma \in K$, then $f(x) = 0 \implies f(\sigma) = 0$. It is full because if $\sigma \in K$ and f is zero on the vertices of σ, then $f(\sigma) = 0$.

Definition. Suppose that L_o is a subcomplex of L. Then we define $N(L_o; L) = \bigcup_{r \in L_o} \overline{\text{star}}(v; L)$ (union over vertices), called the closed simplicial neighborhood of L_o in L.

Definition. Suppose that X is a polyhedron, M an m-manifold, $X \subseteq M$. Let $K_o \subseteq K$ be a triangulation of $X \subseteq M$; i.e., $|K_o| = X$, $|K| = M$; with K_o a full subcomplex of K. Then $N = |N(K'_o; K')|$ is called a derived neighborhood of X in M, where $K'_o \subseteq K'$ is the first derived subdivision of $K_o \subseteq K$.

Definition. If $K_o \subseteq K$ is any triangulation of $X \subseteq M$ and if $K_o^{(r)} \subseteq K^{(r)}$ is the rth subdivision, then $|N(K_o^{(r)}; K^{(r)})|$ is called an rth derived neighborhood of X in M. For $r \geq 2$, an rth derived neighborhood is a derived neighborhood.

Remark. The reason for taking full subcomplexes or at least 2nd deriveds as derived neighborhoods is that we want to be able to prove that a derived neighborhood of X collapses to X. If $M = \Delta^2$, $X = \dot{\Delta}^2$, then the first derived neighborhood of X in M is M, which does not collapse to X. The 2nd derived neighborhood does collapse to X, however.

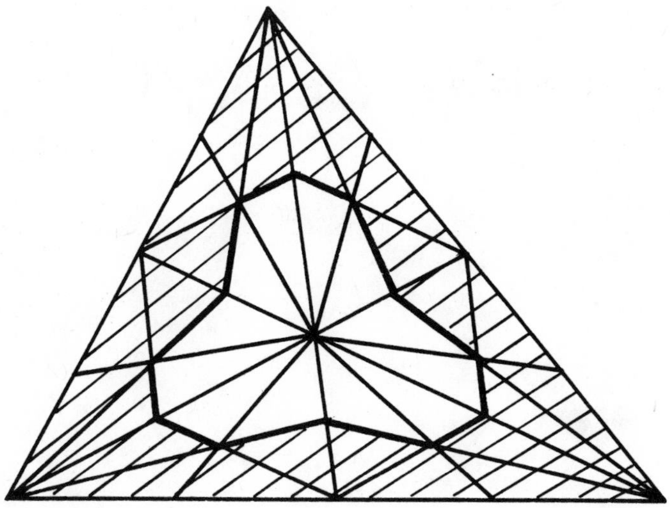

Lemma 2.6. Let K_o be a full subcomplex of K. Suppose $f; K \longrightarrow \mathbb{R}^+$ and $K_o = f^{-1}(0)$, f linear. Suppose $0 < \varepsilon < f(v)$, v any vertex in $K-K_o$. Then $f^{-1}([0, \varepsilon])$ is a derived neighborhood of $|K_o|$ in $|K|$.

Proof. Let K' be obtained from K by starring each simplex A at $\hat{A} \in \mathring{A}$ in order of increasing dimensi on, choosing $\hat{A} \in f^{-1}(\varepsilon)$ if $\mathring{A} \cap f^{-1}(\varepsilon) \neq \emptyset$.

Claim: $|N(K_o' ; K')| = f^{-1}([0, \varepsilon])$. Let σ be a principal simplex of $N(K_o', K')$. $\sigma = \hat{A}_1 \ldots \hat{A}_r$, $A_1 < \ldots < A_r$, $A_i \in K$. Then $\hat{A}_i \in K_o'$, so $A_i \in K_o$, some i.

Take i as large as possible with $A_i \in K_o$. Then $f(\hat{A}_j) = 0$, $j < i$. $A_{i+1}, \ldots, A_r$ have vertices whose values under f are greater than ε. Hence $f^{-1}(\varepsilon) \cap \mathring{A}_{i+k} \neq \emptyset$, $1 \leq k \leq r-i$, by linearity of f. Therefore, $f(\hat{A}_{i+1}) = \ldots = f(\hat{A}_r) = \varepsilon$, so $N(K'_o, K') \subset f^{-1}[0, \varepsilon]$.

Conversely, suppose $\hat{A}_1 \ldots \hat{A}_r \subseteq f^{-1}([0, \varepsilon])$, $A_1 < \ldots < A_r$. Then $f(\hat{A}_i) = 0$ or ε. If $f(A_1) = 0$, then A_1 is a vertex of K'_o. If $f(\hat{A}_1) = \varepsilon$, then A_1 has a vertex in K_o, say v, with $\{v\} \neq A_1$, and so $v.\hat{A}_1 \ldots \hat{A}_r \in K'$ and lies in $f^{-1}([0, \varepsilon])$. But $v.\hat{A}_1 \ldots \hat{A}_r \in N(K'_o; K')$. So $f^{-1}[0, \varepsilon] \subset |N(K'_o, K')|$.

3. Ambient Isotopy

Definition. An ambient isotopy of a polyhedron X is a p.l. homeomorphism $h: X \times I \longrightarrow X \Delta I$ which commutes with projection on I (i.e., is level preserving) and has the property that $h(x, 0) = (x, 0)$, all $x \in X$.

If h is an ambient isotopy, we write h_t for the p.l. homeomorphism of X onto itself defined by setting $h(x, t) = (h_t(x), t)$. If X_1 and X_2 are polyhedra contained in X, we say that h throws X_1 onto X_2 if $h_1(X_1) = X_2$. Two polyhedra contained in X are said to be ambient isotopic if there exists an ambient isotopy throwing one onto the other. The relation "X_1 is ambient isotopic to X_2" is clearly an equivalence relation.

A homeomorphism $k: X \longrightarrow X$ is said to be ambient isotopic to the identity if there exists an ambient isotopy h of X with $h_1 = k$.

If $X_o \subseteq X$, we say that the ambient isotopy h of X keeps X_o fixed if $h | X_o \times I$ = identity map of $X_o \times I$.

Lemma 2.7. Let $K_o \subseteq K$ be simplicial complexes, and let $h: |K| \rightarrow |K_o|$ be a p.l. homeomorphism such that

1) $h| \, |K_o|$ = identity.

2) $h(\sigma) = \sigma$, all $\sigma \in K$.

Then h is ambient isotopic to the identity via an ambient isotopy keeping $|K_o|$ fixed.

Proof. Let $\sigma_1, \ldots, \sigma_n$ be the simplices of $K-K_o$, in order of increasing dimension. Define H on $K_o \times I$ by setting it equal to the identity. Define H

on $K \times 1$ by setting $H(x, 1) = (h(x), 1)$ all $x \in K$. Assume that H has been defined on $\sigma_j \times I$, all $j < i$. Then H is defined on the faces of $\sigma_j \times I$. Extend H to $\sigma_i \times I$ by defining $H(\hat{\sigma}_i, \frac{1}{2}) = (\hat{\sigma}_i, \frac{1}{2})$ and joining linearly, $\hat{\sigma}_i$ a point in $\mathring{\sigma}_i$. This defines a p.l. homeomorphism $H: K \times I \longrightarrow K \times I$. It is easy to check that it is level preserving and is therefore the desired ambient isotopy.

Corollary 2.8. If $h: B \longrightarrow B$, B a p.l. ball, is a p.l. homeomorphism and if $h|\dot{B}$ = identity of $\dot{B}$, then h is ambient isotopic to the identity, keeping $\dot{B}$ fixed.

Proof. Let $K = \Delta$, $K_0 = \dot{\Delta}$ and apply Lemma 2.7.

Lemma 2.9. Let N_1 and N_2 be two derived neighborhoods of the polyhedron X in the polyhedron M. Then there is an ambient isotopy throwing N_1 onto N_2 which is fixed on X.

Proof. Let $K_1 \subsetneq J_1$ and $K_2 \subsetneq J_2$ be triangulations of $X \subsetneq M$, with K_i full in J_i. Let primes denote first derived subdivisions, and suppose $N_1 = |N(K_1'; J_1')|$ and $N_2 = |N(K_2'; J_2')|$. Let $K_0 \subsetneq J_0$ be a common subdivision of $K_1 \subsetneq J_1$ and $K_2 \subsetneq J_2$. (Choose subdivisions making $1 \;:\; |J_0| \longrightarrow |J_1|$ simplicial. They obviously are the same.) Then K_0 is a full subcomplex of J_0 and, so (primes denote first deriveds) $N_0 = |N_0(J_0'; K_0')|$ is a derived neighborhood.

It clearly suffices to find an isotopy throwing N_1 onto N_0 and an isotopy throwing N_2 onto N_0. We will construct an ambient isotopy throwing N_1 onto N_0.

Let $f: |J_1| \longrightarrow R^+$ be a map which is linear on simplices, with $f^{-1}(0) = |K_1|$. Then f is also linear on simplices of J_o. Let ε be such that $0 < \varepsilon < f(v)$ for all vertices v in $J_o - K_o$. Then there exist first derived subdivisions $K_o^* \subseteq J_o^*$ and $K_1^* \subseteq J_1^*$ of $K_o \subseteq J_o$ and $K_1 \subseteq J_1$, respectively, such that $f^{-1}([0, \varepsilon]) = |N(K_1^*; J_1^*)| = |N(K_o^*; J_o^*)| = N^*$, by the proof of Lemma 2.6.

Let $\{A_i\}$ = simplices of J_1. Let J_1' be obtained by starring at points $\hat{A}_i \in \mathring{A}_i$. Say J_1^* is obtained by starring $\hat{\hat{A}}_i \in \mathring{A}_i$. From the proof of Lemma 2.6, it is clear that we may suppose $\hat{A}_i = \hat{\hat{A}}_i$ if $A_i \in K_1$. Define a simplicial homeomorphism $J_1' \xrightarrow{h} J_1^*$ by sending $\hat{A}_i$ to $\hat{\hat{A}}_i$ and extending linearly over simplices. By the Lemma 2.7, h is ambient isotopic to the identity, keeping $|K_1|$ fixed, for if $\sigma \in J_1$, $h(\sigma) = \bar{\sigma}$, and $h \,|\, |K_1| =$ identity. Hence there is an ambient isotopy keeping $|K_1|$ fixed and throwing N_1 onto $N^* = |N(K^*; J^*)|$. Similarly, there is an ambient isotopy keeping $|K_o|$ fixed throwing N_o onto $N^* = |N(K_o^*; J_o^*)|$, and so N_1 is ambient isotopic to N_o, keeping $|K_o|$ fixed.

<u>Lemma 2.10.</u> If X is a polyhedron contained in the polyhedron M, and if N is a derived neighborhood of X in M, then $N \searrow X$.

<u>Proof.</u> In view of Lemma 2.9, it suffices to prove that $N \searrow X$ for <u>one</u> derived neighborhood N. So let $K_o \subseteq K$ be a triangulation of $X \subseteq M$, and assume K_o is full in K. Then let $f: K \longrightarrow R^+$ be linear, with $f^{-1}(0) = K_o$. Let $\varepsilon > 0$ be such that $\varepsilon < f(v)$, all vertices v of $K - K_o$. We have seen that

$N = f^{-1}([0, \varepsilon])$ is a derived neighborhood of K_o. So it suffices to show that $f^{-1}([0, \varepsilon]) \searrow |K_o|$.

Let $\{A_i | i = 1, \ldots, r\}$ be the simplices of $K - K_o$ in order of increasing dimension. Then $C_i = A_i \cap f^{-1}([0, \varepsilon])$ is a convex linear cell and so a p.l. ball. Let $F_i = A_i \cap f^{-1}(\varepsilon)$, a face. Now set $U_o = (K_o)$, and set $U_i = U_o \cup (\cup\{C_j | j = 1, \ldots, i\})$. Then $C_i \cap U_{i-1} = C_i \cap \dot{A}_i = cl\{C_i - F_i\}$ is a face of C_i. So $cl\{U_i - U_{i-1}\} = cl\{C_i - C_i \cap U_{i-1}\} = C_i$ is a ball meeting U_{i-1} in a face. Hence $U_i \overset{e}{\searrow} U_{i-1}$. But $U_r = f^{-1}([0, \varepsilon])$.

4. Existence and Uniqueness of Regular Neighborhoods

Definition. Let X be a polyhedron contained in the p.l. m-manifold M. $N \subseteq M$ is called a regular neighborhood of X in M if

1) N is a closed neighborhood of X in M,

2) N is an m-manifold, and

3) $N \searrow X$.

This section is devoted to the proof of the following theorem.

Theorem 2.11. Let $X \subseteq M$, M and m-manifold, X a polyhedron. Then

1) Any derived neighborhood of X is a regular neighborhood;

2) If N_1 and N_2 are regular neighborhoods of X in M, then there exists a p.l. homeomorphism $h: N_1 \longrightarrow N_2$ such that $h(x) = x$ if $x \in X$; and

3) If X is collapsible ($X \searrow 0$), then any regular neighborhood of X is a p.l. m-ball.

Theorem 2.11 is proven by induction. We consider the following three statements, for each integer $n \geq 0$:

E(n): If X is a polyhedron contained in the m-manifold M, and if $m \leq n$, then every derived neighborhood of X is a regular neighborhood.

U(n): If N_1 and N_2 are derived neighborhoods of X in M^m, an m-manifold, and if $m \leq n$, then there exists a p.l. homeomorphism $h: N_1 \longrightarrow N_2$ which is the identity on X.

B(n): In a manifold of dimension at most n, every regular neighborhood of a collapsible polyhedron is a p.l. m-ball.

Lemma 2.12. U(n) implies B(n).

Proof. Let dim $M \leq n$. If $X \searrow \{x_0\}$ and N is a regular neighborhood of X in M, then X is a regular neighborhood of $\{x_0\}$. Let $M = |K|$ be a triangulation of M with x_0 a vertex of K. Then $|\overline{\text{star}}(x_0; K)| = |x_0 . \text{link}(x_0; K)|$ is a p.l. m-ball, and a closed neighborhood of x_0. Moreover, $|\overline{\text{star}}(x_0; K)| \searrow \{x_0\}$. So U(n) implies that N is homeomorph to the p.l. m-ball $|\overline{\text{star}}(x_0, K)|$.

Lemma 2.13. E(n-1) and B(n-1) implies E(n).

Proof. Let $X \subseteq M$ be a polyhedron contained in the m-manifold M, $m \leq n$. Let $K_0 \subseteq K$ be a triangulation of $X \subseteq M$, with K_0 full in K. Let $N = |N(K_0'; K')|$. N is clearly a closed (topological) neighborhood of X, and we know that $N \searrow X$. So it remains only to show that N is a p.l. m-manifold. To do this, it suffices to prove that $N(K_0'; K')$, for which we also write N, by abuse of notation, is a combinatiorial m-manifold. Using induction and the formula $\text{link}(AB; N) = \text{link}(A; \text{link}(B; N))$ with a single vertex, it is easy to see that N will be a combinatorial m-manifold if (and only if) for every vertex v of N, $\text{link}(v; N)$ is an (m-1)-sphere or ball.

So let v be a vertex of N. If $v \in K_0'$, then $\overline{\text{star}}(v; K') \subset N$, and so $\text{link}(v; N) = \text{link}(v; K')$ = a sphere or ball of dimension (m-1).

Suppose on the other hand that $v \in N - K_0'$. Then $v = \hat{A}$ for some simplex $A \in K$. Let $B = A \cap |K_0|$, a single (simplicial) face of A by fullness of K_0 (B is clearly non-empty).

Let $\sigma \in K'$, and write $\sigma = \hat{A}_1 \ldots \hat{A}_s$, $A_1 < \ldots < A_s \in K$. Then $\sigma \in \text{link}(v; K') \Longleftrightarrow A_j < A < A_{j+1}$ some j, or $A < A_1$ or $A_s < A$. So if $S = \{\hat{B}_1 \ldots \hat{B}_j \mid A \lneq B_1 < \ldots < B_j \in K\}$, then $\sigma \in \text{link}(v; K') \Longleftrightarrow \sigma = \sigma_1 \sigma_2$, where $\sigma_1 \in (\dot{A})'$ and $\sigma_2 \in S$, $(\dot{A})'$ being the induced subdivision of K' on $\dot{A}$. (We allow the possibility $\sigma_i = \emptyset$, $i = 1, 2$, and write $\sigma_1 . \emptyset = \sigma_1$, $\emptyset . \sigma_2 = \sigma_2$.) Thus, $\text{link}(v; K') = \dot{A}.S$.

Let $L = \dot{A}.S$. Now $A < B \Longrightarrow \hat{B} \notin K'_o$. Hence $S \cap K'_o = \emptyset$. Therefore $L \cap K'_o = \dot{A}' \cap K'_o = B'$. Therefore, $L \cap N$ consists of the simplices of L meeting B' and their faces. The fact that B is convex insures that it and its faces form a full subcomplex of any simplicial complex containing it. We have

$$L \cap N = N(B'; L) = N(B'; \dot{A}'S) = N(B'; \dot{A}').S,$$

the last equality being a consequence of the fact that $B' \subseteq \dot{A}'$.

$N(B'; \dot{A}')$ is a derived neighborhood of the collapsible complex B' in the manifold $|\dot{A}'|$ of dimension at most $(n-1)$. Hence by $B(n-1)$ and $E(n-1)$, $|N(B'; \dot{A}')|$ is a p.l. ball whose dimension is $(\dim A - 1)$. However, S is p.l. homeomorphic to $\text{link}(A; K)$. In fact, if $A < B$ and C is the complementary face, the map on vertices which sends $\hat{B}$ to $\hat{C}$ determines a simplicial homeomorphism of S onto $(\text{link}(A; K))'$. Thus, $|S|$ is a p.l. ball of dimension equal to $m - \dim A - 1$. Hence $|\dot{A}'.S|$ is a p.l. ball fo dimension $m-1$.

Thus to complete the proof, it remains only to show that $\text{link}(v; N) = \text{link}(v; K') \cap N$. Certainly, $\text{link}(v; N) \subset \text{link}(v, K') \cap N$. Conversely, if $\sigma \in \text{link}(v; K') \cap N = N(B', \dot{A}').S$, then $\sigma = \sigma_1 \sigma_2$ where $\sigma_1 \in \dot{A}'_1$, $\sigma_2 \in S$ $\sigma_1 < \tau_1$, τ_1 meets B'. So $v\sigma < v\tau_1\sigma_2$ which meets B'. So $v\sigma \in N$, $\sigma \in \text{link}(v, N)$.

Lemma 2.14. If M is an m-manifold, if $X \subseteq M$ is a polyhedron, if $B \subsetneq M$ is an m-ball such that $F = B \cap \dot{M}$ is a face of B, and if $B \cap X = \emptyset$, then there exists a p.l. homeomorphism $h: cl(m-B) \longrightarrow M$ with $h|X$ = identity of X.

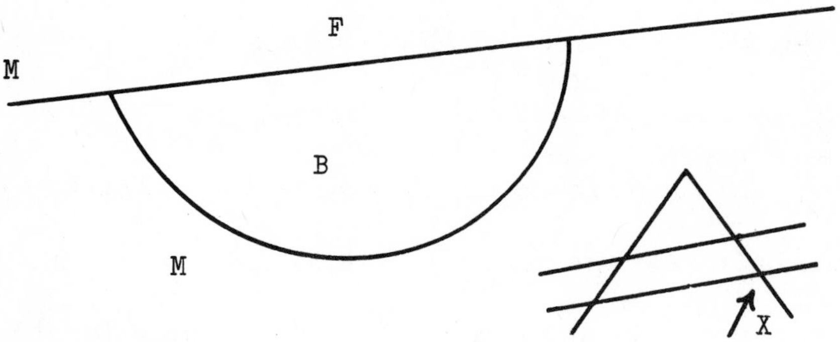

Proof. By induction on m. So assume 2.14 for manifolds of dim $(m-1)$, and say dim $M = m$.

1) $cl(M-B)$ is an m-manifold.

Namely, triangulate M so that B and F are triangulated as subcomplexes, and consider $\text{link}(x; \overline{M-B})$, x a vertex of $\overline{M-B}$. If $x \in M-B$, then $\text{link}(X; \overline{M-B}) = \text{link}(X; M)$, an $(m-1)$ ball or sphere. If $x \in \overline{M-B} \cap B$, suppose first $x \notin \dot{M}$ i.e., $x \notin F$. Then $\text{link}(x; \overline{M-B}) = \overline{\text{link}(x; M) - \text{link}(x; B)}$ is an $(m-1)$ sphere with the interior of an $(m-1)$-ball deleted, and so an $(m-1)$ ball. If $x \in F$, then $x \in \dot{F}$. $[F \cap \overline{M-B} = \dot{F}]$. So $\text{link}(x, F)$ is an $(m-2)$ ball, Moreover, $\dot{\overline{(\text{link}(x; M))}} = \text{link}(x; \dot{M})$, and so $(\text{link}(x; \dot{M})) \cap \text{link}(x; B) = \text{link}(x; \dot{M} \cap B) = \text{link}(x; F)$, a face of the $(m-1)$ ball $\text{link}(x; B)$. Hence by induction, $cl(|\text{link}(x; M)| - |\text{link}(x; B)|)$ is p.l. homeomorphic to $|\text{link}(x; M)|$, an $(m-1)$ ball.

Therefore, $|\text{link}(x; \overline{M-B})|$ is p.l. (m-1) ball. This proves that cl(M-B) is a manifold of dim m.

2) Let $F_1 = \overline{\partial B - F}$. Let $c: \partial(\text{cl}(M-B) \times I \longrightarrow \text{cl}(M-B)$ be a boundary collar. Choose $\varepsilon > 0$ such that $c(F_1 \times [0, \varepsilon])$ does not meet X. Let $D = c(F_1 \times [0, \varepsilon])$. There is a p.l. homeomorphism $B \cup D \longrightarrow D$ which is the identity on $\overline{\dot{D} - F}$. Extend to all of M by the identity, getting a p.l. homeomorphism $M \longrightarrow \text{cl}(M-B)$.

To start the induction, we leave it to the reader to verify that in case m = 1, cl(M-B) is a manifold, and then to proceed as in 2).

Lemma 2.15. E(n-1) and B(n-1) implies U(n).

Proof. Let N be a regular neighborhood of X in M. Then we will show that N is p.l. homeomorphic to a derived neighborhood of X in M. (M an n-manifold, X a polyhedron in M.), via a homeomorphism which is the identity on X. This together with Lemma 2.9 will imply U(n).

Let $K_o \subseteq K \subseteq J$ be triangulations of $X \subseteq N \subseteq M$. We can choose $K_o \subseteq K$ so that $K \overset{s}{\searrow} K_o$. So let $K = K_r \overset{es}{\searrow} K_{r-1} \overset{es}{\searrow} \cdots \overset{es}{\searrow} K_o$ be the collapse. Let K'' = barycentric second derived of K. Let $U_i = N(K_i''; K'')$. Then $U_r = K''$, and U_o is a second derived neighborhood of $|K_o|$ in the n-manifold $|K|$. We are going to construct p.l. homeomorphisms $h_i: U_{i+1} \longrightarrow U_i$ which leave K_o pointwise fixed. We assume by induction that h_{i+1} has been constructed if $i \neq r-1$, so that we may assume in particular that U_{i+1} is an m-manifold.

Now let us observe that $U_i = \bigcup_{\sigma \in K_i} \overline{st}(\hat{\sigma}; K'')$. Since $\hat{\sigma}$ is a vertex of K''_i, the inclusion $\supseteq$ is obvious. Suppose on the other hand, that $\tau \in U_i$. then $\tau \leq \tau_1$, where τ_1 meets K''_i. Suppose $\tau_1 = \hat{B}_1 \ldots \hat{B}_s$, where $B_1 < \ldots < B_s \in K'$. Then for some i, $\hat{B}_i \in K''_i$. Hence $B_i \in K'_i$, so $B_1 \in K'_i$. If B_1 is a point, then $B_1 = \hat{\sigma}$, $\sigma \in K_i$. Otherwise, let $\sigma \in K_i$ be such that $\hat{\sigma}$ is a vertex of B_1. Then $\hat{\sigma}\hat{B}_1 \ldots \hat{B}_s \in K''$. So in either case $\tau_1 \in \bigcup_{\sigma \in K_i} \overline{st}(\hat{\sigma}; K'')$, and hence so does τ.

Now let $K_{i+1} = K_i + A + B$, $A = aB$, $a \in K_i$, $A \notin K_i$. Then the only barycenters of simplices of K_{i+1} which are not barycenters of simplices of K_i are $\hat{A}$ and $\hat{B}$. Therefore

$$U_{i+1} = U_i + P + Q \ , \quad P = \overline{star}(\hat{A}; K''), \quad Q = \overline{st}(\hat{B}; K'').$$

We now claim that the following two statements are true:

a) $U_i \cap P$ is a face of P.

b) $(U_i \cup P) \cap Q$ is a face of Q.

To prove a), let $L = \text{link}(\hat{A}; K') = \dot{A}'.S$, where $S = \{\hat{B}_1 \ldots \hat{B}_s \mid A \underset{\neq}{\leq} B_1 < \ldots < B_s\}$. (See Lemma 2.13.) Let $p\colon \text{lk}(\hat{A}; K'') \longrightarrow L'$ be simplicial homeomorphism which is defined on vertices by sending $\widehat{AC}$ to $\hat{C}$ for any simplex C of L. If $\sigma \in P \cap U_i$, then $\sigma \in \text{lk}(\hat{A}; K'')$, as $\sigma \in \overline{st}(\hat{A}; K'')$ and $\hat{A} \notin \sigma$. In addition, $\sigma \in \text{link}(\hat{D}; K'')$ for some $D \in K_i$ as $\sigma \in \overline{st}(\hat{D}; K'')$ for some $D \in K_i$ but $\hat{D} \notin \overline{st}(\hat{A}; K'')$. Therefore, $\sigma \in P \cap U_i \Longrightarrow \sigma \in \text{link}(\hat{A}; K'') \cap \text{lk}(\hat{D}; K'')$, some $D \in K_i$. Conversely, it is clear that any simplex of such an intersection lies in $P \cap U_i$.

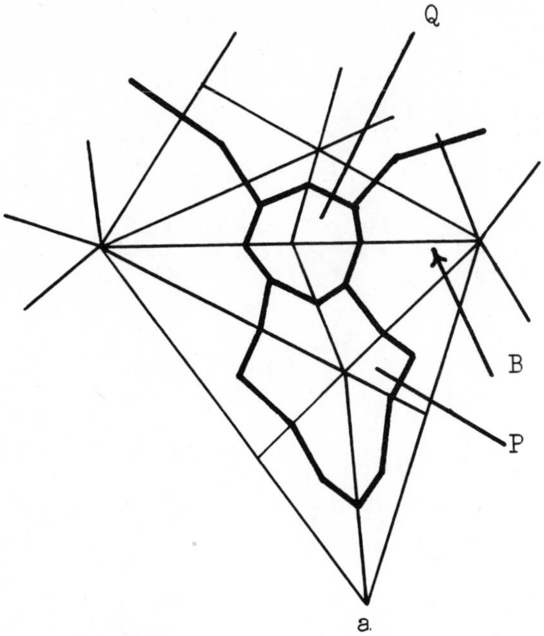

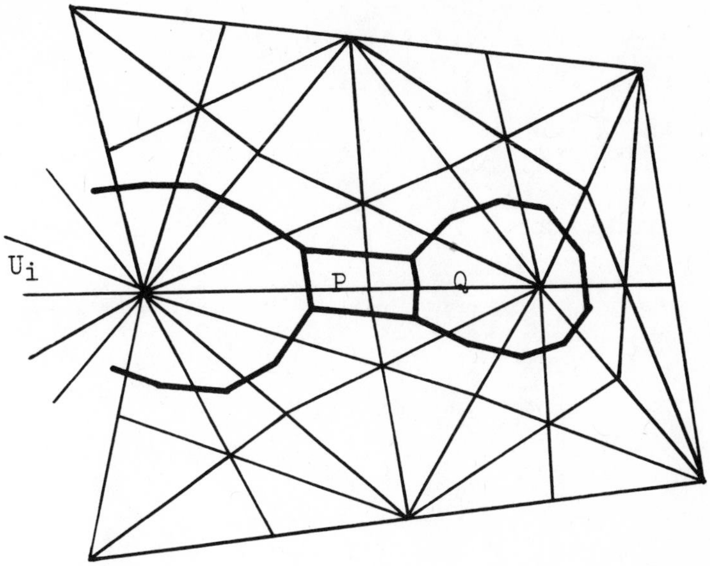

However, $lk(\hat{A}; K'') \cap lk(\hat{D}; K'') \neq \emptyset \iff \hat{A}\hat{D} \in K'$. For if $\sigma = \hat{B}_1 \ldots \hat{B}_s$, $B_1 < \ldots < B_s \in K'$, is a simplex of this intersection, then $\hat{A}$ and $\hat{D}$ must be vertices of B_1, and conversely. So this intersection is non-empty if and only if $A < D$ or $D < A$. But A was a principal simplex of K_{i+1} and $D \in K_i$. So $D < A$ is the only possibility, in which case $D \in a\dot{B}$. So we have proven the following:

$$P \cap U_i = \bigcup_{D \in a\dot{B}} (\text{link}(\hat{A}; K'') \cap \text{link}(\hat{D}; K'')).$$

Since $P \cap U_i \subseteq \text{link}(A; K'')$, we may consider its image under the p.l. homeomorphism $p\colon \text{link}(\hat{A}; K'') \longrightarrow L'$. If $\sigma \in \text{link}(\hat{A}; K'')$ and $D \in a\dot{B}$, then $\sigma \in lk(\hat{D}; K'') \iff p\sigma \in \overline{st}(\hat{D}; L')$. For if $\sigma = \hat{B}_1 \ldots \hat{B}_s$, $B_1 < \ldots < B_s \in K'$, write $B_i = \hat{A}\tau_i$. Then $p(\sigma) = \hat{\tau}_1 \ldots \hat{\tau}_s \in L'$. But
$\sigma \in lk(\hat{D}; K'') \iff \hat{D} < B_1 \iff \hat{D}_1 \leq \tau_1 \iff p\sigma \in \overline{st}(\hat{D}; L')$. So we have:

$$p(P \cap U_i) = \bigcup_{D \in a\dot{B}} \overline{st}(\hat{D}; L') = N((a\dot{B})'', L').$$

The last equality follows an argument similar to that used in deriving a similar expression for U_i (page 62).

However, $(a\dot{B})'$ is full in $\dot{A}'$ and so also in $L = \dot{A}'.S$. Therefore, $(a\dot{B})''$ is full in L'. $|L'|$ is a p.l. manifold of dimension (n-1). Hence $E(n-1) \Longrightarrow N((a\dot{B})'', L')$ is a regular neighborhood of $|a\dot{B}|$ in $|L|$. But $|a\dot{B}| \searrow 0$, so by $B(n-1)$, this regular neighborhood is a p.l. (m-1) ball. Hence $P \cap U_i$ is also a p.l. (m-1) ball. Since $P \cap U_i \subseteq \text{link}(\hat{A}; K'')$, which lies the boundary of $P = \overline{\text{star}}(\hat{A}; K'')$, this proves that $P \cap U_i$ is a face of P.

To prove b), let $L_1 = \text{link}(\hat{B}; K') = \dot{B}'.S_1$, say. Define $p_1 . \text{lk}(\hat{B}; K'') \longrightarrow L_1'$ by defining it on vertices to send $\widehat{BC}$ to $\hat{C}$. As before we have that $\sigma \in Q \cap (U_i \cup P)$ if and only if $\sigma \in \text{link}(\hat{B}; K'') \cap \text{link}(\hat{D}; K'')$ for some $D \in K_i$ or for $D = A$. Once again, this intersection is non-empty if and only if $B < D$ or $D < B$. Since B is a free face of the principal simplex A, the only possibilities are $D = A$ or $D < B$. So this time we find that

$$p_1(Q \cap (U_i \cup P)) = \bigcup_{\substack{D \in \dot{B} \\ \text{or } D = A}} \overline{st}(\hat{D}; L_1) = N((\hat{A}\dot{B})''; L_1').$$

As before, we see that $\hat{A}\dot{B}'$ is full in $L_1 = \dot{B}'S_1$ and is collapsible. So $E(n-1)$ and $B(n-1) \Longrightarrow N((\hat{A}\dot{B})''; L_1')$ is an (n-1) ball, and so $Q \cap (U_i \cap P)$ is a face of Q.

To complete the proof, we are going to apply Lemma 2.14. Recall that the inductive hypothesis implied that U_{i+1} is a manifold. Moreover, $\dot{U}_{i+1} \cap Q = cl(\dot{Q} - FrQ)$, where the frontier of Q is taken with respect to U_{i+1}.

But $FrQ = (U_i \cup P) \cap Q$, a face of Q. Hence $U_{i+1} \cap Q$ is also a face of Q. Hence U_{i+1} is p. l. homeomorphic to $cl\{U_i - Q\} = U_i \cup P$. A similar argument gives a p. l. homeomorphism of $U_i \cup P$ with U_i, using Lemma 2.14 again.

Proof of Theorem 2.11. By the preceding lemma, it suffices to establish B(0), E(0), and U(0). Let M be a zero-manifold, X a polyhedron, $X \subseteq M$. Then M is a finite set of points and X is a subset. Hence any derived neighborhood of X is also X, as if $P \notin X$, $X \cup \{P\}$ does not collapse to X. If X is collapsible, it is a single point, so B(0) is also trivial.

Remark. In the course of proving Lemma 2.1, we also showed that given any regular neighborhood N_1 of X in M^m, there exists a sequence of m-manifolds

$$N_1 = V_r \supseteq \dots \supseteq V_o$$

with V_o a derived neighborhood of X and $cl(V_i - V_{i-1})$ and m-ball, which meets V_{i-1} in a face and also meets ∂V_i in a face.

5. Uniqueness of Regular Neighborhoods which Meet the Boundary Regularly

In Section 3 we proved that derived neighborhoods of a polyhedron in a manifold are ambient isotopic. In this section we extend this result to a larger c lass of regular neighborhoods.

Definition. A regular neighborhood N of the polyhedron X in the p.l. manifold M is said to meet the boundary regularly if either $N \cap \partial M$ is a regular neighborhood of $X \cap \partial M$ in ∂M or both of these intersections are empty.

Note: A derived neighborhood of X in M meets the boundary regularly.

For suppose $f: K \longrightarrow R^+$ is linear, $f^{-1}(0) = K_o$, and $f(v) > \varepsilon$ for all vertices $v \in K - K_o$. If $K_o \cap \partial K = \emptyset$, $\partial K \quad f^{-1}[0, \varepsilon] = \emptyset$. Otherwise $\partial K \cap f^{-1}[0, \varepsilon]$ is a derived neighborhood of $K_o \cap \partial K$ in ∂K. The uniqueness of derived neighborhods shows that the result holds for all derived neighborhoods.

Theorem 2.1 : If N_1 and N_2 are two regular neighborhoods of the polyhedron X in the manifold M which meets ∂M regularly, then there exists an ambient isotopy throwing N_1 onto N_2, fixed on X.

Naturally to prove this theorem we will need some lemmas.

Lemma 2.17. Let $N \subseteq M$ be m-manifolds. Suppose $N \cap \partial M$ is an (m-1) manifold. Let $X \subseteq N$ be a polyhedron, $B \subseteq N$ and m-ball, $B \cap X = \emptyset$. Suppose $B \cap Fr_M(N)$ is a face of B and either

1) $B \subseteq \text{Int } M$ or

2) $B \cap \partial M = B_1$ is a face of B and $B_1 \cap Fr_M(N)$ is a face of B_1.

Then there exists an ambient isotopy of M, throwing N onto cl(N-B), which is constant outside an m-ball contained in M not meeting X.

Pictures:

1) $B \subseteq \mathring{M}$.

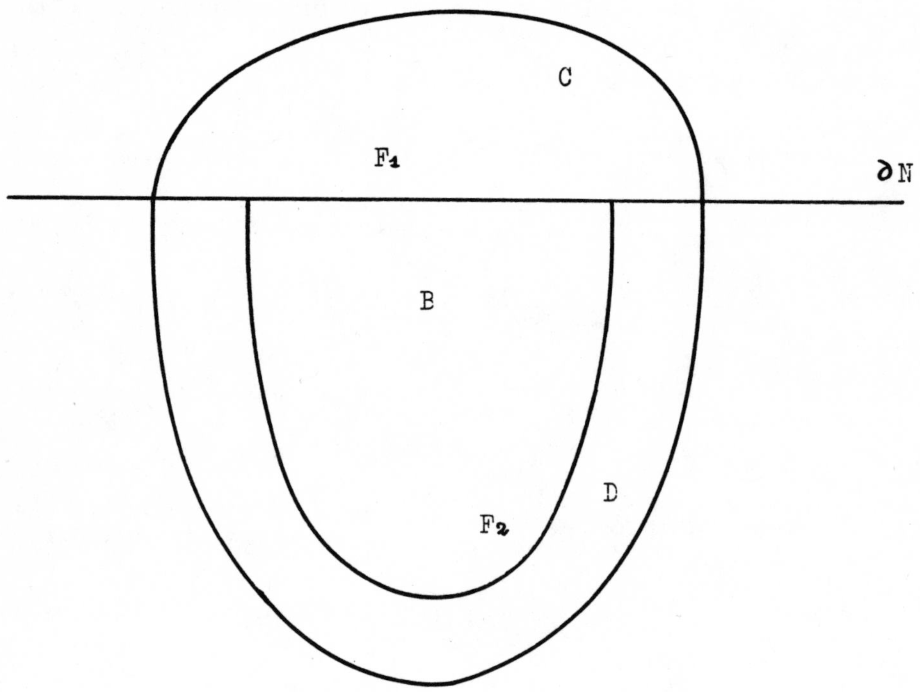

2)

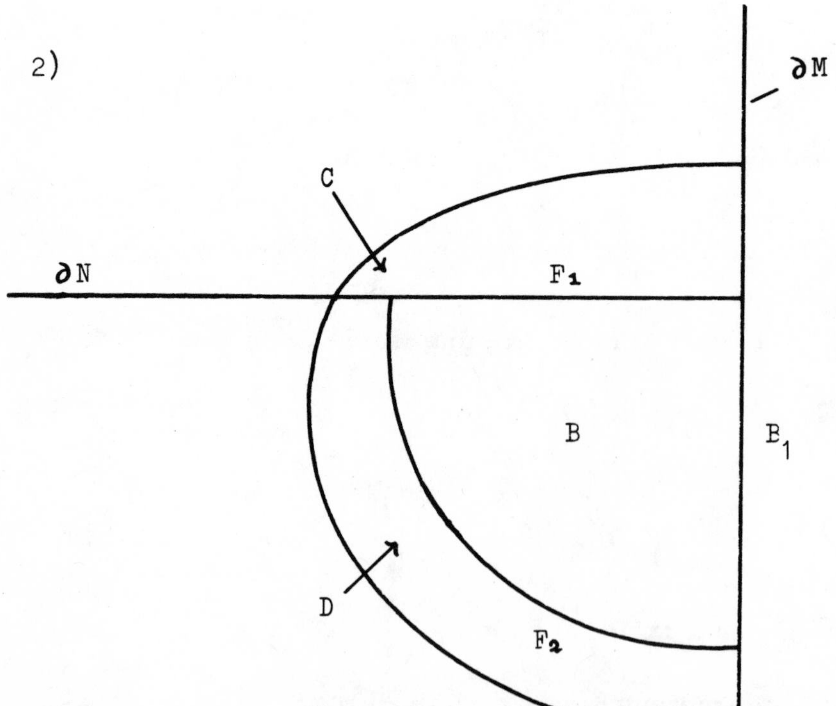

Proof. First of all, cl(M-N) and cl(N-B) are manifolds. Namely, triangulate M with N as a subcomplex and let x be a vertex of $\overline{M-N}$.

1) $x \in M-N$. Then $lk(x; \overline{M-N}) = link(x; M) =$ sphere or ball of dim $m-1$.

2) $x \in (FrN) \cap (\text{Int } M)$. Then $link(x; \overline{M-N}) = \overline{link(x; M) - link(x; N)}$.

But $lk(x; M) \neq link(x; N)$ and $link(x; M)$ is an $(m-1)$ sphere. Hence $link(x; N)$ is an $(m-1)$ ball and the closure of the difference is an $(m-1)$ ball.

3) $x \in \partial M \cap Fr(N)$.

$$Fr_M(N) = \overline{\partial N - N \cap \partial M}\ ,$$ which is a p.l. $(m-1)$-manifold,

since we assumed that $N \cap \partial M$ was, and by 1) and 2).

Now $link(x; \overline{M-N}) = \overline{link(x; M) - link(x; N)}$ and

$link(x; \overline{M-N} \cap N) = \overline{link(x; M) - link(x; N)} \cap link(x; N)$. Let $B_1 = link(x; M)$, $B_2 = link(x; N)$, both $(n-1)$ balls. Then $\overline{B_1 - B_2} \cap B_2$ is a face of B_2. So $\partial B_1 \cap B_2$ is a face of B_2 and $\overline{B_1 - B_2}$ is an n-ball.

This proves cl(M-N) is a manifold. cl(N-B) is a manifold by Lemma 2.14.

Let $F_1 = B \cap Fr(N)$. Let $F_2 = B \cap cl(N-B)$. F_2 is a face of B, for in case 1) of the statement of this lemma $F_2 = cl(\dot{B} - F_1)$; and in case 2, $F_2 = cl(\dot{B} - F_1 \cup B_1)$, and we saw that $F_1 \cup B_1$ is a face of B in the last paragraph. Triangulate M with F_1, $B_1 = B \cap \partial M$, F_2, B, N, and X as subcomplexe Let C = second derived neighborhood of F_1 in $\overline{M-N}$, with respect to this triangulation. Let D = second derived neighborhood of F_2 in $\overline{N-B}$. Note that $D \cap X = \emptyset$.

Since F_1 and F_2 are collapsible, C and D are m-balls, by the uniqueness part of Theorem 2.11. $C \cap B = F_1$, a common face, so $C \cup B$ is an m-ball. $D \cap B = F_2$, a common face, so $D \cup B$ is an m-ball. $E = C \cup B \cup D$ is a second derived neighborhood of B in M and so is an m-ball.

Now we consider the two cases of the statement of this lemma.

1) $B \subseteq \text{Int } M$.

We define $f: E \to E$ as follows. Put $h|\dot{E}$ = identity.

Now $C \cap (B \cup D) = C \cap Fr(cl(M-N)) = C \cap (\partial\, cl(M-N))$, as $C \cap \partial M = \emptyset$. But $F_1 \subseteq Fr N$ and C is a derived neighborhood in cl(M-N) and so meets the boundary regularly. Hence $C \cap (B \cup D)$ is an (m-1) ball. $(C \cup B) \cap D = D \cap \partial(cl(N-B))$ is also an (m-1) ball. Moreover, these two balls have identical boundaries, both contained in $\dot{E}$. Hence the restriction of h to this common boundary extends to a p.l. homeomorphism $h_1: C \cap (B \cup D) \to (C \cup B) \cap D$. Together with h, this defines a p.l. homeomorphism $h_2: \dot{C} \to (C \cup B)^{\cdot}$ and a p.l. homeomorphism $h_3: (B \cup D)^{\cdot} \to \dot{D}$ which agree where they are both defined. Hence h_2 extends to a p.l. homeomorphism $h_4: C \to C \cup B$ and h_3 extends to $h_5: B \cup D \to D$. Let $h = h_4 \cup h_5 : E \to E$. (The reader is advised to consult Picture 1 on page 66).

Now, $h(B \cup D) = B$. Moreover, h is ambient isotopic to 1_E keeping ∂E fixed. Extend this ambient isotopy over M by letting it be the identity at every level for points outside E. The resulting ambient isotopy throws N onto cl(N-B) and leaves X fixed.

2) $B \cap \partial M \neq 0$. Let $C_1 = C \cap \partial M$, $D_1 = D \cap \partial M$, $E_1 = E \cap \partial M$. By arguing as in 1) (one lower dimension), we may find a p. l. homeomorphism $h: E_1 \longrightarrow E_1$ such that $h|\partial E_1$ = identity, $h(c_1) = C_1 \cup B_1$, $h(D_1 \cup B_1) = D_1$. (Recall: $\partial M = \emptyset$.) Define h on FrE by setting $h|FrE = 1$. Then as before, h is defined on $(C \cap (B \cup D))^{\dot{}}$, which it maps homeomoprhically onto $((C \cup B) \cap D)^{\dot{}}$. (These are not equal.) Once again, this definition extends to a p.l. homeomorphism of E which is the identity on Fr(E). Now h is ambient itotopic to the identity via an isotopy fixed on Fr(E), by a corollary to 2.7 which we did not state. Extend this isotopy as in 1).

<u>Notes:</u> 1) The unstated corollary is: If Δ_1 is a principal face of $\Delta = v\Delta_1$, any homeomorphism $h: \Delta \longrightarrow \Delta$ with $h|v\dot{\Delta}_1$ = identity, is ambient isotopic to the identity keeping $v\dot{\Delta}_1$ fixed. This applies because $E \cong vE_1$.

2) The m-ball outside which the isotopy is constant is E.

<u>Lemma 2.18.</u> If $X \subseteq \text{Int } M^m$ and N_1 and N_2 are two regular neighborhoods of X which lie in Int M, then there exists an ambient isotopy throwing N_1 onto N_2.

<u>Proof.</u> In the proof of Theorem 2.11 (see lemma 2.14 and the remark on page 64), we showed that there exists a sequence of m-manifolds, $N_1 = V_r \supset V_{r-1} \supset \ldots \supset V_0$ with V_0 a derived neighborhood of X in M and with $B_i = cl(V_i - V_{i-1})$ and m-ball which meets V_{i-1} and ∂V_i in faces. Since $B_i \subseteq \text{Int } M$, $B_i \cap (\partial V_i) = B_i \cap FrV_i$. Hence Lemma 2.1 applies: there exists an ambient isotopy of M, fixed on X, throwing V_i onto V_{i-1}. Hence N_1 is ambient isotopic to a derived neighborhood. So is N_2, and derived neighborhoods are ambient isotopic.

Lemma 2.19. If $X \subseteq M^m$, and N_1 and N_2 are regular neighborhoods of $X \cap \partial M$ in ∂M, then there exists an ambient isotopy of M, fixed on X, throwing N_1 onto N_2.

Proof. Let M be triangulated with N_1 and X as subcomplexes with $N_1 \overset{s}{\searrow} X \cap \partial M$. Let U_o = 2nd derived neighborhood of X with respect to this triangulation. Then $U_o \cap \partial M$ is a second derived neighborhood in ∂M of $X \cap \partial M$. We saw in the proof of Theorem 2.11 (see Lemma 2.15) that in ∂M, there exists a collection of (m-1) manifolds $N_1 = V_r \supseteq \dots \supseteq V_o = U_o$ such that $cl(V_i - V_{i-1})$ is a ball meeting V_{i-1} and $\partial(V_i)$ in faces. As $\partial(\partial M) = \emptyset$, $\partial V_i = Fr_{\partial M} V_i$. Therefore, Lemma 2.1 applies to each pair V_i V_{i-1} to give an ambient isotopy throwing V_i onto V_{i-1}, constant outside of an (m-1)-ball in ∂M which does not meet X. Call this ambient isotopy H_i, and let E_i be the ball outside of which it is constant (may take E_i = 2nd derived neighborhood of $cl(V_i - V_{i-1})$ in ∂M). $E_i \cap X = \emptyset$.

Now triangulate M with X and E_i as subcomplexes. Let F_i = 2nd derived of E_i in M. $F_i \cap X = \emptyset$. We extend H_i to F_i as follows: Put H_i = identity on $Fr_M(F_i)$ and extend H_1 and H over F_i and $F_i \times I$ in the usual way (see Section 3, Lemma 2.7 and Corollary 2.8.). Now put H_i = identity on the rest of $M \times 1$. This defines an ambient isotopy of M throwing V_i onto V_{i-1}. Composing these isotopies defines an isotopy throwing N_1 onto $U_o \cap \partial M$, fixed on X. Similarly, N_2 is ambient isotopic to $U_o' \cap \partial M$, U_o' a derived neighborhood of X also. But U_o' is ambient isotopic to U_o, and any ambient isotopy throwing U_o

onto U'_o must throw $U_o \cap \partial M$ onto $U'_o \cap \partial M$, as p.l. homeomorphisms of manifolds preserve boundary.

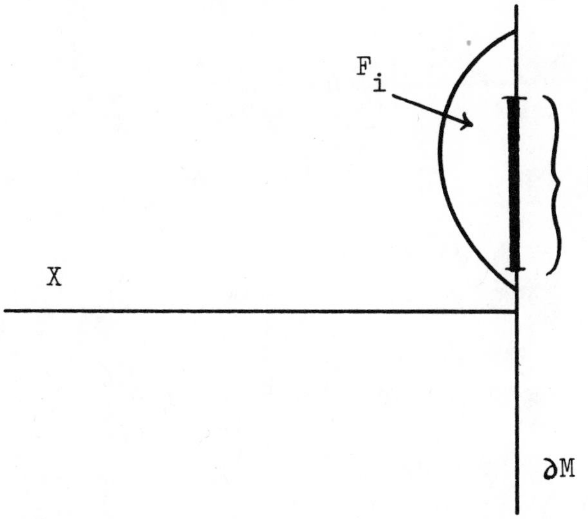

Lemma 2.20. If N is a regular neighborhood of X in M and if N meets ∂M regularly, then $N \searrow X \cup (N \cap \partial M) \searrow X$.

Proof. First suppose that N is a derived neighborhood of X, i.e., $N = |N(K'_o ; K')|$, where $K_o \subseteq K$ is a triangulation of $X \subseteq M$ with K_o a full subcomplex. Let $A_1, \ldots, A_r$ be the simplices of $K-K_o$ which meet K_o, ordered so as to satisfy the following tow properties:

a) Simplices of $\mathring{K}$ preceed those of $\dot{K}$.

b) A_i preceeds its faces.

$A_i \cap |K_o| = B_i$, a single face of A_i. $A_i \cap N = |N(B'_i ; A'_i)|$, a ball. $|\dot{A}_i| \cap N = N(B'_i; \dot{A}'_i)$, a face of this ball. Hence

$$U_i = |K_o| \cup \{\bigcup_{j=1}^{r} (N \cap A_j)\} \searrow |K_o| \cup \{\bigcup_{j=i+1}^{r} (N \cap A_j)\} = U_{i+1},$$

as $\bigcup_{j=1}^{r} (N \cap A_j) \searrow \bigcup_{j=i+1}^{r} (N \cap A_j)$ and by Lemma 2.1, (applied to a subdivision in which the collapses are simplicial). Lemma 2.1 applies because $|K_o| \cap (\bigcup_{j=1}^{r} (N \cap A_j)) = |K_o| \cap (\bigcup_{j=1}^{r} A_j) \subseteq |K_o| \cap (\bigcup_{j=i+1}^{r} A_j)$, for if a point of K_o is contained in A_j, some j, it is contained in a proper face of A_j. Now, $U_o = N$. Clearly, there exists an i such that $U_i = X \cup (N \cap \partial M)$, by a). $U_r = X$.

Now suppose that N is a regular neighborhood of X which meets the boundary regularly. Then $N \cap \partial M$ is a regular neighborhood of $X \cap \partial M$ in ∂M.

<u>Claim:</u> $N \cap \partial M \subseteq \partial N$ is a regular neighborhood of $X \cap \partial N$ in ∂N. $N \cap \partial M$ is a neighborhood of $X \cap \partial N$ in ∂N because $X \cap \partial N = (X \cap \mathrm{Fr} N) \cup (X \cap N \cap \partial M) = X \cap \partial M$ as $X \cap \mathrm{Fr} N = \emptyset$ and $N \cap \partial M$ is obviously a neighborhood of $X \cap \partial M$ in ∂N. $N \cap \partial M$ is an $(m-1)$ manifold which collapses to $X \cap \partial M = X \cap \partial N$.

Let N_1 be a derived neighborhood of X in M. Then N_1 meets ∂M regularly. Now, there exists a p.l. homeomorphism $h: N \longrightarrow N_1$ such that $h|X$ = identity and $h(N) = N_1$. Moreover, $h(N \cap \partial M)$ and $N_1 \cap \partial M$ are both regular neighborhoods of $X \cap \partial N_1$ in ∂N_1. Hence there exists an ambient isotopy of N_1, fixed on X, throwing $h(N \cap \partial M)$ on $N_1 \cap \partial M$. In particular, there exists a p.l. homeomorphism h' of N onto N_1 with $h'|X$ = identity, such that $h'(N \cap \partial M) = N_1 \cap \partial M$. But $N_1 \searrow X \cup (N_1 \cap \partial M) \searrow X$. Hence $N \searrow X \cup (N \cap \partial M) \searrow X$, since $(h')^{-1}$ preserves collapses.

Proof of Theorem 2.16. We are going to show that any regular neighborhood which meets the boundary regularly is ambient isotopic to a derived neighborhood. Since derived neighborhoods are ambient isotopic, this will prove 2.16.

So let N be a regular neighborhood of X in M meeting ∂M regularly. Then $N \searrow X \cup (\partial M \cap N) \searrow X$. Let K be a triangulation of M such that X and N are triangulated as subcomplexes, K_o and L, say. We may suppose that $L \overset{s}{\searrow} K_o \cup (L \cap \dot{K}) \overset{s}{\searrow} K_o$. Let $L = K_r \overset{es}{\searrow} \cdots \overset{es}{\searrow} K_o$ be these two collapses, with $K_s = K_o \cup (L \cap \dot{K})$, some $s \leq r$. Let $U_i = N(K''_i ; K''_r)$, where K'' = 2nd derived of K. Let $K_i = K_{i-1} + A + B$, $A = aB$. Then we have seen (Lemma 2.15) that $U_i = U_{i-1} \cup P \cup Q$, where $P = \overline{\mathrm{st}}(\hat{A}; K'')$, $Q = \overline{\mathrm{star}}(\hat{B}; K'')$, and that there exists a p.l. homeomorphism $U_i \cong U_{i-1} \cup P \cong U_{i-1}$. We are going to use Lemma 2.16 to show that in fact U_i is ambient isotopic to $U_{i-1} \cup P$ and $U_{i-1} \cup P$ is ambient isotopic to U_i, keeping X fixed. This will complete the proof.

Either A and B are both in ∂M or neither is in ∂M. In the latter case, P and Q both do not meet ∂M. In this case, $P \cap \mathrm{Fr}(U_{i-1} \cup P) = P \cap \partial(U_{i-1} \cup P)$, and we have seen (page 63) that $P \cap \partial(U_{i-1} \cup P)$ is a face of P. Similarly, $Q \cap \mathrm{Fr}(U_i) = Q \cap \partial(U_i)$ is a face of Q. Hence by Lemma 2.16, there are ambient isotopies throwing U_i onto $U_{i-1} \cup P$ and $U_{i-1} \cup P$ onto U_i.

Suppose on the other hand that A and B are both in ∂M. Then $\mathrm{star}(\hat{A}; K'') \cap \dot{K}'' = \mathrm{star}(\hat{A}; \dot{K}'')$ and similarly for $\hat{B}$, so P and Q each meets ∂M in a face. We still have that $P \cap \mathrm{Fr}(U_{i-1} \cup P)$ is a face of P, and $Q \cap \mathrm{Fr}\, U_i$ is a face of Q. Hence in order to conclude the proof by applying

Lemma 2.16. we must show that $(P \cap \partial M) \cap Fr(U_{i-1} \cup P)$ and $(Q \cap \partial M) \cap FrU_i$ are faces of $P \cap \partial M$ and $Q \cap \partial M$, respectively.

Now, $N \cap \partial M = |K_r'' \cap \dot{K}''|$ is a regular neighborhood of $|K_o \cap \dot{K}''| = X \cap \partial M$. Moreover, $K_r \cap \dot{K} = \ldots = K_s \cap \dot{K} \searrow^{es} \ldots \searrow^{es} K_o \cap \dot{K}$. (We are assuming here that $i < s$.) Clearly, we have that $U_i \cap \partial M = N(K_i'' \cap \dot{K}''; K_s'' \cap \dot{K}'') = N((K_i \cap \dot{K})''; (K_r \cap \dot{K})'')$. Also, we just noted that $P \cap \partial M = \text{star}(\hat{A}; \dot{K}'')$ and $Q \cap \partial M = \text{star}(\hat{B}; \dot{K}'')$. Hence, the arguments of Lemma 2.15 (see page 63) apply in ∂M to show that $(P \cap \partial M) \cap \partial[(U_{i-1} \cup P) \cap \partial M]$ and $(Q \cap \partial M) \cap \partial(U_i \cap \partial M)$ are faces of $P \cap \partial M$ and $Q \cap \partial M$, respectively. But $\partial[(U_{i-1} \cup P) \cap \partial M] = [Fr(U_{i-1} \cup P)] \cap \partial M$, and $\partial(U_i \cap \partial M) = (FrU_i) \cap \partial M$. Thus $P \cap \partial M \cap Fr(U_{i-1} \cup P)$ is a face of $P \cap \partial M$ and $Q \cap \partial M \cap Fr(U_i)$ is a face of $Q \cap \partial M$.

<u>Corollary 2.16.1</u> (Annulus Property): Say $B_1 \subseteq \text{Int } B_2$, B_1 and B_2 p.l. m-balls. Then $cl(B_2 - B_1)$ is p.l. homeomorphic to $\dot{B}_1 \times I$

<u>Corollary 2.16.2.</u> (Generalized Annulus Property): If N_1 and N_2 are regular neighborhoods of X in M with $N_1 \subseteq \text{Int}_M N_2$ and if N_1 meets ∂M regularly, then there exists a p.l. homeomorphism

$$h: cl(N_2 - N_1) \longrightarrow (Fr_M N_1) \times I .$$

<u>Proof.</u> Clearly, 2.16.2 implies 2.16.1, since a ball is a regular neighborhood of any interior point. To prove 2.16.2, let K_o be a full subcomplex of K, $|K| = M$, with $|K_o| = X$. Let $\Phi: K \longrightarrow [0,1]$ be a <u>simplicial</u> map (vertices of $[0,1]$ are 0 and 1) with $\Phi^{-1}(0) = K_o$. Choose $0 < \varepsilon_1 < \varepsilon_2 < 1$. Then by 2.11,

there exists a p.l. homeomorphism $h: N_2 \longrightarrow \phi^{-1}[0, \varepsilon_2]$, $h|K_o$ = identity. Now, $h(N_1)$ and $\phi^{-1}[0, \varepsilon_1]$ are regular neighborhoods of X in $\phi^{-1}[0, \varepsilon_2]$ which meet the boundary regularly (in fact, N_1 meets ∂N_2 regularly and $\phi^{-1}[0, \varepsilon_1]$ is a derived neighborhood). Hence these two neighborhoods are ambient isotopic; in particular, there exists a p.l. homeomorphism $k: \Phi^{-1}[0, \varepsilon_2] \longrightarrow \Phi^{-1}[0, \varepsilon_2]$ such that $k(h(N_1)) = \phi^{-1}[0, \varepsilon_1]$. So $cl(N_2 - N_1) \cong \phi^{-1}[\varepsilon_1, \varepsilon_2] \cong \phi^{-1}(\varepsilon_1) \times I \underset{h^{-1}k^{-1} \times 1}{\cong} FrN_1 \times I$.

<u>Addendum 2.16.3.</u> Let N_1, N_2, N_3 be regular neighborhoods of X in M^m meeting ∂M regularly. Suppose N_1 and N_2 are (topological) neighborhoods of N_3. Let $P \subseteq M - (N_1 \cup N_2)$ be a polyhedron. Then there exists an ambient isotopy of M, fixed on $P \cup N_3$, throwing N_1 onto N_2.

<u>Proof.</u> 2.17.2 implies $cl(N_1 - N_3) \cong (Fr_M N_3 \times I)$. Hence $cl(N_1 - N_3) \longrightarrow FrN_3$. Hence $N_1 \searrow N_3$ (Lemma 2.1). Similarly, N_2 is a regular neighborhood of N_3. Let N_4 be a second derived neighborhood of P. Then $N_1 \cup N_4$ and $N_2 \cup N_4$ are regular neighborhoods of $N_3 \cup P$ meeting ∂M regularly. ($N_i \cap N_4 = \emptyset$, $i = 1, 2$.) Hence there exists an ambient isotopy throwing $N_1 \cup N_4$ onto $N_2 \cup N_4$, keeping $N_3 \cup P$ fixed. Since a p.l. homeomorphism is continuous and so maps connected components onto connected components, it follows that this ambient isotopy throws N_1 onto N_2.

Chapter III -- P. L. Spaces and Infinite Complexes

1. Introduction.

Chapters I and II have been confined to the study of compact polyhedra and p.l. manifolds contained in given Euclidean spaces. As in Differential Topology, where one can introduce abstract manifolds, one can define P. L. spaces and manifolds without reference to an ambient Euclidean space and without the hypotheses of compactness. In this chapter we propose to study abstract P. L. spaces and manifolds and to indicate how to extend the preceding results to such objects.

One can also define the notion of a locally finite infinite complex contained in a given Euclidean space (possibly E^{∞}). We will show that the notions of P. L. space and infinite complex are essentially equivalent. In particular, compact P. L. spaces and manifolds are no more general than the finite polyhedra and p.l. manifolds which we have been considering.

2. Triangulation of P. L. Spaces and Manifolds.

Definition. Let X be a topological space. A co-ordinate map (f, P) is a topological embedding $f: P \longrightarrow X$ of a Euclidean polyhedron P. Two such maps (f, P) and (g, Q) are compatible provided that if $f(P) \cap g(Q) \neq \emptyset$ there exists a coordinate map (h, R) such that $h(R) = g(Q) \cap f(P)$ and $f^{-1}h$ and $g^{-1}h$ are p.l. maps. Equivalently, we say that (f, P) and (g, Q) are compatible if $f^{-1}(gQ)$ is a subpolyhedron of Q and $g^{-1}f: f^{-1}(gQ) \longrightarrow Q$ is a p.l. map. (Put $h = g|f^{-1}gQ$), assuming $f(P) \cap g(Q) = \emptyset$.

Definition. A P.L. structure $\mathcal{F}$ on X is a family of coordinate maps such that

1) Any two elements of $\mathcal{F}$ are compatible.

2) For all $x \in X$, there exists $(f, P) \in \mathcal{F}$ such that $f(P)$ is a topological neighborhood of x in X.

3) $\mathcal{F}$ is maximal, i.e., if (f, P) is compatible with every map of $\mathcal{F}$, then $(f, P) \in \mathcal{F}$.

If X is a 2nd countable Hausdorff space, the pair $(X, \mathcal{F})$ is called a P.L. space.

Definition. A family of coordinate maps $\mathcal{F}$ on X satisfying 1) and 2) is called a base for a P.L. structure on X.

Lemma 3.1. Every base $\mathcal{B}$ for a P.L. structure on the topological space X is contained in a unique P.L. structure $\mathcal{F}$.

Proof. Let $\mathcal{F}$ = the set of all coordinate maps in X compatible with those in $\mathcal{B}$. The elements of $\mathcal{F}$ are compatible. For if (f, P) and (g, Q) are in $\mathcal{F}$ and $f(P) \cap g(Q) \neq \emptyset$, we may find a finite collection $(h_1, B_1), \ldots, (h_r, B_r)$ of maps in $\mathcal{B}$ such that $f(P) \cap g(Q) \subseteq \bigcup_{i=1}^{r} h_i(B_i)$. By definition f and g are compatible with each h_i, so if we let $R_i' = h_i^{-1} fP$ and $R_i'' = h_i^{-1} gQ$, R_i' and R_i'' are subpolyhedra of B_i. Let $R_i^* = R_i' \cap R_i''$. Then $U h_i R_i^* = f(P) \cap g(Q)$. Therefore, $P_1 = f^{-1}(gQ) = f^{-1}(U h_i R_i^*) = U f^{-1} h_i R_i^*$ is a polyhedron, and $g^{-1} f$ is p.l. on P_1 because in each piece $f^{-1} h_i R_i^*$ it agrees with the p.l. map

$g^{-1}h_ih_i^{-1}f$ which also is defined on this piece. It is clear that $\mathcal{F}$ satisfies 2) and 3) in the definition of a P.L. space and is the unique structure containing $\mathcal{B}$.

<u>Lemma 3.2.</u> If $f: P \longrightarrow X$ and $g: Q \longrightarrow X$ are two compatible coordinate maps, X a topological space, then there exists $h: R \longrightarrow X$, a coordinate map, with $h(R) = f(P) \cup g(Q)$ and with $h^{-1}f$ and $h^{-1}g$ p.l. maps.

<u>Proof.</u> Let $|K| = P$ and $|L| = Q$ be triangulations with K_o and L_o, subcomplexes, triangulating $f^{-1}gQ$ and $g^{-1}fP$ respectively. Let K_o' and L_o' be subdivisions of K_o and L_o such that $g^{-1}f: K_o' \longrightarrow L_o'$ is simplicial. Let K' and L' be extensions of these subdivisions. Let $\Delta \subsetneq F^N$ be a simplex which has one vertex $j(v)$ for each vertex v of $L' - L_o'$ and one vertex $i(v)$ for each vertex v of K', and no others. Consider the simplicial homeomorphism $i: K' \longrightarrow \Delta$ determined by the definition for i already given on vertices and the homeomorphism $j: L' \longrightarrow \Delta$ defined by putting $j(v) = i(f^{-1}g(v))$ if $v \in L_o'$ and extending linearly to all of L'. (j is already defined on vertices of $L' - L_o'$.) Let R be the union of the images of these simplicial homeomorphisms, a simplicial complex. Define $h: R \longrightarrow X$ by defining

$$h(x) = fi^{-1}(x) \text{ if } x \in \text{Image } i.$$

$$h(x) = g \circ j^{-1}(x) \text{ if } x \in \text{Image } j.$$

The definitions agree on the overlap, since if $x \in (\text{Im } i) \cap \text{Im } (j)$ $g \circ j^{-1}(x) = gg^{-1}fi^{-1}(x) = fi^{-1}(x)$. It is not hard to see that $h: R \longrightarrow X$ is a homeomorphism with image $f(P) \cup g(Q)$, and that $h^{-1}f$ and $h^{-1}g$ are p.l. maps.

Corollary 3.3. If $(X, \mathcal{F})$ is a P.L. space and $C \subseteq X$ is compact, then there exists $(h, R) \in \mathcal{F}$ with $C \subseteq \operatorname{Int} h(R)$.

Proof. Let $(h_1, R_1), \ldots, (h_r, R_r)$ be in $\mathcal{F}$ with $C \subseteq \operatorname{Int}(h_1(R_1) \cup \ldots \cup h_r(R_r))$. There exists a coordinate map $h: R \to X$ with $h(R) = h_1(R_1) \cup \ldots \cup h_r(R_r)$, and with h compatible with each h_i (i.e., $h^{-1}h_i: R_i \to R$ is p.l., all i). By arguing as in Lemma 3.1, it is not hard to show that h is compatible with every element of $\mathcal{F}$ and so in $\mathcal{F}$.

Definition. The P.L. space $(X, \mathcal{F})$ is called a P.L. m-manifold if for all $x \in X$ there exists $h: \Delta^m \to X$ with $(h, \Delta^m) \in \mathcal{F}$ and $x \in \operatorname{Int}_X h(\Delta^m)$.

Lemma 3.4. If $(X, \mathcal{F})$ is a P.L. m-manifold and $C \subseteq X$ is compact, then there exists $(h, R) \in \mathcal{F}$ with

1) R is a p.l. m-manifold.
2) $C \subseteq \operatorname{Int}_X h(R)$.

Proof. By Lemma 3.2, choose (f, P) and (g, Q) in $\mathcal{F}$ with $C \subseteq \operatorname{Int} f(P)$, $f(P) \subseteq \operatorname{Int} g(Q)$. Let K_o be a full subcomplex of K, $|K| = Q$, $|K_o| = g^{-1}fP$. Let N be the second derived neighborhood of K_o in K. Then N is an m-manifold, for though K need not be a combinatorial manifold, every point of $|K_o|$ has a neighborhood in $|K|$ which is a p.l. m-ball. So $\operatorname{link}(v, K)$ = an m-1 sphere or ball for all $v \in K_o$, and $\operatorname{link}(A, K)$ is a sphere or ball for all simplices A meeting K_o. So the proof that N is a manifold goes through (see proof of Lemma 2.13). $g|N \to X$ is the required coordinate map of this lemma.

Note: Strictly speaking, the last two lemmas have been using the fact that if in the P.L. space $(X, \mathcal{F})$, (h, P) is a coordinate map such that $h(P)$ may be covered by the images of a finite number of maps in $\mathcal{F}$ with which h is compatible, then $(h, P) \in \mathcal{F}$. The proof is left to the reader (see Lemma 3.1).

The next lemma may be viewed as affirming the possibility of "triangulating" P.L. spaces and manifolds, as we shall see following the introduction of locally finite (infinite) complexes.

Lemma 3.5. Let $(X, \mathcal{F})$ be a P.L. space. Then there exists a countable set of simplicial complexes and subcomplexes, $K_i \subseteq J_i$, $L_i \subseteq J_i$ and embeddings $f_i: |J_i| \longrightarrow X$ such that

1) $X = \bigcup_{i=1}^{\infty} f_i(|J_i|)$.

2) $f_i(|J_i|) \cap f_k(|J_k|) = \emptyset$ if $|i-k| \geq 2$.

3) $f_i(|J_i|) \cap f_{i+1}(|J_{i+1}|) = f_i(|L_i|) = f_{i+1}(|K_{i+1}|)$.

4) $f_{i+1}^{-1} f_i: L_i \longrightarrow K_{i+1}$ is a simplicial homeomorphism.

If $(X, \mathcal{F})$ is a P.L. m-manifold, we can take J_i to be a combinatorial m-manifold and K_i and L_i to be combinatorial $(m-1)$ manifolds in ∂J_i.

Proof. X is locally compact and 2nd countable. Hence X is σ-compact. Let $X = \bigcup_{i=1}^{\infty} C_i$, C_i compact. Let $(h_1, R_1) \in \mathcal{F}$. Define inductively $(h_i, R_i) \in \mathcal{F}$, $i \geq 2$, such that $C_i \subseteq h_{i-1}(R_{i-1}) \subseteq \operatorname{Int} h_i(R_i)$. Let $P_i = \operatorname{cl}(R_i - h_i^{-1} h_{i-1} R_i)$, a polyhedron. Let $Q_i = h_i^{-1} \operatorname{Fr}_X (h_{i-1} R_{i-1})$, $S_i = h_i^{-1}(\operatorname{Fr} h_i R_i)$. Let $f_i = h_i | P_i$. Let K_i, L_i J_i be triangulations of

Q_i, S_i, P_i. For each i, let L_i' and K_{i+1}' be subdivisions such that $f_{i+1}^{-1} f_i : L_i' \longrightarrow K_{i+1}'$ is simplicial. Since $K_i \cap L_i = \emptyset$, this defines a subdivision of $K_i \cup L_i$ which we extend to a subdivision J_i' of J. Then J_i', K_i', L_i' and f_i satisfy the first part of the lemma.

The proof of the second part of the lemma is similar, using Lemma 3.4 instead of Lemma 3.2. The details are left to the reader.

To make the notion of a triangulation of a P.L. space more precise, we introduce infinite complexes. First of all, we view $E^n \subseteq E^{n+1}$ by identifying $(x_1, \ldots, x_n)$ with $(x_1, \ldots, x_n, 0)$. Note that under these identifications, the convex hull of a subset S of E^n is the same as its convex hull viewed as a subset of E^{n+1}. Let $E^\infty = \bigcup_{i=1}^{\infty} E^i$, with the weak topology. E^∞ may be viewed as all (∞)-tuples $(x_1, \ldots, x_n, \ldots)$ with all but a finite number of x_i being zero, and the topology of E^∞ may be viewed as the topology of pointwise convergence. The convex hull of any subset of E^∞ is defined in the obvious way. In particular, by Δ^∞ we denote the convex hull of the points $(1, 0, \ldots)$, $(0, 1, 0, \ldots)$, $(0, 0, 1, 0, \ldots)$, etc.

Definition. A locally finite simplicial complex K in E^∞ is a collection of (finite) simplices, K, such that

1) $\sigma, \tau \in K \Longrightarrow \sigma \cap \tau = \emptyset$ or a common face.

2) $\sigma \in K$, $\tau < \sigma \Longrightarrow \tau \in K$.

3) For all $x \in |K|$, there exists a neighborhood U of x in E^∞ meeting only finitely many simplices of K. (Exercise: Prove that every finite subcomplex of K lies in some E^n.)

Let $(X, \mathcal{J})$ be a P.L. space. Using Lemma 3.5, and the technique of Lemma 3.2 one can construct an infinite locally finite complex K whose vertices are vertices of Δ^{∞} and a homeomorphism $h: |K| \longrightarrow X$ of $|K|$ onto X such that the restrictions of h to finite subcomplexes are elements of $\mathcal{J}$. Moreover, if $(X, \mathcal{J})$ is a P.L. m-manifold, then we may insist that $|K|$ is also; that is, every point of $|K|$ lies in the interior of a p.l. m-ball contained in $|K|$. In the case that there is a bound on the dimensions of the simplexes of Lemma 3.5, one can take $K \subset E^N$ for some finite N. In this case, the complex K is constructed within a suitable Euclidean space by "bare hands", using the instructions provided by Lemma 3.5. Details are left to the reader.

Definition. The pair (K, h) is called a triangulation of $(X, \mathcal{J})$ if K is a locally finite complex and $h: |K| \longrightarrow X$ is a homeomorphism such that the restrictions of h to finite subcomplexes are elements of $\mathcal{J}$.

3. P.L. Maps and Subidivision Theorems

Definition. Let $(X, \mathfrak{F})$ and $(Y, \mathfrak{G})$ be P.L. spaces. Then $\phi: X \longrightarrow Y$ is called a P.L. map if for all $(f, P) \in \mathfrak{F}$ and all $(g, Q) \in \mathfrak{G}$, $f^{-1}\phi^{-1}gQ$ is either empty or a subpolyhedron of P, and if the latter, then

$$g^{-1} \circ \phi \circ f: f^{-1}\phi^{-1}gQ \longrightarrow Q$$

is a p.l. map.

Notes: 1) It is easy to check that a P.L. map is continuous.

2) By an argument similar to that of Lemma 3.1, to show that a given map ϕ is a P.L. map, it suffices to check the condition in the definition for elements (f, P) of a base of $\mathfrak{F}$ and elements (g, Q) of a base of $\mathfrak{G}$.

Definition. If $\phi\ |K| \longrightarrow |L|$, K and L locally finite simplicial complexes, we say ϕ is P.L. if it maps each finite subcomplex piecewise linearly into a finite subcomplex of L.

Remark. The two definitions of P.L. map are consistent. That is, if $(X, \mathfrak{F})$ and $(X, \mathfrak{G})$ are P.L. spaces and if (K, h) and (L, j) are triangulations of X and Y respectively, and if ϕ and ψ are maps such that the following diagram commutes:

$$\begin{array}{ccc} X & \xrightarrow{\ \phi\ } & Y \\ {\scriptstyle h}\uparrow & & \uparrow{\scriptstyle j} \\ |K| & \xrightarrow{\ \psi\ } & |L| \end{array}$$

Then ϕ is a P.L. map if and only if ψ is a P.L. map.

Definition. A map $f: X \longrightarrow Y$ of topological spaces is said to be a proper map if the inverse images of compact sets in Y are compact.

Definition. A subdivision K' of a locally finite complex K is a locally finite simplicial complex such that

1) $|K| = |K'|$.

2) Every simplex of K is contained in a simplex of K'.

Using Lemma 1.2 and local finiteness, it is easy to see that every simplex of K is a union of finitely many simplices of K'. Moreover, if K' is a subdivision of K, then K' induces a subdivision (in the finite sense) of every finite subcomplex of K.

Theorem 3.6. A. If S is a locally finite family of polyhedra in $|K|$, then there exists a subdivision K' of K containing (finite) triangulations of each element of S.

B. If $f: K \longrightarrow L$ is a P.L. map of locally finite complexes, then there exists a subdivision K' of K such that $f: K' \longrightarrow L$ maps simplices linearly into simplices.

C. If $f: K \longrightarrow L$ is proper P.L. map, then there exist subdivisions K' and L' with $f: K' \longrightarrow L'$ simplicial.

Proof. A) Write $K = \bigcup_{i=1}^{\infty} K_i$, K_i finite subcomplexes, $K_i \cap K_j = \emptyset$ if $|i-j| \geq 2$. For example, if K is connected, let R_1 be a finite subcomplex and define R_i = closed simplicial neighborhoods of R_{i-1}, for each i. Let

$K_i = \overline{R_i - R_{i-1}}$. The R_i cover K because any vertex of K can be connected to a vertex of R_1 by a finite edge path.

Each K_i meets finitely only finitely many polyhedra in S. Proceed by induction subdividing K_i to contain subdivisions of its intersections with members of S and with the preceding subdivision of K_{i-1}. Then since K_i is not changed after the (i+1)st step is over, it is clear that this defines the required subdivision of K.

B). $S' = \{\sigma \cap f^{-1}(\tau) | \sigma \in K, \tau \in L\}$ is a locally finite set of polyhedra of K. Let K' be a subdivision of K containing subdivisions of the elements of S.

C). We may assume by B that f is linear on simplices of K. As f is proper, $\{f\sigma \mid \sigma \in K\}$ is a locally finite family of polyhedra in $|L|$. Let L' have these polyhedra as subcomplexes. Then $\{\sigma \cap f^{-1}\tau \mid \sigma \in K, \tau \in L'\}$ is a locally finite <u>cell</u> subdivision of K. As in the finite case this cell subdivision has a locally finite simplicial subdivision with no extra vertices. (See Lemma 1.4).

<u>Warning:</u> C) is false for non-proper maps. For example, triangulate the real line with vertices at the integers. There is a PL map $f: R \rightarrow [0, 1]$ mapping R homeomorphically onto the open interval (0, 1). It is impossible to find locally finite subdivisions to make f simplicial.

4. P.L. Subspaces

Definition. Let $(X, \mathcal{F})$ be a P.L. space. Let $(X_o, \mathcal{F}_o)$ be another P.L. space with $X_o \subseteq X$. Then $(X_o, \mathcal{F}_o)$ is called a P.L. subspace of $(X, \mathcal{F})$ provided

1) X_o has the relative topology induced by X, and

2) $i: X_o \longrightarrow X$, $i(x) = x$, is a P.L. map.

Remark. If $(X_o, \mathcal{F}_o)$ is a P.L. subspace, then $\mathcal{F}_o = \{(f, P) \in \mathcal{F} \mid f(P) \subseteq X_o\}$.

Examples: 1) If $X_o \subset X$ is open and if $\mathcal{F}_o = \{(f, P) \in \mathcal{F} \mid f(P) \subseteq X_o\}$, then $(X_o, \mathcal{F}_o)$ is a P.L. subspace of $(X, \mathcal{F})$.

2) E^n has the natural P.L. structure generated by the inclusion maps of polyhedra in E^n. A compact subspace X_o of E^n must be a polyhedron in E^n (with its natural structure). For suppose $X_o \subset E^n$ is a compact P.L. subspace. Then there is a coordinate map (f, P) in the structure of X_o with $f(P) = X_o$. But X_o is a P.L. subspace, so the composition $P \xrightarrow{f} X_o \subset E^n$ is a P.L. map. Therefore $X_o = f(P)$ is a polyhedron in E^n.

3) In E^n, $\{x \mid d(x, x_o) < 1\}$ is a P.L. subspace,

$\{x \mid d(x, x_o) \leq 1\}$ is not.

4) If $P_o \subset P$ are polyhedra in E^n, $P - P_o$ is a P.L. subspace of E^n.

Lemma 3.7. If $(X_o, \mathcal{F}_o)$ is a P.L. subspace of $(X, \mathcal{F})$ and if X_o is a closed subset of X, then there exists a locally finite triangulation $h: |K| \longrightarrow X$ and a subcomplex K_o of K such that $h \mid |K_o|: |K_o| \longrightarrow X_o$ is a triangulation of X_o.

<u>Proof.</u> Let $h: |L| \longrightarrow X$ be a locally finite triangulation of X. Then let $k: |M| \longrightarrow X_o$ be a locally finite triangulation of X_o. Let $\emptyset = h^{-1} i k$, $i: X_o \longrightarrow X$ the inclusion map. Let M' and K be subdivisions of M and L respectively, making the proper P.L. map (X_o is closed) $\emptyset$ simplicial. Let K_o = Image $\emptyset$.

5. Collapsing and Regular Neighborhood Theory.

Definition. If X_o is a closed P. L. subspace of the compact P. L. space X, then we say $X \searrow X_o$ if there exists a finite sequence of P. L. subspaces of X,

$X_o \subseteq X_1 \subseteq \ldots \subseteq X_r = X$ such that $\overline{X_i - X_{i-1}} = cl(X_i - X_{i-1})$

is a p. l. (P. L.) ball having $cl(X_i - X_{i-1}) \cap X_{i-1}$ as a face.

Definition. If M is a P. L. manifold, let $h: |K| \longrightarrow M$ be a triangulation of a neighborhood of x in M (h in the structure). We say $x \in \partial M$ if $link(h^{-1}x; K)$ is a ball. This does not depend upon the choice of (h, K).

Definition. Let X_o be a compact P. L. subspace of the P. L. manifold M. Then a regular neighborhood N of X is a topological neighborhood N, compact, such that $N \searrow X$ and N is an m-dimensional P. L. submanifold (i. e., a subspace which is a manifold) of X. N meets the boundary regularly if $N \cap \partial M = \emptyset$ or is a regular neighborhood of $X \cap \partial M$ in ∂M.

Theorem 3.8. Let X_o be a compact P. L. subspace of the P. L. m-manifold M. Then a regular neighborhood of X_o which meets the boundary regularly exists. If N_1 and N_2 are any two regular neighborhoods of X, then there exists a P. L. homeomorphism of N_1 onto N_2 pointwise fixed on X_o. If N_1 and N_2 meet the boundary regularly, then there exists an ambient isotopy $H: M \times I \longrightarrow M \times I$ throwing N_1 onto N_2 and leaving X_o fixed.

Proof. Let (f, K) be an element of the P. L. structure $\mathcal{F}$ of X such that $X_o \subseteq Int_M f(K)$ and K is a p. l. m-manifold. Let N be the image under f of a regular neighborhood of $f^{-1}(X_o)$ in K.

The uniqueness theorems follow similarly by taking $N_1 \cup N_2 \subseteq \mathrm{Int}_M f(P)$.

One can also define regular neighborhoods of non-compact subspaces of a P. L. manifold. If X and X_o are closed P. L. spaces, X_o a subspace of X, we say X_o collapses to X by an elementary generalized collapse if $cl(X-X_o)$ is the union of a disjoint locally finite family of P. L. subspaces B_i of X, where, for each i, B_i is a p.l. ball having $B_i \cap X_o$ as a face. A generalized collapse is a finite sequence of elementary generalized collapses. We write $X \searrow^{g} X_o$ if X collapses to X_o by an elementary generalized collapse.

A generalized regular neighborhood of X_o in the P. L. m-manifold M, X_o a closed P. L. subspace, is a closed topological neighborhood which is an m-submanifold and which collapses to X by an elementary generalized collapse.

This definition gives rise to the analogous existence and uniqueness theorems as for the compace case. However, these generalized regular neighborhoods have had no importance so far.

Chapter IV - General Position

§1. Definitions

Let K and L be P. L. subspaces of the P. L. manifold Q, $q = \dim Q$. Then K and L are in general position (or K is in gen. pos. w.r.t. L) if $\dim (K \cap L) \leq \dim K + \dim L - q$. (Note the similarity between this condition and the condition in dimensions that is necessary and sufficient for two subspaces of a finite dimensional vector space to span that space.)

If $f: P \longrightarrow Q$ is a map, $S'_r(f) = \{x \in P \mid f^{-1}f(x)$ has at least r-points$\}$, and $S_r(f) = \overline{S'_r(f)}$. If P & Q are P. L. spaces and f is a P. L. map, then it follows from the fact that P and Q may be triangulated to make f linear that $S'(f)$ is a P. L. subspace of P. If f is proper, then $S_r(f)$ is a closed P. L. subspace, and $\dim S_r(f) = \dim S'_r(f)$.

If $f: P \longrightarrow Q$ is a map, P & Q P. L. spaces of dimension p and q respectively, we say that f is in general position provided

1) f is P. L. and proper.

2) for all r, $\dim S'_r(f) \leq rp + (r-1)q$

3) $S_\infty(f) = \emptyset$ (i.e. f is non-degenerate).

Let f and g be two maps $P \longrightarrow Q$, P and Q P. L. spaces. Let $\mathcal{E}: P \longrightarrow \mathbb{R}_+$ be a positive, continuous function. Let ρ be a metric for the topology of Q. Then we say f is an $\mathcal{E}$-approximation to g (with respect to ρ) provided that $\forall x \in P$, $\rho(f(x), g(x)) < \mathcal{E}(x)$.

If f and g are maps, $f \simeq f'$ (rel K) means that f is homotopic to f' by a homotopy which is the constant homotopy on K.

§2. Approximation of Continuous Functions by P.L. Maps.

Lemma 4.1. Let P_1, P_2, and P_3 be subpolyhedra of the polyhedron P. Let $f: P \longrightarrow I^n$ be a continuous map, with $f|P_3$ a p.l. map. Assume $P_1 \cap P_2 = \emptyset$. Given $\mathcal{E} > 0$, there exists $f': P \longrightarrow I^n$ with the following properties:

1) $f'|P_1$ is a p.l. map

2) $f|P_2 \cup P_3 = f'|P_3 \cup P_3$.

3) f' is an $\mathcal{E}$-approximation to f (w.r.t the usual metric on I^n.)

Proof. Let ρ be a metric for P and choose $\delta > 0$ such that $\rho(x, y) < \delta$ implies $d(fx, fy) < \mathcal{E}/2$. Let $K_1, K_2, K_3 \subseteq K$ be simplicial triangulations of $P_1, P_2, P_3 \subseteq P$, such that K_1 is full in K, mesh (K) $< \delta$, and $f|K$ is linear. Now define $f': |K| \longrightarrow I^n$ by first putting $f'(v) = f(v)$ for every vertex $v \in K$. Then $f'|\sigma$, σ any simplex of K_1, be defined by extending linearly the definition of f' on vertices of σ. If $\sigma \cap |K_1| = \emptyset$, however, (i.e., σ has no faces in K_1, put $f'|\sigma = f|\sigma$. Finally if $\sigma \in K - K_1$, but $\sigma \cap |K_1| \neq \emptyset$, we may put $\sigma = \sigma_1\sigma_2$, $\sigma_1 \in K_1$, $\sigma_2 \cap |K_1| = \emptyset$, as K_1 is full. Then we define $f'|\sigma$ by extending linearly the map f' already given on σ_1 and σ_2. Clearly, $f'|K_2 \cup K_3 = f|K_2 \cup K_3$, and $f'|K_1$ is linear. Since $\forall \sigma \in K$, diam $f\sigma < \mathcal{E}/2$ and diam $f'\sigma < \mathcal{E}/2$ by construction, f' is an $\mathcal{E}$-approximation to f.

Remark. f is homotopic to f' (rel $P_2 \cup P_3$) by the homotopy $H_t(x) = tf(x) + (1-t)f'(x)$. Then $d(H_t(x), H_s(x)) < \mathcal{E}$, all $x \in I^n$, all $s, t \in I$. In other words, we can choose the homotopy H of f and f' to a "arbitrarily small."

<u>Lemma 4.2.</u> Let $f: P \to Q$ be a continuous map of the P.L. space P into the P.L. g-manifold Q. Let $P_o \subseteq P$ be a closed P.L. subspace of P on which f is already a P.L. map. Let $\mathcal{E}: P \to \mathbb{R}$ be a continuous positive function. Then there exists $f': P \to Q$ such that

1) $f' \simeq f$ (rel P_o),

2) $\rho(fx, f'x) < \mathcal{E}(x)$ all x (ρ some given distance function for the topology of Q),

3) f' is a P.L. map.

<u>Proof.</u> Let $\{B_i\}$ be a locally finite countable family of q-balls in Q, with $Q \subseteq \bigcup_i \text{Int}_Q B_i$. (For example, triangulate Q and take closed vertex stars.) Let $K_o \subseteq K$ be (locally finite) simplicial complexes triangulating $P_o \subseteq P$, such that if $\sigma \in K$, $f\sigma \subseteq \text{Int}_Q B_j$, some j. This is possible because there is a triangulation L of P, containing a triangulation of P_o, such that $L = \bigcup_{i=1}^{\infty} L_i$, L_i finite subcomplexes such that $L_i \cap L_j = \emptyset$ if $|i-j| \geq 2$. Subdivide each L_i to get L_i' such that $\sigma \in L_i'$ implies $f\sigma \subseteq \text{Int } B_j$, some j. Then further subdivide (proceed inductively) to get L_i'' such that for all i, L_i'' and L_{i+1}'' are compatible; this gives the required subdivision, K, of L.

Let $\{A_i \mid i = 1, \ldots, \infty\}$ be the simplices of $K - K_o$, ordered so that a simplex follows its faces. (For example: first take the vertices of $L_o'' - K_o$, then the 1-simplices and $L_o'' - K_o$ and the vertices of $(L'' - L_o'') - K_o$, then the 2-simplices of $L''_o - K_o$, the 1-simplices of $(L_1'' - L''_o) - K_o$ and the zero-simplices of $(L_2'' - L_1'') - K_o$, etc. ...) Put $K_i = K_o \cup \bigcup_{j=1}^{i} A_j$. We are going to define inductively maps $f_i: K \longrightarrow Q$

1) $f_i \mid |K_i|$ is P. L.

2) $f_i \simeq f$ (rel P_0)

3) if $\sigma \in K$, $f_i(\sigma) \subseteq \mathrm{Int}_Q B_j$, some j.

4) $\rho(f_i(x), f_{i-1}(x)) < \varepsilon/2^i$, all x.

We start with $f_0 = f$. Suppose f_{i-1} is defined. Then $f_{i-1}(A_i) \subseteq \mathrm{Int}_Q B_j$, some j. Let K' be a subdivision of K such that $N(A_i' ; K') \subseteq f_{i-1}^{-1}(\mathrm{Int}_Q B_j)$. Let $h: B_j \longrightarrow I^q$ be a P. L. homeomorphism. Put $R = N(A_i' ; K')$, $R_1 = A_i'$, $R_2 = \mathrm{Fr}_{|K|} N(A_i'; K')$, $R_3 = R \cap K_{i-1}'$. Then $R_1 \cap R_2 = \emptyset$ and $h \circ (f_{i-1} | R)$ is P. L. on R_3. Hence for every $\varepsilon > 0$ there exists $\alpha : R \longrightarrow I^q$ such that $\alpha | R_1$ is P. L., $\alpha | R_2 \cup R_3 = h \circ (f_{i-1} | R_2 \cup R_3)$, and $\rho(\alpha(x), h \circ f_{i-1}(x)) < \varepsilon$, if $x \in R$. Define $f_i: K \longrightarrow Q$ by

$$f_i | R = h^{-1} \alpha$$

$$f_i | \mathrm{cl}(|K| - R) = f_{i-1} | \mathrm{cl}(|K| - R).$$

Now R is compact, so by choosing ε small enough we can ensure that $d(f_i(x) - f_{i-1}(x)) < \varepsilon(x)/2^i$ for all $x \in |K|$, and also that every $f_i(\sigma)$ is contained in some $\mathrm{Int}_Q B_j$. Then f_i is a well-defined map which clearly satisfies 1), 3), and 4). Moreover, from the remark following Lemma 4. 1, we see that $(f_i | R) \simeq f_{i-1} | R$ (rel. $R_2 \cup R_3$) and so, extending the homotopy by the identity, we see that 3) holds. Call this homotopy H_i.

By construction, f_i agrees with f_{i-1} except on a simplicial neighborhood of A_i, R_i. If $\sigma \in K$, σ meets only finitely many of the R_i. Therefore the f_i

eventually agree on σ. Hence putting $f' = \lim_{i \to \infty} f_i$ defines a P. L. map $|K| \to Q$. Similarly, the homotopies H_i are eventually the identity on any given $\sigma \in K$ and so $H = \lim_{i \to \infty} H_i \circ \ldots \circ H_1$ is a well defined continuous map $|K| \times I \to Q$, and so $f \simeq f'$ (rel $|K_o|$).

Remark. Using the remark following 4.1, the reader can easily show that under the hypotheses of 4.2, we can find a homotopy H of f, fixed on P_o, such that $f' = H_1$ satisfies the conclusions of 6.2 and in addition, for every $x \in P$ and every s, t in $[0,1]$, $d(H_s x, H_t x) < \mathcal{E}(x)$.

§3. Approximation of P. L. maps by Non-Degenerate P. L. Maps.

Definition. If X is a finite set of points in E^n, let ΩX be the union of all proper affine subspaces of E^n spanned by subsets of X. ΩX is a closed subset of E^n of measure zero, so $E^n - \Omega X$ is dense in E^n.

Lemma 4.3. Let P_1 and $P_2 \subseteq P$ be polyhedra, dim $P \leq n$. Let $f: P \to I^n$ be a p.l. map with $f|P_1 \cap P_2$ non-degenerate. Given $\mathcal{E} > 0$ there exists a p.l. map $f': P \to I^n$ such that

1) $f'|P_1$ is non-degenerate
2) $f'|P_2 = f|P_2$
3) $f(P - P_2) \subseteq \mathring{I}^n$
4) for all $x \in P$, $\rho(f'x, fx) < \mathcal{E}$

Note: In general we cannot shift f to be non-degenerate on $P_1 - P_2$, without changing it on P_2, if it is not already non-degenerate on P_2 for example, let P_2 = 1-face of a 2-simplex P, $P_1 = P$, and suppose $f(P_2)$ is a point.

Proof of Lemma 4.3. Let $K_1, K_2 \subseteq K$ be triangulations of $P_1, P_2 \subseteq P$ so that $f: K \longrightarrow I^n$ is linear. Let $v_1, \ldots, v_r$ be the vertices of $K_1 \cap K_2$ and that $v_{r+1}, \ldots, v_s$ be the vertices of $K_1 - K_1 \cap K_2$. For $i \leq r$ put $w_i = f(v_i)$. For $r < i \leq s$ we may choose points w_i, w_i arbitrarily close to $f(v_i)$, such that $w_i \notin \Omega\{w_1, \ldots, w_{i-1}\}$, and $w_i \in \mathring{I}_n$. If we define $f': K \longrightarrow I^n$ to be the unique linear map such that $f'(v_i) = w_i$, $1 \leq i \leq s$, and $f'(v) = f(v)$ for all other vertices v, then by choosing each w_i close enough to $f(v_i)$, we may ensure that f' satisfies 4). It clearly satisfies 2) and 3). To show that such an f' is non-degenerate on K_1, it suffices to show that its restriction to each $\sigma \in K$ is. This we prove by induction on dim σ. If $\sigma \in K_1 \cap K_2$, $f'|\sigma = f|\sigma$, so there is nothing to prove. If $\sigma \notin K_1 \cap K_2$, put $\sigma = v_{j_1} \ldots v_{j_t}$, $j_1 < \ldots < j_t$, $j_t > r$. By induction, $f'|v_{j_1} \ldots v_{j_{t-1}}$ is non-degenerate. As $\dim P \leq n$, span $\{fv_{j_1}, \ldots, f'v_{j_{t-1}}\} \neq E^n$, so $f'(v_{j_t})$ is not in this affine subspace. Therefore the points $\{f'(v_{j_1}), \ldots, f'(v_{j_t})\}$ are independent; so. $f'|\sigma$ is non-degenerate.

Lemma 4.4. Let $f: P \longrightarrow Q$ be a P.L. map, Q a P.L. manifold and P a P.L. space with $\dim P \leq \dim Q$. Let $P_o \subseteq P$ be a closed P.L. subspace Suppose $f|P_o$ is non-degenerate. Then $f \simeq f'$ (rel P_o), where f' is a non-degenerate P.L. map and $f'(P-P_o) \subseteq \text{Int } Q$. Moreover, given $\mathcal{E}: P \longrightarrow \mathbb{R}_+$ a positive continuous function, we may insist that $\rho(f(x), f'(x)) < \mathcal{E}(x)$, all x, ρ a given metric for the topology of Q.

Proof. Exactly as Lemma 4.2, using Lemma 4.3 instead of 4.1.

Remarks.

1) As in 4.2, we could actually insist that there be a homotopy $H: f \simeq f'$ (rel P_o) such that for all $x \in P$ and all s, t in $[0,1]$

$$d(H_s, x, H_t x) < \epsilon(x).$$

2) In 4.2 and 4.4, one can insist that if the given map f is proper, then so is the map f'.

§4. Shifting Subspaces to General Position.

Lemma 4.5. Let $P_o \subsetneq P$ and $R_1, \ldots, R_r$ be polyhedra contained in I^n, with $P \cap \partial I^n \subset P_o$. Given $\epsilon > 0$ there exists an ambient isotopy h of I^n such that

1) h is fixed on $\partial I^n \cup P_o$

2) $h_1(P-P_o)$ is in general position w.r.t. each R_i

3) for all t, $d(h_t x, x) < \mathcal{E}$.

Proof. Let J be a triangulation of I^n having as subcomplexes triangulations $K_o \subsetneq K, L_1, \ldots, L_r$ of $P_o \subsetneq P, R_1, \ldots, R_r$, with K_o full in J. Let $v_1, \ldots, v_s$ be the vertices of $K-K_o$, and let X be the set of all the vertices of J.

Let $w_1, \ldots, w_s$ be points in Int I^n, such that $w_i \notin \Omega(X \cup \{w_1, \ldots, w_{i-1}\})$ all i; we may choose each w_i to be less than any preassigned distance from v_i. In particular, we may choose the w_i so that if ℓ is the linear map $J \longrightarrow I^n$ determined by putting $\ell(v_i) = w_i$ and $\ell(v) = v$ if $v \in X$, and $v \neq v_i$ all i, then ℓ is ambient isotopic to 1 via an ambient isotopy h satisfying 3) and 1).

(Certainly we can make ℓ isotopic to the identity by "small" moves. Then see proof that isotopy by moves implies ambient isotopy, Chapter V, §1, Lemma 5.1.)

To check 2), let $\sigma \in K-K_o$, $\tau \in R_i$. Write $\sigma = \sigma_1\sigma_2$, $\sigma_1 \in K_o$ and $\sigma_2 \cap |K_o| = \emptyset$ ($\sigma_1 = \emptyset$ possible). Let $\sigma_2 = v_{i_1} \ldots v_{i_s}$, $i_1 < \ldots < i_s$. Then $\ell\sigma = \sigma_1 \cdot (w_{i_1} \ldots w_{i_s})$. If $\ell\sigma$ and τ span E^n, then

$$\dim(\ell\sigma \cap \tau) \leq \dim \sigma + \dim\tau - n \leq \dim P + \dim R_i - n .$$

If $\ell\sigma$ and τ do not span E^n, then since $w_{i_s} \notin \Omega(X \cup \{w_1, \ldots, w_{i_s - 1}\})$, w_{i_s} is not the affine subspace spanned by $\sigma_1 \cdot w_{i_1} \ldots w_{i_{s-1}}$ and τ. This implies $\mathring{\sigma} \cap \tau = \emptyset$. Since $P-P_o = |K| - |K_o| = \bigcup_{\sigma \in K-K_o} \mathring{\sigma}$, this shows that

$$\dim[(P-P_o) \cap R_i] \leq \dim(P-P_o) + \dim R_i - n ,$$

for all i, $1 \leq i \leq r$.

Lemma 4. . Let $P_o \subseteq P$, $R_1, \ldots, R_r$ be closed P.L. subspaces of the P.L. g-manifold Q, with $P \cap \partial Q \subseteq P_o$. Let $\mathcal{E}: Q \to \mathbb{R}$ be a continuous positive function. Then there exists an ambient isotopy h of Q such that:

1) h fixes the points of $\partial Q \cup P_o$,

2) $h_1(P-P_o)$ is in general position w.r.t. each R_i,

3) $d(h_t x, x) < \mathcal{E}(x)$ for all x (d a metric for the topology of Q.).

Proof. Let $\{B_i\}$ be a locally finite countable family of q-balls such that $Q = \bigcup_{i=1}^{\infty} \text{Int}_Q B_i$. Let $K_o \subseteq K$ be triangulations of $P_o \subseteq P$ such that, for every $\sigma \in K$, $\sigma \subseteq \text{Int}_Q B_i$ for some i. Let $\{A_j\}$ be the simplices of $K-K_o$, ordered so that any simplex follows its faces. Let $K_i = K_o \cup \bigcup_{j=1}^{i} A_j$. We are going to define P. L. homeomorphisms h_i $(i \geq 0)$ of Q and ambient isotopies $H^{(i)}$ of Q $(i \geq 1)$ fixing $\partial Q \cup P_o$, such that

1) $H_1^{(i)} \circ h_{i-1} = h_i$,

2) $\forall \sigma \in K$, $\forall t$, $H_t^{(i)}(\sigma) \subsetneq \mathrm{Int}_Q B_j$, some j,

3) $\forall x$, $d(H_t^{(i)}x, x) < \mathcal{E}(x)/2^i$, all t.

4) $h_i(|K_i| - |K_o|)$ is in general position w. r. t each of the R_i.

We start by putting h_o = identity. Now suppose h_{i-1} is constructed, some $i \geq 1$. Let $A_i \subsetneq \mathrm{Int}_Q B_j$. Let $\alpha: B \longrightarrow I^q$ be a P. L. homeomorphism. Let $V_o = \alpha((h_{i-1}K_{i-1}) \cap B_j)$, let $V = \alpha(h_{i-1}K_i \cap B_j) = V_o \cup \alpha h_{i-1}A_i$, and let $W = \alpha(R_k \cap B_j)$. Note that $V \cap \partial I^q \subsetneq V_o$.

By Lemma 4. 5, for every $\mathcal{E} > 0$ there exists an ambient isotopy k of I^q fixed on $V_o \cup \partial I^q$, such that $k_1(V - V_o)$ is in general position with respect to each W_k and such that, for every t, $\rho(x, k_t x) < \mathcal{E}$. Now define $H^{(i)}$ by

$$H^{(i)}|B_j \times I = (\alpha^{-1} \times 1) \circ k \circ (\alpha \times 1)$$

$$H^{(i)}|\ \mathrm{cl}(Q - B_j) \times I = \text{identity}.$$

Put $h_i = H_1^{(i)} \circ h_{i-1}$. By choosing $\mathcal{E}$ small enough we can ensure that $d(H_t^{(i)}x, x) < \mathcal{E}(x)/2^i$ for all $x \in |K|$, $t \in I$, and also that, given $\sigma \in K$, $t \in I$, $H_t^{(i)}(\sigma) \subset \mathrm{Int}_Q B_j$, for some j.

To complete the proof, we observe that, by the construction of the $H^{(i)}$, we may have that each is the identity outside the interior of some B_j. Hence if C is any compact subset of Q, then on $C \times I$ all but a finite number of the $H^{(i)}$ are the identity. Hence it makes sense to define

$$h = \lim_{i \to \infty} H^{(i)} \circ H^{(i-1)} \circ \ldots \circ H^{1} .$$

Then h is an ambient isotopy and by construction satisfies 1), 2), and 3) in the statement of the lemma.

§5. Shifting maps to General Position.

Lemma 4.7. Let K be a (locally finite) simplicial complex and let $f: K \to Q$ be a P.L. map which embeds each simplex. Let $K_o \subseteq K$, and let $R_1, \ldots, R_n$ be closed P.L. subspaces of the P.L. manifold Q. Assume $f(|K| - |K_o|) \subseteq \operatorname{Int} Q$. Let $\mathcal{E}: K \to \mathbb{R}_+$ be a positive continuous function. Then there is a map $f': K \to Q$ and a homotopy $H: K \times I \to Q$ of f and f' such that

1) H is the constant homotopy

2) H is a P.L. map

3) f' embeds each simplex of K and $f'(|K| - |K_o|) \subseteq \operatorname{Int} Q$

4) $\forall \sigma_1, \ldots, \sigma_r$ in $K - K_o$

$$\dim\left(\bigcap_1^r f' \mathring{\sigma}_i\right) \leq \sum_1^r \dim \sigma_i - (r-1)q$$

and

$$\dim\left[\left(\bigcap_1^r f' \mathring{\sigma}_i\right) \cap R_j\right] \leq \sum_1^r \dim \sigma_i + \dim R_j - rq \quad , \quad \text{all } j.$$

5) $d(H_s x, fx) < \mathcal{E}(x)$ for all x and s, (d a metric on Q)

6) $f'(|K| - |K_o|) \subseteq \operatorname{Int} Q$.

<u>Proof.</u> Let $\{A_i | i = 1, 2, \ldots\}$ be the simplices of $K-K_o$, with each simplex following its faces. Let $K_i = K_o \cup \bigcup_{j=1}^{i} A_j$, a subcomplex. We are going to define, inductively, P.L. maps f_i, $i \geq 0$, and P.L. homotopies $H^{(i)}$, $i \geq 1$, such that

1) $\forall \sigma \in K$, $f_i | \sigma$ is an embedding;

2) $H^{(i)}$ is a homotopy of f_{i-1} to f_i which leaves K_{i-1} fixed;

3) $\forall \sigma_1, \ldots, \sigma_r \in K_i - K_o$,

$$\dim\left(\bigcap_{j=1}^{r} f_i \mathring{\sigma}_j\right) \leq \sum_{j=1}^{r} \dim \sigma_j - (r-1)q$$

$$\dim\left(\bigcap_{j=1}^{r} f_i \mathring{\sigma}_j) \cap R_k\right] \leq \sum_{j=1}^{r} \dim \sigma_j + \dim R_k - rq, \quad \text{all } k.$$

4) $d(H_s^{(i)} x, f_{i-1} x) < \varepsilon(x)/2^i$,

5) $f_i(|K| - |K_o|) \subseteq \operatorname{Int} Q$.

Put $f_o = f$. Now assume f_{i-1} is defined, $i \geq 1$. Let $L_1, \ldots, L_N$ be all the following P.L. subspaces of Q:

a) R_j, $1 \leq j \leq n$,

b) $\bigcap_{j=1}^{r} (f_{i-1} \sigma_j)$, all $\sigma_1, \ldots, \sigma_r$ in K_{i-1},

c) $[\bigcap_{j=1}^{r} f_{i-1} \sigma_j] \cap R_k$, all $\sigma_1, \ldots, \sigma_r$ in K_{i-1} and $1 \leq k \leq n$.

(Note: r <u>not</u> fixed.)

Now we are going to apply Lemma 4.6. Let $L = \text{link}(A_i; K)$. Let $P_o = f_{i-1}(\mathring{A}_i . L)$, and let $P = P_o \cup f_{i-1}(A_i)$. Note that $P \cap \partial Q \subseteq P_o$.

By Lemma 4.6, there exists an ambient isotopy h of Q, fixed on $P_o \cap \partial Q$, such that $h_1(P-P_o)$ is in general position w.r.t. each L_i, and $\forall s$ and $\forall x$,

$$d(h_s x, x) < \frac{1}{2^i} \min\{\varepsilon(y) \mid y \in A_i . L\} .$$

Define $H^{(i)}$ on $(A_i . L) \times I$ by putting $H_s^{(i)}(x) = h_s f(x)$. Extend $H^{(i)}$ to $K \times I$ by the constant homotopy outside $(A_i . L) \times I$, and put $f_i = H_1^{(i)} = h_1 \circ f_{i-1}$.

Clearly $H^{(i)}$ and f_i satisfy 2) and 4). Condition 5) holds because $h_1(\text{Int } Q) \subseteq \text{Int } Q$ and because f_{i-1} satisfies 5). Condition 1) holds for f_i because f_i differs from f_{i-1} only on simplices of $A_i . L$, where it is the composite of f_{i-1} and a homeomorphism.

To check 3), we first observe that $f_{i-1}(\mathring{A}_i) \subseteq P-P_o$ (in fact have =). For suppose $x \in P_o \cap f_{i-1}(A_i)$. Then $x = f_{i-1}y$, say, where $y \in \dot{A}_i L$, and $x = f_{i-1}(z)$, $z \in A_i$. Let $y \in \rho . \tau$, $\rho \in \dot{A}_i$ and $\tau \in L$. Then $A_i \tau$ is a simplex of K and so is embedded by f_{i-1}. Therefore $y = z$, so $x \in f_{i-1}(\dot{A}_i)$. Therefore $P_o \cap f_{i-1}(A_i) \subseteq f_{i-1}(\dot{A}_i)$. Therefore, as f_{i-1} embeds A_i, $f_{i-1}(\mathring{A}_i) \cap P_o = \emptyset$. Condition 3) now follows for f_i from the corresponding condition for f_{i-1} and the fact that $f_i(\mathring{A}_i)$ is in general position with respect to all the L_i.

To complete the proof, put $H = \lim_{i \to \infty} H^{(i)}$ and $f' = H_1 = \lim_{i \to \infty} H_1^{(i)} = \lim_{i \to \infty} f_i$. These are well defined p.l. maps because $H^{(i)} | A_i \times I = H^{(j)} | A_i \times I$ for $j \geq i$.

Finally we put some of the above results together to get:

Lemma 4.8. Let P be a P.L. space, P_o a closed subspace. Let Q be a P.L. manifold, $\dim P \leq \dim Q$. Let $f: P \to Q$ be a continuous map such that $f|P_o$ is P.L. and non-degenerate. Let $R_1, \ldots, R_N$ be closed P.L. subspaces of Q. Let $\varepsilon: P \to \mathbb{R}$ be a positive continuous function. Then there exist $g: P \to Q$ and a homotopy $H: f \simeq g$ (rel P_o) such that

1) g is a P.L., non-degenerate map,

2) $g|P-P_o$ is in general position,

3) $g(P-P_o)$ is in general position w.r.t. each R_i,

4) $g(P-P_o) \subseteq \text{Int } Q$,

5) $\forall x$, $d(H_s x, fx) < \varepsilon(x)$ $\forall s \in [0,1]$ (d some metric for the topology of Q).

Proof. By 4.2 and 4.4 we can find $f' \simeq f$ (rel P_o) and a homotopy H' between f and f' relative P_o, with f' P.L. and non-degenerate, $f'(P-P_o) \subseteq \text{Int } Q$, and $d(H'_s x, fx) < \varepsilon(x) \cdot \frac{1}{2}$. Let $K_o \subseteq K$ be triangulations of Q, so that $f': K \to L$ is linear on simplices. Then f' embeds the simplices of K. Let H'' be a homotopy of f' to a map g, relative P_o, satisfying

a) g is P.L. non-degenerate;

b) $g(P-P_o) \subseteq \text{Int } Q$

c) $\dim \bigcap_1^r g\mathring{\sigma}_i \leq \sum_1^r \dim \sigma_i - (r-1)q$, $\sigma_1, \ldots, \sigma_r$ in $K-K_o$;

d) $\dim(g\mathring{\sigma} \cap R_j) \leq \dim \sigma + \dim R_j - q$, $\sigma \in K-K_o$;

e) $d(H''_s x, f'x) < \frac{1}{2}\varepsilon(x)$, all x.

Then c) and 4) imply 2) and 3) in the statement of the lemma. Put

$$H(x,t) = \begin{cases} H'(x, 2t) & 0 \leq t \leq \frac{1}{2} \\ H''(x; 2t-1) & \frac{1}{2} \leq t \leq 1 \end{cases}$$

By the triangle inequality, H satisfies 5). Certainly, g satisfies 1) and 4).

<u>Definition.</u> Let $P_o \subset P$ be polyhedra. We say that P_o is of <u>local codimension</u> $\geq r$ in P if, for any triangulation $K_o \subset K$ of $P_o \subset P$, and for any simplex A of K_o, there is a simplex B of K with $A < B$ and $\dim B - \dim A \geq r$.

<u>Lemma 4.9.</u> Let Q be a P.L. manifold, and $p: Q \times I \to Q$ the projection on the first coordinate. Suppose X is a polyhedron in $Q \times I$ with $X \subset (\partial Q \times I) = X_o$. If $\dim X \leq m-r$, $r \geq 1$, and $\dim X_o \leq m-r-1$, then there is a level-preserving P.L. homeomorphism $h: Q \times I \to Q \times I$, arbitrarily close to the identity, such that $S_2(p|hX)$ is of local codimension $\geq r$ in hX.

Furthermore, if $S_2(p|X_o)$ is already of codimension $\geq r$ in X_o, we can insist that $h|\partial Q \times I$ is the identity.

<u>Note:</u> 'Level-preserving' means that h commutes with projection onto the second factor.

Before proceeding with the proof of lemma 4.9 we need another technical lemma.

<u>Lemma 4.10</u>. Let K_o be a full subcomplex of K. Let K' be the subdivision of K obtained by starring all simplexes of $K-K_o$ in order of decreasing dimension. Then K_o is a subcomplex of K' and if $A \in K'-K_o$, then $\text{link}(A; K') \cap K_o$ is either empty or a single simplex.

<u>Proof</u>. One may readily check, by induction on dimension, that a general simplex of K' may be written in the form $B.\hat{C}_1.\hat{C}_2 \ldots \hat{C}_r$ where $B \in K_o$, and $C_i \in K$ and $B < C_1 < \ldots < C_r$. Now if $A \in K'-K_o$ is written in the above form $D \in \text{link}(A; K') \cap K_o$ if and only if $AD \in K'$ and $D \in K_o$. In which case $AD = BD.\hat{C}_1 \ldots \hat{C}_r$ and $BD < C_1 < C_2 < \ldots < C_r$. Now K_o is full in K, and so $C_1 \cap K_o$ is a single simplex σ say, and the above conditions are satisfied if and only if $BD < \sigma$. So $\text{link}(A; K') \cap K_o = \text{link}(B; \sigma) =$ a single simplex (if it is not empty).

<u>Proof of Lemma 4.9.</u>

Case 1: First consider the case when $Q = \Delta^q$ and when $S_2(p|X_o)$ is already of local codimension $\geq r$ in X_o, and we wish to keep $\partial Q \times I$ fixed. Let $K_o \subseteq K \subsetneq \beta(\Delta \times I)$ be triangulations of $X \subseteq X \subsetneq \Delta \times I$, with K_o full in K. Let $K' \subset \beta'(\Delta \times I)$ be obtained from $\mathring{K} \subset \beta(\Delta \times I)$ by starring at interior points the simplices of $K-K_o$ in order of decreasing dimension.

Let $x_1, \ldots, x_s$ be the vertices of K_o, $v_1, \ldots, v_t$ the vertices of $K'-K_o$. For every $\varepsilon > 0$ let $v_1', \ldots, v_t'$ be points in $\Delta \times I$ such that the following hold:

1) there is a linear homeomorphism $\emptyset: \beta(\Delta \times I) \to \Delta \times I$, sending v_i to v_i' and z to itself if z is any other vertex of $\beta(\Delta \times I)$;

2) v_i and v_i' are on the same level; $d(v_i, v_i') < \varepsilon$, for all i,

and

3) for every i, $pv_i' \notin \Omega\{px_1, \ldots, px_s, pv_1', \ldots, pv_{i-1}'\}$.

Note: Condition 3) does not in fact depend upon the order of the vertices $(v_1, \ldots, v_t)$.

Let $h: \beta(\Delta \times I) \longrightarrow \Delta \times I$ be the linear homeomorphism of 1) above. We claim that h is the desired homeomorphism.

To prove this claim, let σ, τ be simplices of the simplicial complex hK'. We consider $(p|\sigma)^{-1}(p\tau)$.

Case 1: $p\sigma$ and $p\tau$ together span E^m. Then

$$\dim(p\sigma \cap p\tau) \leq \dim p\sigma + \dim p \quad - m \leq \dim p\sigma - r.$$

Therefore $\dim(p|\sigma)^{-1}p\tau \leq \dim \sigma - r$.

Case 2: $p\sigma$ and $p\tau$ do not span E^m.

A) $\sigma \in \mathring{\Delta} \times I$. Write $\sigma = \rho\sigma_1$, $\tau = \rho\tau_1$, $\sigma_1 \cap \tau_1 = \emptyset$. By 3) on page 102, the vertices of $p(\sigma_1)$ are linearly independent of the vertices of $p(\tau)$. Therefore $(p|\sigma)^{-1}(p\tau) = \rho = \sigma \cap \tau$.

B) σ and τ both meet K_o and $\sigma \cap \tau \in K_o$.

Put $\sigma = \sigma_1\sigma_2$, $\sigma_2 \in K_o$, $\sigma_1 \cap K_o = \emptyset$. ($K_o$ is full.) Put $\tau = \tau_1\tau_2$, $\tau_1 \cap K_o = \emptyset$, $\tau_2 \in K_o$. Then the vertices of $p(\sigma_1)$ are linearly independent of those of $p\sigma_2$ and $p\tau$ together. Therefore $(p|\sigma)^{-1}(p\tau) = (p|\sigma_2)^{-1}(p\tau) \subset K_o$.

And so is of codimension $\geq r$ in K_o by the given conditions.

C) σ, τ both meet K_o, $\sigma \cap \tau \notin K_o$.

Let $\rho = \sigma \cap \tau$. $\sigma = \rho\sigma_1\sigma_2$ where $\sigma_1 \cap K_o = \emptyset$, $\sigma_2 \in K_o$. Let $\tau = \rho\tau_1\tau_2$, $\tau_1 \cap K_o = \emptyset$, $\tau_2 \in K_o$. Now $\rho \in K'-K_o$. Hence $\mathrm{link}(\rho; K') \cap K_o =$ a single simplex, ρ_1 say. By 3), the vertices of $p\sigma_1$ and $p\tau_1$ are independent of the (space spanned by the) vertices of $p\sigma_2, p\tau_2$ and $p\rho$ and of each other. Therefore $p\sigma \cap p\tau = p(\rho\sigma_2) \cap p(\rho\tau_2)$. But $p\sigma_2, p\tau_2$ are faces of $p\rho_1$, and $p|\rho\rho_1$ is one-one because $S_2(p|K_o)$ has loc. codim $\geq r$ and so $S_\infty(p|K_o) = \emptyset$. Therefore $(p|\sigma)^{-1}(p\tau) = \rho$.

Now,

$$S_2(p\,|hK') \cap \sigma = \bigcup_{\tau} \mathrm{cl}[(p|\sigma)^{-1}p\tau - \sigma \cap \tau],$$

where τ ranges over hK'. So $S_2(p\,|\,hK')$ is of local codimension $\geq r$ in hK'.

Proof of Lemma 4.9 continued -- The General Case.

Let K triangulate X, J triangulate Q, be such that $p|X$: $K \longrightarrow J$ is simplicial. Let K' and J' be first derived subdivisions such that $p|X$: $K' \longrightarrow J'$ is still simplicial.

Let $A_1, \ldots, A_n$ be the simplices of J. Let $A_i^* =$ dual cell of A_i in J'. Let $K_i = (p|X)^{-1}A_i^* \cong |K| \cap (A_i^* \times I)$. K_i is a subcomplex.

Claim: $\dim K_i \leq \dim A_i^* - r$.

For let $\sigma \in K_i$. Put $\sigma = \hat{B}_1 \ldots \hat{B}_r$, $B_1 < \ldots < B_r$. Then $p\sigma = p\hat{B}_1 \ldots p\hat{B}_r$ (with possible repetitions). Now, $p\sigma \in A_i^*$ if and only if $A_i \leq pB_1$. Therefore $\dim A_i \leq \dim pB_1 \leq \dim B_1$.

However, $\dim B_1 \leq \dim B_r - (r-1) = \dim B_r - \dim \sigma \leq \dim X - \dim \sigma$.

Therefore $\dim \sigma \leq \dim X - \dim B_1 \leq \dim X - \dim A_i$. So $\dim \sigma \leq (m-r) - \dim A_i$.

But $m - \dim A_i = \dim A_i^*$. Hence $\dim \sigma \leq \dim A_i^* - r$.

Suppose that $A_1, \ldots, A_s$, $s < n$, are the simplices of the boundary $\dot{J}$.

Let $A_i^{\#} = $ dual cell of A_i in $\dot{J}'$. Then, since $\dim X_o \leq m-r-1$, if

$L_i = (p|X_o)^{-1} A_i^{\#}$, then $\dim L_i \leq \dim A_i^{\#} - r$, $i \leq s$, by the same argument

as in the last paragraph.

Now let $B_1, \ldots, B_t$ be the dual cells A_i^* and $A_i^{\#}$ in order of increasing

dimension, and let $K_j = (p|X)^{-1} B_j$, changing notation. We recall from the

theory of dual cells that the B_i cover $|J|$, that their interiors are disjoint, and

that ∂B_i is the union of some of the B_j with $j < i$.

Now we construct inductively p.l. homeomorphisms $h_i : B_i \times I \longrightarrow B_i \times I$

such that

  1) if $B_j \subseteq \partial B_i$, $h_i | B_j \times I = h_j$.

  2) $S_2(p | h_i K_i)$ is of local codimension $\geq r$ in K_i.

Suppose that h_j is defined for $j \leq i-1$. Then the maps h_j, $j \leq i-1$

define a p.l. homeomorphism

$$h' : \partial B_i \times I \longrightarrow \partial B_i \times I.$$

Since B_i is a ball, h' extends to a p.l. homeomorphism of $(\partial B_i \times I) \cup (B_i \times \partial I)$

onto itself, and this homeomorphism extends in turn to a p.l. homeomorphism

$h'' : B_i \times I \longrightarrow B_i \times I$, which is level preserving. To define h_i, we now apply the

Case 1 of this proof with $X = h'' K_i$ and $Q = B_i$.

Clearly $S_2(p|h\ K|) = \bigcup_i S_2(p|h_i\ K_i|)$, where h is the p.l. homeomorphism, $h: |J| \times I \longrightarrow |J| \times I$, defined by the h_i. Therefore h satisfies the requirements of the first paragraph in Lemma 4.9.

The proof in case $S_2(p|X_o)$ is already of local codimensi on at least r is nearly the same. We start out by defining h to be the identity on $(\partial J) \times I$ and then extend the definition inductively in order of increasing dimensions over the dual cells A_i^* of J (<u>not</u> $\dot{J}$) using Case 1.

Chapter V: Sunny Collapsing and Unknotting of Spheres and Balls

§1. Statement of the Problem

Suppose that $S^n \subseteq S^q$ are P. L. spheres of dimension n and q respectively. Then the pair $(S^q; S^n)$ is called a sphere pair of type (q, n). The pair $(\dot{\Delta}^{n+1} . \dot{\Delta}^{q-n}, \dot{\Delta}^{n+1})$ called the standard pair of type (q, n). The sphere pair (S^q, S^n) is called unknotted if it is P. L. homeomorphic to the standard pair; i. e., if there exists a P. L. homeomorphism $h: S^q \longrightarrow \dot{\Delta}^{n+1} . \dot{\Delta}^{q-n}$ such that $h(S^n) = \dot{\Delta}^{n+1}$.

Question: Is a sphere pair always unknotted?

Answer: Yes if $q-n \geq 3$

No if $q-n = 2$ (e. g., Trefoil knot in 3-sphere.)

Unknown if $q-n = 1$ (Schoenflies Conjecture.)

We are going to show in this chapter that the answer to this question is indeed affirmative if $q-n \geq 3$.

A related question is that of the unknotting of ball pairs. A proper ball pair (B^q, B^n) of type (q, n) is a P. L. m-ball B^m contained in P. L. g-ball B^q in such a way that $\partial B^m = B^m \cap \partial B^g$. The standard (proper) pair of type (q, m) is the pair $(\Delta^m . \dot{\Delta}^{q-m}, \Delta^m)$, and a proper ball pair is said to be unknotted if it is P. L. homeomorphic to the standard pair.

Question: Is a proper ball pair always unknotted ?

Answer: Yes if $q-n \geq 3$ -- we will prove this.

No if $q-n = 2$

? if $q-n = 1$.

In order to prove that pairs of codimension ≥ 3 (i.e. $q-n \geq 3$) are unknotted, we shall also have to consider the

<u>Factorization Question</u>: If $K_o \subseteq K \subseteq M$ are compact P.L. spaces, with M an m-manifold, and if $K \searrow K_o$ and $M \searrow K_o$, soes $M \searrow K$

In some cases the answer is always affirmative:

<u>Lemma 5.1</u>. If, in addition to the hypotheses of the factorization question, $K \subseteq \text{Int } M = M - \partial M$, then $M \searrow K$.

<u>Proof</u>. Let N be a derived neighbourhood of K in M. Then $N \subseteq \text{Int } M$ and $N \searrow K \searrow K_o$. So N is a regular neighbourhood of K_o, meeting the boundary regularly. By the generalized annulus theorem, $\overline{M-N} \simeq (\text{FrN}) \times I$. Therefore $M \searrow N \searrow K$, so $M \searrow K$.

However, the result we will need for the unknotting question is:

<u>Theorem 5.2</u>. If $K_o \subseteq K \subseteq M$ are compact P.L. spaces, M an m-manifold, then if $M \searrow K_o$ and $K \searrow K_o$ and if $\dim (K-K_o) \leq m-3$, then $M \searrow K$.

Here $\dim(K-K_o)$ = largest dimension of simplices of K not in K_o.

The proof of this theorem occupies the next few sections.

§2. <u>Sunny Collapsing</u>

<u>Definition.</u> Say $X_o \subseteq X \subseteq M \times I$ are compact P.L. spaces. If (x, t) and $(x', t') \in M \times I$, we say (x, t) is directly below (x', t') if $x = x'$ and $t < t'$. If $U = M \times I$, the shadow of U is defined to be the set $\{y \in M \times I \mid y$ is directly below a point of $U\}$. We write sh(U) for this set.

Picture:

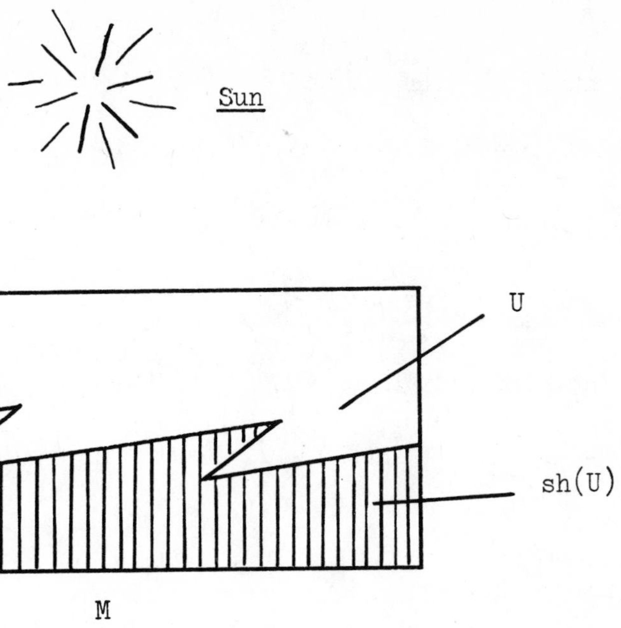

<u>Definition</u>. X <u>sunny collapses to</u> X_o <u>in</u> $M \times I$ if there exist triangulations $K_o \subset K$ of $X_o \subset X$ and J of M such that

1) The inclusion $K \longrightarrow J \times I$ is linear (on simplices),

and

2) there exists a sequence of elementary simplicial collapses:

$$K = K_r \overset{es}{\searrow} K_{r-1} \overset{es}{\searrow} \cdots \overset{es}{\searrow} K_o \text{ such that } (|K_i| - |K_{i-1}|) \cap sh(K_i) = \emptyset .$$

Picture:

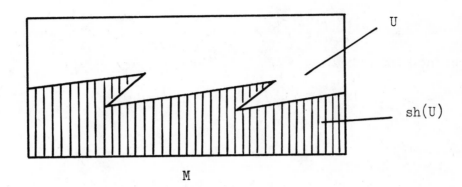

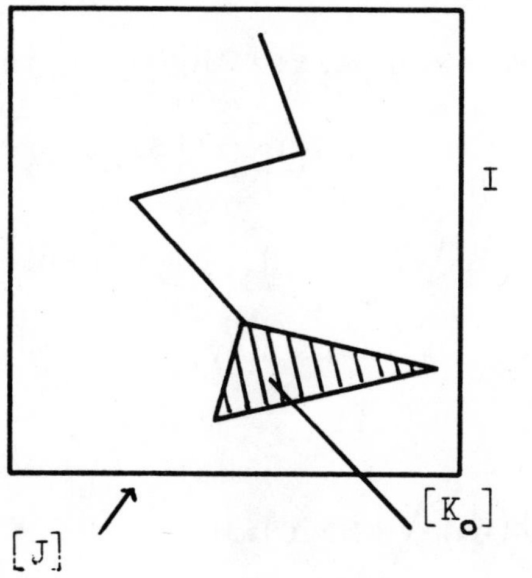

If K = entire figure inside the box, then $|K|$ sunny collapses to $|K_o|$.

Lemma 5.3. Suppose $X \subseteq M \times I$ are compact P.L. spaces. Let $X_o = X \cap [(M \times 0) \cup (\partial M \times I)]$. Suppose that X sunny collapses to X_o in $M \times I$. Then $M \times I \searrow (M \times 0) \cup (\partial M \times I) \cup X$.

Proof. Let $M = |J|$, $X_o = |K_o|$, $X = |K|$, where $K_o \subsetneq K$, and K is contained linearly in $J \times I$. Let $K = K_r \overset{es}{\searrow} K_{r-1} \overset{es}{\searrow} \cdots \overset{es}{\searrow} K_o$ with $(|K_i| - |K_{i-1}|) \cap sh(K_i) = \emptyset$ be the sunny collapse.

Step 1): $|J| \times I \searrow (|J| \times 0) \cup (|\partial J| \times I) \cup |K| \cup sh(|K|)$.

Let $\beta(J \times I)$ and $\gamma(J)$ be simplicial subdivision such that $\beta(J \times I)$ contains a subdivision of K and P_1: $\beta(J \times I) \longrightarrow \gamma(J)$, projection on the first coordinate, is simplicial. Let $\{A_i\}$ be the simplices of $\gamma(J) - \gamma(\partial J)$ in of order of decreasing dimension. For each i, $\beta(J \times I)$ contains a triangulation of $A_i \times I$. Consider $cl\{A_i \times I - (A_i \times I) \cap (K \cup sh(K))\}$. Now, if this set is non-empty it is a convex linear cell with $A_i \times 1$ as a principal face. Hence it collapses to the closure of the difference of its boundary and $A_i \times 1$. So $A_i \times I \searrow (\dot{A}_i \times I) \cup (A_i \times 0) \cup \{(A_i \times I) \cap (K \cup sh(K)\}$.

So doing these collapses in order of increasing i we find that

$$|J \times I| \searrow (|J| \times 0) \cup (|K| \cup sh(|K|)) \cup (|\partial J| \times I) .$$

Step 2): $(J \times 0) \cup (\partial J \times I) \cup K \cup sh\, K \searrow (J \times 0) \cup (\partial J \times I) \cup K$.

In this step we use the existence of the sunny collapse. We are going to show that

$$(J \times 0) \cup (\partial J \times I) \cup K \cup sh(K_i) \searrow (J \times 0) \cup (\partial J \times I) \cup K \cup sh(K_{i-1}).$$

Let $K_i = K_{i-1} \cup A \cup B$, with $A = aB$, $A \cap K_{i-1} = a\dot{B}$. Therefore $A \cap sh(K_i) \subseteq a\dot{B}$.

Let $\hat{B}$ be an interior point of B. Let b be a point directly below $\hat{B}$. Then for b near enough to $\hat{B}$, $b.A \cap K_{i-1} = a\dot{B}$; note that b is joinable to A because A can contain no vertical line segments. So $b.A \cap K_i = A$. Since $bA \subset sh(K_i) \cup K_i$, this implies that $bA \cap K = A$. So, collapsing bA from the face bB

$$K \cup sh\, K_i \searrow K \cup sh\, K_i - \text{Int } bA - \text{Int } bB = K \cup sh\, K_{i-1} \cup sh\, ba\dot{B} \cup ba\dot{B}$$

Using the fact that $(ba\dot{B}) \cap (K \cup shK_{i-1}) \subseteq a\dot{B} \subset K_{i-1}$ collapse vertically as in Step 1. $K \cup sh\, K_{i-1} \cup sh\, baB \searrow K \cup sh\, K_{i-1}$.

Picture:

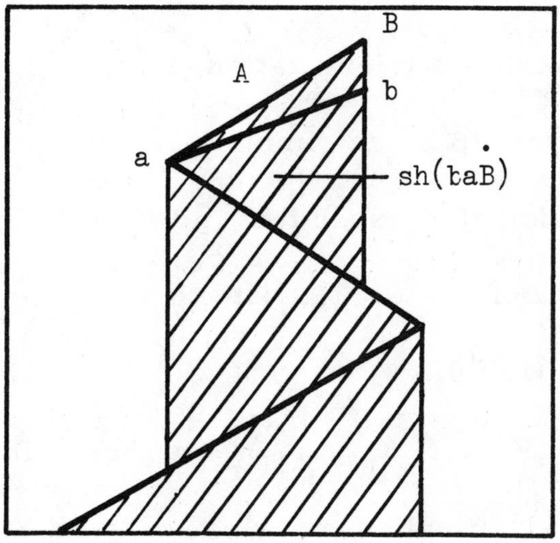

$sh(K_{i-1})$

Recall the definition: if **P** and Q are (compact) P. L. spaces, $P \subseteq Q$, we say P is of local codimension greater than or equal to c in Q provided that, for any triangulation $K_o \subseteq K$ of $P \subseteq Q$, and say $\sigma \in K_o$, there exists $\tau \in K$ with $\sigma < \tau$ and $\dim \sigma \leq \dim \tau - c$.

Lemma 5.4. Let $F: X \times I \to M \times I$ be a P.L. embedding, X and M compact P.L. spaces, such that

$$F^{-1}((M \times 0) \cup (\partial M \times I) = X \times 0.$$

Let $\pi: X \times I \to X$, $p: M \times I \to M$ be projections on the 1st factors. Suppose that

1) $S_2(p \circ F)$ is of local codimension ≥ 2 in $X \times I$

2) $\pi | S_2(p \circ F)$ is non-degenerate.

Then $F(X \times I)$ sunny collapses to $F(X \times 0)$ in $M \times I$.

Proof. By induction on dim K. Let K and J be simplicial complexes triangulating X and M, respectively. Let $\alpha(K \times I)$ and $\beta(K)$ be subdivisions of $K \times I$ and K, respectively, such that

1) $\alpha(K \times I)$ contains a triangulation L of $S_2(p| F)$.

2) $\pi : \alpha(K \times I) \to \beta(K)$ is simplicial.

Let γL be a subdivision of L such that $p \; F \mid \gamma L: wL \to J'$ is simplicial for a suitable subdivision J' of J. Note that γL contains a subdivision $\gamma(L \cap K \times 0)$ of $L \cap (K \times 0)$.

Let dim K = r and let $A_1, \ldots, A_r$ be the r-simplices of βK. Let $B_1, \ldots, B_s$ be the (r-1) simplices of $\gamma L - \gamma(L \cap (K \times 0))$. Any (r-1) simplex of. L is a face of. an (r+1) simplex of $\alpha(K \times I)$. Hence each B_i lies in a face of some simplex of $\alpha(A_j \times I)$, some j. Since $\pi: \alpha(A_j \times I) \to A_j$ is simplicial, this means that each B_i is contained in $\dot{A}_j \times I$, some j.

Now we are going to construct "blisters" on the B_i as follows. For each i, let $\hat{B}_i$ = barycenter of B_i. Choose X_i directly below $\hat{B}_i$ and near it (how near will be specified in a moment). If $B_i \not\subset X \times 1$, choose Y_i near and directly above $\hat{B}_i$. Choose A_j such that $B_i \subseteq A_j \times I$, and let $Z_i \in \mathring{A}_j \times I$ be a point on the same level as $\hat{B}_i$ and near it (how near to be specified shortly). Let

$$E_i = \begin{cases} X_i Y_i Z_i \dot{B}_i & \text{if } B_i \subseteq X \times 1 \quad (\text{i.e. } \hat{B}_i \notin X \times 1); \\ X_i Z_i B_i & \text{if } B_i \subseteq X \times 1 \quad . \end{cases}$$

We choose X_i, Y_i, and Z_i near enough to $\hat{B}_i$ so that $E_i \cap E_j = B_i \cap B_j$ and, if $B_i \nsubseteq X \times 1$, $E_i \cap (X \times 1) = B_i \cap (X \times 1)$, and $E_i \cap (X \times 0) = B_i \cap (X \times 0)$.

We observe that X_i and Y_i are not in B_i because $S_\infty(\pi | S_2(p \circ f)) = \emptyset$, and so no simplices of $\gamma(L)$ may contain a vertical line segment.

<u>Picture</u> (of 4 blisters):

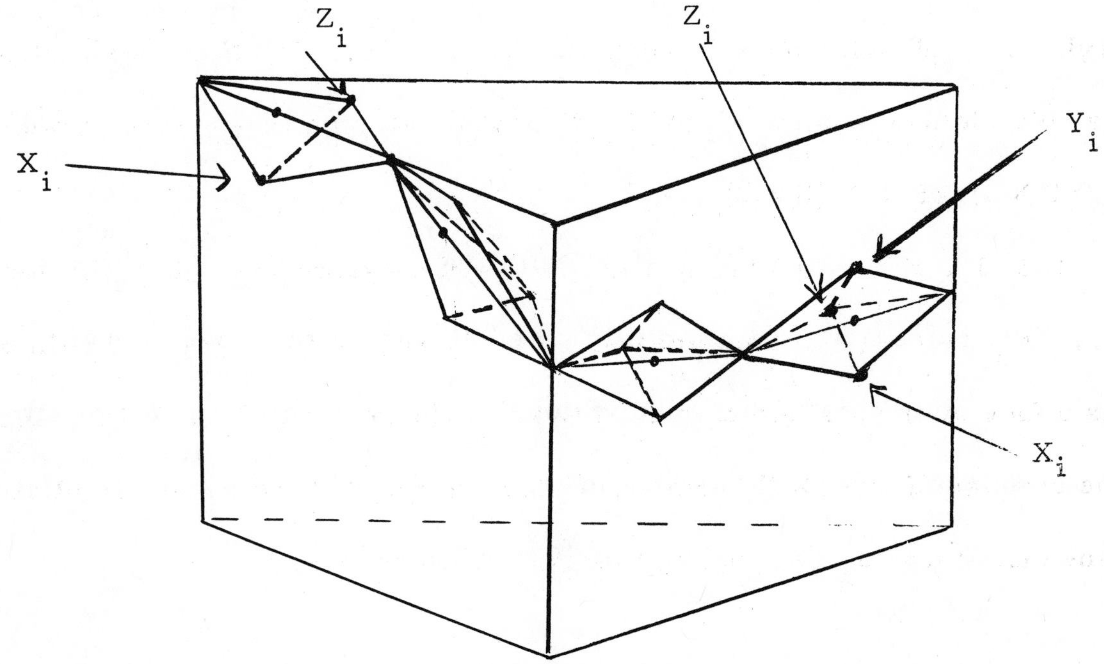

Let $E'_{j_1}, \ldots, E_{j_{R(j)}}$ be the blisters which meet $\mathring{A}_j \times I$. Each blister is a ball of dim $(r \times 1)$ and meets $\partial(A_j \times I)$ in a face. Hence $cl(A_j \times I - E_{j_1})$ is an $(r+1)$-ball. Since $E_{j_2} \cap E_{j_1} = B_{j_2} \cap B_{j_1}$, it is not hard to see that $E_{j_2} \cap \partial(cl(A_j \times I - E_{j_1})) = E_{j_2} \cap \partial(A_j \times I)$ = a face of E_{j_2}. Hence $cl(\mathbf{A}_j \times I - E_{j_1} \cup E_{j_2})$ is an $(r+1)$-ball. Continuing thusly, we at last find that $cl(A_j \times I - E_{j_1} \cup \ldots \cup E_{j_{R(j)}})$ is an $(r+1)$-ball. A similar argument shows that $cl(A_j \times 1 - (A_j \times 1) \cap (E_{j_1} \cup \ldots \cup E_{j_{R(j)}}))$ is a face of $cl[A_j \times I - E_{j_1} \cup \ldots \cup E_{j_{R(j)}}]$. Hence the closure of the complement of this face is also a face of $cl[A_j \times I - E_{j_1} \cup \ldots . \cup E_{j_{R(j)}}]$, to which this last polyhedron collapses. So, $A_j \times I \searrow [(A_j \times 0) \cup (\partial A_j \times I)] \cup (E_{j_1} \cup \ldots \cup E_{j_{R(j)}})$.

Let Λ = $(r-1)$ skeleton of $\beta K = \beta K - \{A_i\}$. Then, by what we have just proved

$$\beta K \times I \searrow (\beta K \times 0) \cup (\Lambda \times I) \cup (E_1 \cup \ldots \cup E_s),$$

and so

$$R = F(\beta K \times I) \searrow F((\beta K \times 0) \cup (\Lambda \times I) \cup (E_1 \cup \ldots \cup E_s)) = S.$$

Moreover $sh(R) \cap R \subseteq S$. For if $F(x) \in sh(R) \cap R$, then $x \in S_2(p \circ F)$ and so $x \in \Lambda \times I$. Since there exist subdivisions making the collapse $R \searrow S$ simplicial, it follows that R sunny collapses to S.

Now let $U_i = \begin{cases} Z_i X_i \dot{B}_i & B_i \subseteq X \times 1 . \\ Z_i X_i \dot{B}_i \cup Z_i Y_i \dot{B}_i & B_i \not\subseteq X \times 1 \end{cases}$

Let $V_i = \begin{cases} X_i B_i & B_i \subseteq X \times 1. \\ X_i B_i \cup Y_i B_i & B_i \not\subseteq X \times 1 . \end{cases}$

Then $E_i \searrow U_i$, as a ball always collapses to a face.

Recall that $B_1, \ldots, B_s$ are the $(r-1)$ simplices of γI and that $p \circ F: \gamma L \longrightarrow J'$ is simplicial. We may suppose in addition that the B_i are ordered so that if $F(B_i)$ overshadows $F(B_j)$ (i.e. has interior points of $F(B_j)$ in its shadow and therefore all of $F(B_j)$ in its shadow) then $i < j$. (Note that since $S_2(p \circ F)$ is of local codim. at least two, none of the polyhedra $F(B_j)$ may contain a vertical line segment.)

Since $E_j \searrow U_j$ all j, we have:

$(K \times 0) \cup (\Lambda \times I) - \bigcup_1^{i-1} V_j + \bigcup_1^{i-1} U_j + \bigcup_i^s E_j$ collapses to

$(K \times 0) \cup (\Lambda \times I) - \bigcup_1^{i} V_j + \bigcup_1^{i} U_j + \bigcup_{i+1}^s E_j$. Hence

$$(1) \qquad F[(K \times 0) \cup (\Lambda \times I) - \bigcup_1^{i-1} V_j + \bigcup_1^{i-1} U_j + \bigcup_i^s E_j] \searrow$$

$$F[(K \times 0) \cup (\Lambda \times I) - \bigcup_1^{i} V_j + \bigcup_1^{i} U_j + \bigcup_{i+1}^s F_j].$$

Moreover, $F(\text{Int } E_i) = \text{Int } F(E_i)$ misses the shadow of $F[(K \times 0) \cup (\Lambda \times I) - \bigcup_1^{i-1} V_j + \bigcup_1^{i-1} U_j + \bigcup_i^s E_j]$. For otherwise, we would have

Int $F(E_i)$ meeting $sh(F(E_j))$, some $j \geq i$. From the construction of the blisters E_k, this implies that $F(B_j)$ overshadows $F(B_i)$, an impossibility for $i \leq j$. It now follows that any simplicial subdivisions which make (I) a simplicial collapse make it a sunny collapse. Hence we may conclude that $F(K \times I)$ sunny collapses to $F((K \times 0) \cup (\Lambda \times I) - \bigcup_1^s V_i + \bigcup_1^s U_j)$.

Now let $k: \Lambda \times I \longrightarrow \Lambda \times I - \bigcup_1^s V_i + \bigcup_1^s U_i$ be the p.l. homeomorphism which sends $\hat{B}_i$ to Z_i and is the identity on $cl(\Lambda \times I - \bigcup V_j)$. Let $F' = F \circ k: \Lambda \times I \longrightarrow M \times I$. Then F' satisfies the hypotheses of this lemma. For $S_2(p \circ F') \subseteq \gamma L - \{B_j \mid J = 1, \ldots, s\}$ and so $S_2(p \circ F')$ has local co-dimension at least two in $\Lambda \times I$, and $\pi | S_2(p \circ F')$ is the restriction of a non-degenerate map and so is non-degenerate. Hence by induction $F' \circ k(\Lambda \times I)$ sunny collapses to $F' \circ k(\Lambda \times 0)$; therefore $F(\Lambda \times I - \bigcup_1^s V_j + \bigcup_1^s U_j)$ sunny collapses to $F(\Lambda \times 0)$. This means that

$$F((\Lambda \times I) \cup (K \times 0) - \bigcup V_j + \bigcup U_j) \searrow F((\Lambda \times 0) \cup (K \times 0)) .$$

Since $F(K \times 0) \subseteq (J \times 0) \cup (\partial J \times I)$, this collapse is also a sunny collapse. This completes the proof.

§3. <u>Factorization of Collapses -- Proof of Theorem 1.2.</u>

<u>Lemma 5.5</u>. Let $B \subseteq Q \times I$ be an n-ball, Q a compact q-manifold. Suppose that $B \cap [(Q \times 0) \cup (\partial Q \times I)]$ is a face of B. Suppose that $n \leq q-2$. Then $(Q \times I) \searrow (Q \times 0) \cup (\partial Q \times I) \cup B$.

Proof. Let $F = B \cap [(Q \times 0) \cup (\partial Q \times I)]$. Let $h: F \times I \to B$ be a P.L. homeomorphism with $h(x, 0) = x$. By Lemma 4.9, there is a P.L. homeomorphism $k: Q \times I \to Q \times I$, level preserving, such that $S_2(p|kB)$ is of local co-dimension ≥ 2 in kB. Consider $K = h^{-1}(S_2(pk|B))$. (p = proj. on the first coordinate). It is of local codim ≥ 2 in $F \times I$, and so its intersection with $(\dot{F} \times I) \cup (F \times 0)$ is of local codimension ≥ 1 in $(\dot{F} \times I) \cup (F \times 0)$. Hence we may apply Lemma 4.9 to find $k': F \times I \to F \times I$, a level preserving homeomorphism, such that $S_2(\pi|k'(K))$ has local codim ≥ 1 in $k'(K)$, π the projection of $F \times I$ onto F.

Let $\varphi = k \circ h \circ (k')^{-1}: F \times I \to Q \times I$. Then $S_2(p \circ \varphi) = k' \circ h^{-1} \circ k^{-1}(S_2(p|kB))$ is of local codimension ≥ 2 in $F \times I$. Moreover, $S_2(\pi|S_2(p \circ \varphi))$ is of local codimension ≥ 1 in $S_2(p \circ \varphi)$; hence $\pi|S_2(p \circ \varphi)$ is non-degenerate. Finally, $\varphi^{-1}(\overline{\partial Q \times I} \cup \overline{Q \times 0}) = F \times 0$. This is because k' and k are level preserving and boundary preserving, and because of the definition of h. Hence by Lemma 5.4, $kh(F \times I)$ sunny collapses to $kh(F \times I) \cap ((Q \times 0) \cup (\partial Q \times I))$. Hence by Lemma 5.2, $(Q \times I) \searrow (Q \times 0) \cup (\partial Q \times I) \cup kh(F \times I)$. Applying k^{-1} to both sides of this collapse, we see that

$$(Q \times I) \searrow (Q \times 0) \cup (\partial Q \times I) \cup B.$$

Theorem 5.2. Let $K_0 \subset K \subseteq M$, K_0, K P.L. subspaces of the compact P.L. m-manifold M. Suppose $M \searrow K_0$, $K \searrow K_0$, and $\dim(K - K_0) \leq m-3$. Then $M \searrow K$.

<u>Proof.</u> It suffices to suppose that $K \overset{e}{\searrow} K_o$; i.e. $cl(K-K_o) = B$, a p.l. r-ball and $B \cap K_o = F$, a face of B. Subdivide M with K, K_o, and B triangulated as subcomplexes. Let N be a 2nd derived neighborhood of K_o in M. M is also a regular neighborhood of K_o and N also meets the boundary regularly. Hence, by the generalized annulus theorem, there exists a p.l. homeomorphism

$$h: cl(M-N) \longrightarrow Fr\, N \times I$$

with

$$h(x) = (x, 0) \quad \text{if } x \in Fr\, N.$$

Now, $N \cap B$ is a regular neighborhood of F in B meeting ∂B regularly. So $N \cap B$ is an r-ball and $N \cap \dot{B}$ is an (r-1) ball, being regular neighborhoods of collapsible sets. Therefore $(Fr\, N) \cap B$ is also an (r-1) ball.

Let $B_1 = cl(B-N)$. $F_1 = B \cap Fr\, N$. Let $Q = Fr\, N$. Let $h: F_1 \longrightarrow Q \times I$ be the restriction of h above. We must now construct a p.l. homeomorphism $\mu: Q \times I \longrightarrow Q \times I$ throwing $Q \times 0$ into $(Q \times 0) \cup (\partial Q \times I)$.

Let $\lambda: I^2 \longrightarrow I^2$ be a p.l. homeomorphism such that $\lambda(1, t) = (1, t)$ for every t, and $\lambda(I \times 0) = ((I \times 0) \cup (0 \times I))$. (Exercise: Construct λ.) Set $\lambda = (\lambda_1, \lambda_2)$. Let $c: \partial Q \times I \longrightarrow Q$ be a boundary collar. Then define $\mu: Q \times I \longrightarrow Q \times I$ by

$$\mu(c(x, s), t) = (c(x, \lambda_1(s, t)), \lambda_2(s, t)) \qquad \text{if } x \in \partial Q$$

$$\mu(y, t) = (y, t) \qquad \text{if } y \in cl(Q - \text{Im } c).$$

The two definitions agree on the overlap (where $s = 1$ in the first definition). The map μ is p.l. For on $\text{Im}(c) \times I$, it is the composite:

$$\mathrm{Im}(c) \times I \xrightarrow{c^{-1} \times 1} \partial Q \times I \times I \xrightarrow{1 \times \lambda} \partial Q \times I \times I \xrightarrow{c \times 1} \mathrm{Im}(c) \times I .$$

This also shows that is is a homeomorphism.

Now, $\mu(hB_1)$ is a ball in $Q \times I$ meeting $(Q \times 0) \cup (\partial Q \times I)$ in the face μhF_1. $\dim B_1 \leq \dim M - 3 \leq \dim Q - 2$. Therefore $Q \times I \searrow (Q \times 0) \cup (\partial Q \times I) \cup \mu hB_1$. Hence $cl(M-N) \searrow (Fr\, N) \cup B_1$, applying $h^{-1} \circ \mu^{-1}$ to the preceding collapse. Therefore $M \searrow N \cup B_1$. $N \cup B_1 = N \cup B$, so $M \searrow N \cup B$. But $N \cup B \searrow K_0 \cup B = K$.

(Note: If $L_0 \subsetneq L \subset J$ are simplicial, L_0 full in J and $L'_0 \subsetneq L' \subset J'$ are first deriveds, then $N(L'_0 ; J') \cup L' \searrow L'$.

Proof. Let $\{A_i\}$ = simplices of $J-L$ which meet L_0, in order of decreasing dimension. Then $A_i \cap N(L'_0 ; J') \searrow \dot{A}_i \cap N(L'_0 ; J')$. For $A_i \cap N(L'_0 ; J')$ is a regular neighborhood of $A_i \cap L_0$ which meets A_i regularly, and so $\dot{A}_i \cap N(L'_0 ; J')$ is a face of the ball $A_i \cap N(L'_0 ; J')$.)

§4. Unknotting of Ball Pairs and Sphere Pairs

Notation: If $P = (B^q, B^n)$ is a proper ball pair, then ∂P denotes the sphere pair $(\partial B^q, \partial B^n)$; and vP denotes ball pair (vB^q, vB^n), v a joinable point. Note that vP is proper.

Lemma 5.6. Let P and Q be two unknotted ball pairs of type (q, m). Let $h: \dot{P} \to \dot{Q}$ be a p.l. homeomorphism. Then there exists a P.L. homeomorphism $k: P \to Q$ with $k|\dot{P} = h$.

<u>Proof.</u> $(\Delta^m . \dot{\Delta}^{q-m}, \Delta^m) \cong (\hat{\Delta}^m \dot{\Delta}^m \dot{\Delta}^{q-m}, \hat{\Delta}^m \dot{\Delta}^m) \cong v.(\dot{\Delta}^m \dot{\Delta}^{q-m}, \dot{\Delta}^m)$. So there are P. L. homeomorphisms $P \longrightarrow v\dot{P}$, $Q \longrightarrow v\dot{Q}$ and we can extend $h: \dot{P} \longrightarrow \dot{Q}$ conically.

<u>Lemma 5.7.</u> The cone and suspension (join with a sphere) of an unknotted ball or sphere pair is an unknotted ball or sphere pair.

<u>Proof.</u> Exercise.

By $B_{q,m}$ we denote the statement: all proper ball pairs of type (q, m) are unknotted. Let $S_{q,m}$ = "all sphere pairs of type (q, m) are unknotted."

<u>Lemma 5.8.</u> $B_{q,m}$ implies $S_{q,m}$.

<u>Proof.</u> Let $P = (S^q, S^m)$. Let $K_o \subseteq K$ be a triangulation of $S^m \subsetneq S^q$. Let v be a vertex of K_o. Let $P_1 = (\overline{st}(v; K), \overline{st}(v, K_o))$. Let $P_2 = cl(P - P_1) = (|\overline{K - st(v; K)}|, |\overline{K_o - st(v; K_o)}|)$. Then P_1 and P_2 are both proper ball pairs, and $\dot{P}_1 = \dot{P}_2$. The identity $\dot{P}_1 \longrightarrow \dot{P}_1$ extends to a p.l. homeomorphism $P_1 \longrightarrow v\dot{P}_1$ and a p.l. homeomorphism $P_2 \longrightarrow v'\dot{P}_2$. So P is p.l. homeomorphic (as a pair) to $v\dot{P}_1 \cup v'\dot{P}_1$, a suspension of $\dot{P}_1$ and so unknotted.

<u>Definition.</u> <u>A face</u> of the proper ball pair $P = (B^q, B^m)$ is a proper ball pair $F = (A^{q-1}, A^{m-1})$ with $A^{q-1} \subseteq \partial B^q$ and $A^{m-1} = A^{q-1} \cap \partial B^m$. We define $cl(\dot{P} - F) = (\partial B^q - A^{q-1}, \partial B^m - A^{m-1})$, which is also a face of P.

<u>Lemma 5.9.</u> Let P and Q be unknotted ball pairs of type (q, m) which meet in a common face. Then if $B_{q-1,m-1}$ is true, $P \cup Q$ is an unknotted ball pair.

Proof. Let F be the common face. Let $P_1 = cl(P-F)$, $Q = cl(Q-F)$. $B_{q-1,m-1}$ implies F, P_1, P_2 are unknotted. Then $\dot{F}$ is unknotted as p.l. homoemorphisms preserve boundaries. By 5.6, the identity $\dot{F} \longrightarrow \dot{F}$ extends to p.l. homeomorphisms:

$$h_1 : P_1 \longrightarrow a\dot{F},$$

$$h_2 : F \longrightarrow b\dot{F},$$

$$h_3 : P_2 \longrightarrow c\dot{F}$$

$h_1 \cup h_2 : \dot{P} \longrightarrow a\dot{F} \cup b\dot{F}$ extends to $k_1 : P \longrightarrow ab\dot{F}$ and $h_2 \cup h_3 : \dot{Q} \longrightarrow b\dot{F} \cup c\dot{F}$ extends to $k_2 : Q \longrightarrow bc\dot{F}$, both homeomorphisms. So $k_1 \cup k_2 : P \cup Q \longrightarrow ab\dot{F} \cup bc\dot{F} \cong aF \cup cF$ is unknotted.

Lemma 5.10. Let (B^q, B^m) be a proper ball pair. Let N be a regular neighborhood of B^m in B^q. Then $B_{q-1,m-1}$ and $S_{q-1,m-1}$ imply (N, B^m), a proper ball pair, is unknotted.

Proof. Let $K_0 \subsetneq K$ triangulate $B^m \subset B^q$, and suppose that $K_0 \overset{s}{\searrow} K$. By uniqueness of regular neighborhoods, we may also suppose that $N = N(K_0''; K'')$ without loss of generality. Let $K_0 = L_r \overset{es}{\searrow} \cdots \overset{es}{\searrow} L_0 = v \in K_o$. Let $E_i = (N(L_i''; K''), N(L_i''; K_0''))$, where K'' = 2nd derived subdivision. $E_r = (N, K_0)$. Moreover, E_i is a ball pair, by regular neighborhood theory, it is easily seen to be proper.

$E_0 = (\overline{star}(v; K''), \overline{star}(v, K_0'')) = v(link(v; K''), link(v; K_0''))$, a cone on a sphere pair of type $(q-1, m-1)$. Hence E_0 is unknotted. Suppose by induction that E_{i-1} is unknotted. Put $L_i = L_{i-1} \cup A$, $A \cap B$, $A = aB$. Then $E_i = E_{i-1} \cup P \cup Q$,

$E_i = E_{i-1} \cup P \cup Q$, where

$$P = (\mathrm{st}(\hat{A}; K''), \mathrm{st}(\hat{A}; K''_o))$$

$$Q = (\mathrm{st}(\hat{B}; K''), \mathrm{st}(\hat{B}; K''_o))$$

(See regular neighborhood theory, Chapter III.)

Now $P = \hat{A}(\mathrm{link}(\hat{A}; K''), \mathrm{link}(\hat{A}; K''_o))$. The link pair is either a sphere pair or a ball pair, according as $\hat{A} \in \mathrm{Int}\, K''_o$ of $\hat{A} \in \dot{K}''_o$. Since $\partial(\mathrm{link}(\hat{A}; K''_o)) = \mathrm{link}(\hat{A}; \dot{K}''_o) \subseteq \mathrm{link}(\hat{A}; \dot{K}'') = \partial(\mathrm{link}(\hat{A}; K''))$, in the event $\hat{A} \in \dot{K}''_o$, this pair is a proper ball pair or a sphere pair of type $(q-1, m-1)$. Hence P is unknotted.

Now we are going to prove that $P \cap E_{i-1}$ is a face of P and E_{i-1}. Let $L = (\mathrm{link}(\hat{A}; K'), \mathrm{link}(\hat{A}; K'_o))$. Let $P_1 = (\mathrm{link}(\hat{A}; K''), \mathrm{link}(\hat{A}; K''_o))$. Then $P = \hat{A}P_1$. Let $p: P_1 \longrightarrow L$ be the pseudo-radial projection given by

$$P(\widehat{\hat{A}\sigma}) = \hat{\sigma} \quad \text{if} \quad \sigma \in \mathrm{link}(\hat{A}; K').$$

(See regular neighborhood theory.).

We now introduce some new notation, by writing $P = (P_b, P_s)$ (P"big" and P"small"), $Q = (Q_b, Q_s)$, etc. Then P sends $P_b \cap (E_{i-1})_b$ onto the derived neighborhood of $(a\dot{B})$ in L_b and sends $P_s \cap (E_{i-1})_s$ onto the derived neighborhood of $(a\dot{B})$ in L_s. Using the sublemma appearing at the end of this proof, we see that the image of $P \cap E_{i-1}$ is a proper ball pair of type $(q-1, m-1)$ and so a face of P and of E_{i-1}. Therefore $P \cup E_{i-1}$ is an unknotted pair. Similarly, (see reg. nbhd. theory) $(P \cup E_{i-1}) \cap Q$ is a face of $P \cup E_{i-1}$ and of Q; hence E_i is unknotted.

Sublemma 5.10.1. Let $X \subseteq M \subseteq Q$, $M \subseteq Q$ a manifold pair, $M \cap \partial Q = \partial M$. Assume everything is triangulated so that X is full in both M and Q. Let N = derived neighborhood of X in Q. Then $\partial(N \cap M) = (\partial N) \cap M$.

Proof. First, $Fr_M(N \cap M) = Fr_Q(N) \cap M$. For say $L \subseteq K_o \subseteq K$ triangulates $X \subseteq M \subseteq Q$, with L full in K_o, K_o full in K. Let $L' \subseteq K'_o \subseteq K'$ be first derived subdivisions, and suppose $N = N(L'; K')$. Then $N \cap M = N(L'; K'_o)$. Say $A \in K'_o$. Then $A \in Fr_M(N \cap M)$ if and only if $A \cap L = \emptyset$ but there exist $B \in L$ with $BA \in K'_o$. $A \in Fr_Q(N) \cap M$ if and only if $A \in K_o$, $A \cap L_1 = \emptyset$ and there exists $B \in L'$ with $AB \in K'$. It is clear that these conditions are equivalent. Therefore $Fr_M(N \cap M) = Fr_Q(N) \cap M$.

Now, $(\partial N) \cap M = ((Fr_Q N) \cap M) \cup (N \cap M \cap \partial Q)$.

$\partial(N \cap M) = Fr_M(N \cap M) \cup (N \cap \partial M)$.

But $M \cap \partial Q = \partial M$.

Corollary 5.11. If $q-m \geq 3$, then $B_{m-1,q-1}$ and $S_{m-1,q-1}$ imply $B_{m,q}$.

Proof. If $q-m \geq 3$, then by Theorem 5.2, $B^q \searrow B^m$ (since both collapse to a point.) Hence B^q is a regular neighborhood of B^m. So (B^q, B^m) is unknotted by 5.10.

Theorem 5.12. If $q-m \geq 3$, then every proper ball pair or sphere pair of type (m, q) is unknotted.

Proof. We already have the following implications:

$$B_{m,q} \Longrightarrow S_{m,q} \text{ and } S_{m,q} \Longrightarrow B_{m+1,q+1}, \text{ if } q-m \geq 3 .$$

To start the induction, assume $m = 0$, $q \geq 3$. So we have a point, P say, in the interior of B^q. Triangulate B^q with P as a vertex. By the uniqueness of regular neighborhoods $[P \subset B^q] \cong [P \subset \overline{\text{star}}(P, K)]$ which is clearly unknotted.

§5. Unknotting of Embeddings of Balls in Balls.

Now we ask the following question: given P. L. embeddings $f, g: B^m \longrightarrow B^q$, with $f|\partial B^m = g|\partial B^m$, $\partial B^m = f^{-1}(\partial B^q) = g^{-1}(\partial B^q)$, is there an ambient isotopy throwing $f(x)$ onto $g(x)$, all $x \in B^m$?

Lemma 5.13. If $B^m \subseteq B^q$ is an unknotted proper ball pair and if $h: B^m \cup \partial B^q \longrightarrow B^m \cup \partial B^q$ is a P. L. homeomorphism, then there exists a P. L. homeomorphism $k: B^q \longrightarrow B^q$ extending h.

Proof. By Lemma 5.6, there exists $k': (B^q; B^m) \xrightarrow{\cong} (B^q; B^m)$ such that $k'|\partial B^q = h|\partial B^q$. So $k'h^{-1}|\partial B^m$ = identity. Let $\alpha: (B^q; B^m) \longrightarrow (\Delta^m \dot{\Delta}^{q-m}, \Delta^m)$ be a P. L. homeomorphism. Let $\beta = \alpha k' h^{-1} \alpha^{-1}: \Delta^m \longrightarrow \Delta^m$. Let $\Sigma\beta: \Delta^m . \dot{\Delta}^{q-m} \longrightarrow \Delta^m \dot{\Delta}^{q-m}$ be the suspension of β (i. e. join up β with the identity on $\dot{\Delta}^{q-m}$). Then $\Sigma\beta$ is the identity on $\dot{\Delta}^m \dot{\Delta}^{q-m} = \partial(\Delta^m . \dot{\Delta}^{q-m})$. Therefore $k'' = \alpha^{-1}(\Sigma\beta)\alpha: B^q \longrightarrow B^q$ is the identity on ∂B^q. Moreover, $k''|B^m = k'h^{-1}$. Let $k = (k'')^{-1}k'$. Then $k|\partial B^q = k'|\partial B^q = h|\partial B^q$, $k|\partial B^m = (k'h^{-1})^{-1}k' = h$.

Lemma 5.14. Let $f, g: B^m \longrightarrow B^q$ be P. L. embeddings, $f^{-1}\partial B^q = g^{-1}\partial B^q = \partial B^m$. Assume $q-m \geq 3$ and $f|\partial B^m = g|\partial B^m$. Then f and g are ambient isotopic keeping ∂B^q fixed. (That is, there exists an ambient isotopy h such that $h_1 \circ f = g$ and h leaves ∂B^q fixed.)

Proof. There exists a P. L. homeomorphism $h: B^q \to B^q$ such that $h(fB^m) = g(B^m)$, as (B^q, fB^m) and (B^q, gB^m) are unknotted proper ball pairs. The map $fg^{-1}h: fB^m \to fB^m$ is a P. L. homeomorphism, and $fg^{-1}h|f(\partial B^m) = h|f(\partial B^m)$. So $h \cup fg^{-1}h: \partial B^q \cup fB^m \to \partial B^q \cup fB^m$ is a P. L. homeomorphism. By 5.13, there exists a P. L. homeomorphism $k: B^q \to B^q$ with $k|\partial B^q = h$ and $k|fB^m = fg^{-1}h$. The map $\alpha = hk^{-1}: B^q \to B^q$ is a P. L. homeomorphism, and $\alpha|fB^m = gf^{-1}$. So $\alpha f = g$. Moreover, $\alpha|\partial B^q$ = identity, so α is ambient isotopic to the identity keeping ∂B^q fixed.

§6. Unknotting Cones

We state the following without proof: (Lickorish's Theorem)

If f and g are P. L. embeddings of $v.K$ into B^q, K a polyhedron and v a joinable point, with $f^{-1}(\partial B^q) = g^{-1}(\partial B^q) = K$, and if $f|K = g|K$, and if $\dim v.K \leq q-3$, then f and g are ambient isotopic keeping ∂B^q fixed.

Chapter VI: Isotopy

§1. Concordance, Isotopy, Ambient Isotopy, and Isotopy by Moves.

Definition. The embeddings f and g of M into Q (PL spaces) are called isotopic if there exists a PL map $F: M \times I \longrightarrow Q$ such that

1) $F_o = F$, $F_1 = g$

2) F_t is an embedding. ($F_t(x) = F(x,t)$.)

Equivalently, we say that f and g are isotopic if there exists a level preserving embedding $\overline{F}: M \times I \longrightarrow Q \times I$ such that $\overline{F}_o = f$ and $\overline{F}_1 = g$, ($\overline{F}(x,t) = (\overline{F}_t(x), t)$). The relation between F and $\overline{F}$ is $\overline{F}(x,t) = (F(x,t),t)$.

We say that f and g are ambient isotopic if there exists an ambient isotopy $h: Q \times I \longrightarrow Q \times I$ with $h \circ f = g$.

We say that f and g are concordant if there exists a PL embedding $F: M \times I \longrightarrow Q \times I$ with $F(x,0) = (f(x), 0)$ and $F(x,1) = (g(x),1)$ for all $x \in M$.

Definition. If Q is a PL space and $h: Q \longrightarrow Q$ is a PL homeomorphism, $\sup(h) = \{x \in Q \mid hx \neq x\}$ = support of h. We say h is supported by X if $\sup(h) \subseteq X \subseteq Q$. Then h is supported by X if and only if $h|Q-X$ is the identity.

If Q is a PL q-manifold and h is supported by a PL q-ball contained in Q as a PL subspace, then h is called a move. We call the move h a proper move if either $h|\partial Q$ = identity or there exists $B^q \subseteq Q$, B^q a q-ball with $\sup(h) \subseteq B^q$, such that $B^q \cap \partial Q$ is a face of B^q.

<u>**Definition.**</u> If f and g are embeddings of M into the q-manifold Q, we say that f and g are <u>isotopic by moves</u> if there exists a finite sequence $h_1, \ldots, h_r$ of proper moves of Q with

$$h_1 \circ \ldots \circ h_r \circ f = g.$$

<u>Lemma 6.1.</u> Each of the following statments implies the ones below it (f and g embeddings $M \longrightarrow Q^q$).

a) f and g are isotopic by moves.

b) f and g are ambient isotopic

c) f and g are isotopic.

d) f and g are concordant.

<u>Proof.</u> b) $\Rightarrow$ c). Let $h: Q \times I \longrightarrow Q \times I$ be an ambient isotopy with $h_1 f = g$. Define $F: M \times I \longrightarrow Q \times I$ by $F = h \circ (f \times 1)$.

c) $\Longrightarrow$ d). Clear.

a) $\Longrightarrow$ b). It suffices to show that any <u>move</u> is ambient isotopic to the identity. So let $h: Q \longrightarrow Q$ be a move.

<u>Case 1:</u> $\text{Sup}(h) \subseteq B^q \subseteq Q$ and $h|\partial Q$ = identity. Then $h|\partial B^q$ is the identity, so $h|B^q$ is ambient isotopic to the identity keeping ∂B^q fixed. Hence h is ambient isotopic to the identity (keeping $Q - B^q$ fixed).

<u>Case 2:</u> Supp $h \subseteq B^q \subseteq Q$, $B^q \cap \partial Q$ = a face F of B^q. Let $F_1 = \text{cl}(\partial B^q - F)$. Then by continuity, $h|F_1$ = identity. Let $\alpha: B^q \longrightarrow \Delta^q$ be a PL homeomorphism sending F into a principal face Δ_1 of Δ^q. Define $k: \Delta^q \times I \longrightarrow \Delta^q \times I$ by first putting $k|\Delta^q \times 0$ = identity, $k|\Delta^q \times 1 = \alpha h \alpha^{-1}$, $k|\text{cl}(\dot{\Delta} - \Delta_1) \times I$ = identity, $k(\hat{\Delta}_1; 1/2) = (\hat{\Delta}_1, 1/2)$ and

$\hat{\Delta}_1$ = barycenter of Δ_1; then extending k, by joining up linearly, to $\Delta^q \times I$. Then k is an ambient isotopy ending in $\alpha h \alpha^{-1}$ and keeping $cl(\dot{\Delta} - \Delta_1)$ fixed. Therefore $h|B^q$ is ambient isotopic to the identity keeping $cl(B^q - F)$ fixed, and so h is itself ambient isotopic to the identity.

Theorem 6.2. If Q is a compact q-manifold and $H: Q \times I \to Q \times I$ is an ambient isotopy, then there exists a finite sequence $h_1, \ldots, h_r$ of proper moves of Q such that $H_1 = h_1 \circ \ldots \circ h_r$.

Proof. Let K triangulate Q. Assume $|K| \subseteq E^n$, and view $|K| \times I \subseteq E^{n+1}$. Given a linear map $\phi : K \to I$, $(1, \phi): K \to K \times I$ is an embedding. Let $p_1 : K \times I \to K$ be projection on the first factor. Given ϕ, let $\phi^* = p_1 \circ H \circ (1, \phi)$.

Let $\alpha(K \times I)$ and $\beta(K \times I)$ be subdivisions making $H: \alpha(K \times I) \to \beta(K \times I)$ simplicial. Let $\sigma \in \beta(K \times I)$. Let $\ell \subseteq \sigma$ be a vertical line segment in σ (i.e. a line whose projection under $P_2: K \times I \to I$ is a point). $H^{-1}(\ell)$ is a line in the simplex $H^{-1}(\sigma)$. Since H is level preserving, $H^{-1}(\ell)$ makes an angle of less than $\pi/2$ with the vertical. (More precisely, if ℓ is viewed as an upward pointing vector, then $H^{-1}(\ell)$ is a vector which makes an angle of less than $\pi/2$ with, say, the vertical unit vector; equivalently, the last ω-ordinate of the vector $H^{-1}(\ell)$ is positive.) Moreover, by linearity of H on simplices, this angle is independent of the choice of ℓ in σ, ℓ vertical. Since $\beta(K \times I)$ is a finite simplicial complex, there exists $\varphi < \pi/2$ such that $H^{-1}(\ell)$ makes an angle $\leq \varphi$ with the vertical if ℓ is any vertical line in a simplex of $\beta(K \times I)$.

On the other hand, there exists $\delta > 0$ such that if $\emptyset(K)$ has diameter $< \delta$, then if $\sigma \in K$, any line segment contained in the (convex linear cell) $(1,\emptyset)(\sigma)$ makes an angle of at least φ with the vertical.

Now $(1,\emptyset)K$ separates $K \times I$. That is, a path from $K \times 1$ to $K \times 0$ meets $(1 \times \emptyset)K$ in at least one point. This is because if $\lambda: I \longrightarrow K \times I$ is such a path and $\lambda_1 = p_2 \circ \lambda$, then if $\lambda(I) \cap (1,\emptyset)K = \emptyset$, the sets $\{s \mid \lambda_1(s) > \emptyset(s)\}$ and $\{s \mid \lambda_1(s) < \emptyset(s)\}$ form a splitting of I by disjoint, non-empty open sets, contradicting the connectedness of I. Therefore the "broken line" $H^{-1}(X \times I)$, $X \in K$, meets $(1,\emptyset)K$ in at least one point.

However,: $(1,\emptyset)K$ and $H^{-1}(X \times I)$ meet in at most one point. For if ξ is a point of intersection whose co-ordinate in I is $t_0 \neq 1$, and if $\eta \in H^{-1}(X \times I)$ and η has t co-ordinate greater than t_0, then η lies inside the solid cone consisting of all rays starting at ξ and (when when directed away from ξ) making an angle of at most φ with the upward vertical. If $\eta \in (1,\emptyset)K$, however, η lies outside this cone. This proves that the point of intersection with smallest t co-ordinate is the only point of intersection.

Therefore $\emptyset^* = p \circ H \circ (1,\emptyset)$ is a homeomorphism if diam $\emptyset(K) < \delta$. Then there exists a finite sequence $\emptyset_1, \dots, \emptyset_N$ of linear maps of K into I such that

1) $\emptyset_0(K) = \{0\}$ and $\emptyset_N(K) = \{1\}$
2) diam $\emptyset_i(K) < \delta$ all i.
3) $\emptyset_i$ and $\emptyset_{i+1}$ agree on all but one vertex of K.

Then $\phi_o^* = 1$ and $\phi_N^* = H_1$. Consider $\phi_i^* \circ (\phi_{i-1}^*)^{-1}$. Let v be the vertex such that $\phi_i(v) \neq \phi_{i-1}(v)$. Then $\phi_i^*(\phi_{i-1}^*)$ is supported by ϕ_{i-1} $\phi_{i-1}^*(\mathrm{star}(v; K))$ and is the identity on $\phi_{i-1}^*(\mathrm{link}(v; K))$. Therefore if $v \notin \partial K$, $\phi_i^*(\phi_{i-1}^*)^{-1}$ does not move ∂K. If $v \in \partial K'$, $|\mathrm{star}(v; K')| \cap (\partial K') = |\mathrm{star}(v; \partial K')|$ is a face of $|\mathrm{star}(v; K')|$. Since ϕ_{i-1}^* is a homeomorphism, it follows that $\phi_i^*(\phi_{i-1}^*)$ is a proper move.

Theorem 6.2 has several improvements in each of the following, $H: Q \times I \longrightarrow Q \times I$ is an ambient isotopy. In all but the last, Q^q is a compact PL q-manifold.

6.2.1. If α is an open cover of Q, then one may choose the moves h_i such that $H_1 = h_1 \circ \ldots \circ h_r$ to be supported by elements of α.

Proof. Let $\alpha \times I = \{U \times I | \, U \in \alpha\}$. $H^{-1}(\alpha \times I)$ covers $Q \times I$. Let $\epsilon > 0$ be the Lesbesgue number of $H^{-1}(\alpha \times I)$ with respect to the metric induced by the triangulation K of Q. Let $K^{(r)}$ be the r-th barycentric subdivision of K, r such that mesh $K^{(r)}$ = maximum diameter of a simplex of $K^{(r)} < \frac{1}{4}\epsilon$. (In general mesh $K' \leq \frac{n}{n+1}$ mesh K, n = dim K, K' = first barycentric subdivision.)

Let $\delta > 0$ be such that 1) $\delta < \frac{1}{2}\epsilon$, 2) dim $\phi(K^{(r)}) < \delta$ implies ϕ is an embedding. Now construct ϕ_i as in 5.2, but with K replaced throughout by the triangulation $K^{(r)}$ of Q, and let $h_i = \phi_i(\phi_{i-1})$. Then $\sup(h_i) \subseteq \phi_{i-1}(\mathrm{star}(v; K^{(r)}))$. But $\mathrm{diam}[(1 \times \phi_{i-1})(\mathrm{star}(v; K^{(r)})] < \epsilon$; for the diameter of $\mathrm{star}(v; K^{(r)})$ is at most $\frac{1}{2}\epsilon$. Therefore $(1 \times \phi_{i-1})(\mathrm{star}(v; K^{(r)}))$

lies in some element of $H^{-1}(\alpha \times I)$, and so $\phi_{i-1}(\mathrm{star}(v; K^{(r)})$ lies in some element of α.

6.2.2. If H keeps the boundary fixed, then we may assume each proper move h_i keeps the boundary fixed.

6.2.3. If the hypothesis of 6.2.1 and 6.2.2 hold simultaneously, then the moves h_i may be chosen so that the conclusions hold simultaneously.

Proof. Clear.

6.2.4. Let $H: Q \times I \to Q \times I$ be an ambient isotopy, Q^q not compact. Let $X \subsetneq Q$ be a compact PL subspace. Then there exists a sequence of moves $h_1, \dots, h_r$ such that $H_1 = h_1 \circ \dots \circ h_r$ on a neighborhood of X.

Proof. Let $K_o \subsetneq K$ be finite complexes triangulating two neighborhoods of X in Q, with $\mathrm{Int}|K| \supseteq |K_o|$. Let $N = N(K_o; K)$. We may also suppose that $|N| \subsetneq \mathrm{Int}\, K$ by choosing K suitably. If $\phi: N \to I = [0,1]$ is a linear map we may still define $\phi^* = p \cdot H \circ (1, \phi): N \to Q$. By the same argument as for 6.2, there exists $\delta > 0$ such that diam $\phi(N) < \delta$ implies ϕ^* is an embedding.

Now suppose that $\phi_1, \phi_2: N \to I$ are such that diam $\phi_i(N) < \delta$ and $\phi_1(\mathrm{Fr}\, N) = \phi_2(\mathrm{Fr}\, N) = \{t_o\}$. Then $\phi_1^*\, \mathrm{Fr}\, N = \phi_2^*\, \mathrm{Fr}\, N$. So $\mathrm{Fr}\, \phi_1^* N = \mathrm{Fr}\, \phi_2^* N$.

Now $x \in \phi_1^*\, \mathrm{Int}\, N$ if and only if $H^{-1}(x \times 1)$ intersects $(1 \times \phi_1)N$, which happens if and only if $H^{-1}(x \times 1)$ homologically links $(1 \times \phi_1)(\mathrm{Fr}\, N)$. Similarly for ϕ_2. Thus $\phi_1^* N = \phi_2^* N$. Then by arguing as in the proof of 6.2, one can find a sequence of proper moves of $\phi_1^* N$, fixed on $\mathrm{Fr}\, \phi_1^* N$, whose composite is $(\phi_2^*)^{+1}(\phi_1^*)^{-1}$. Extending these moves to all of Q by the identity outside of N, we see that $(\phi_2^*)(\phi_1^*)^{-1}$ is isotopic by moves to the identity. Therefdre ϕ_2^* is isotopic by moves to ϕ_1^*.

Now let $0 = t = t_0 < t_1 < \ldots < t_r = t_{r+1} = 1$, with $t_i - t_{i-1} < \frac{1}{2}\delta$. Choose $\phi_i : N \longrightarrow I$, $-1 \leq i \leq r$, such that $\phi_i(v) = t_i$ if $v \in \mathrm{Fr}\, N$ is a vertex, and $\phi_i(v) = t_i + \frac{1}{2}(t_{i+1} - t_i)$ if $v \in N - \mathrm{Fr}\, N$ is a vertex. Define $\psi_i(v) = t_i$ if $v \in \mathrm{Fr}\, N$ and $\psi_i(v) = t_i - \frac{1}{2}(t_i - t_{i-1})$ if $v \in N - \mathrm{Fr}\, N$, v always a vertex. Then ψ_{i+1} and ψ_i agree on K_0. ϕ_i, ψ_i agree on $\mathrm{Fr}\, N$. So ψ_i^* and ϕ_i^* are isotopic by moves. Let h_i be an isotopy by moves throwing ψ_i^* onto ϕ_i^*. Then $h = h_r h_{r-1} \ldots h_1$ is an isotopy by moves and $h | K_0 = H_1 | K_0$.

<u>Corollary 6.3:</u> If $f, g: M^n \rightarrow Q^q$ are two embeddings, M compact, then f and g ambient isotopic implies f and g isotopic by moves.

§2. <u>Locally Unknotted Manifold Pairs and the "Weak" Isotopy Extension Theorem.</u>

<u>Definition.</u> Say (Q, M) is a PL <u>manifold pair</u>; i.e. Q and M are PL manifolds, and M is a PL subspace of Q. We say that (Q, M) is a <u>proper manifold pair</u> if $M \cap \partial Q = \partial M$. (Q, M) is said to be <u>locally unknotted</u> if given any $x \in M$, there exists a neighborhood V of x in Q such that $(V, V \cap M)$ is an unknotted ball pair; observe that it is a proper ball pair if it is a ball pair at all.

Lemma 6.4. If $K_o \subseteq K$ triangules $M \subseteq Q$, then (Q, M) is locally unknotted if and only if given any $A \in K_o$, $(\text{link}(A;K), \text{link}(A;K_o))$ is an unknotted sphere or ball pair.

Proof. $\Longrightarrow$. First we consider the case when $A = v$ is a vertex. If $K'_o \subseteq K'$ is any subdivision, then the radial projection $\text{link}(v;K') \longrightarrow \text{link}(v;K)$ carries the simplices of $\text{link}(v;K'_o)$ into simplices of $\text{link}(v;K'_o)$. Hence the same is true of the pseudo-radial projection, a PL homeomorphism. Hence it suffices to show $(\text{link}(v;K'), \text{link}(v;K'_o))$ is unknotted. But by choosing a suitable subdivision (for example, the rth barycentric, some large r), we may suppose that the link pair of v with respect to this subdivision lies in a neighborhood V of v such that $(V, V \cap M)$ is an unknotted proper ball pair. In other words, it suffices to consider the case $Q = \Delta^r . \dot{\Delta}^{i+1}$ and $M = \Delta^r$, and $v \in \Delta^r$ is a given point (not necessarily a vertex) of Δ^r.

If $v \in \Delta^r$, stellar subdivide by starring Δ^r at r, getting the pair $(v . \dot{\Delta}^r \dot{\Delta}^{i+1}, v . \dot{\Delta}^r)$. Then the link pair of r is $(\dot{\Delta}^{i+1} \dot{\Delta}^r, \dot{\Delta}^r)$, the standard unknotted sphere pair of type $(r+i-1, r-1)$. If $v \in A$, where $\Delta^r = A . B$, $(B \neq \emptyset)$, stellar subdivide by starring A at r to get the pair $(v\dot{A}B\dot{\Delta}^{i+1}, v\dot{A}B)$. The the link pair of v is $(\dot{A}B\dot{\Delta}^{i+1}, \dot{A}B)$, an unknotted ball pair.

To prove the result of an arbitrary simplex A of K_o, assume the result by induction for simplices of lower dimension than A. Let a be a vertex of A, and put $A = a . B$. $(\text{link}(A;K), \text{link}(A, K_o)) =$ $[\text{link}(a; \text{link}(B, K)), \text{link}(a; \text{link}(B; K_o))]$. By inductive hypothesis,

$\text{link}(B; K_o) \subseteq \text{link}(B; K)$ is an unknotted ball or sphere pair and so a locally unknotted proper manifold pair. Hence we may apply the result for vertices to the link pair of a in this manifold pair.

$\Leftarrow$. As $(\text{link}(v; K), \text{link}(v; K_o))$ unknotted implies $(\overline{\text{star}}(v; K), \overline{\text{star}}(v; K_o))$ unknotted.

<u>Lemma 6.5</u> (weak isotopy extension theorem): Let (Q, M) be a proper locally unknotted manifold pair, with M compact. Suppose that $h: M \to M$ is a homeomorphism which is ambient isotopic to the identity 1_M. Then there exists a PL homeomorphism $k: Q \to Q$ with $k|M = h$. If h is ambient isotopic to 1_M keeping ∂M fixed, then we can assume that k is fixed in ∂Q.

<u>Proof.</u> Let $K_o \subseteq K$ triangulate $M \subseteq Q$. Then let α be the <u>star convering</u> of M; i.e., $\alpha = \{\mathring{\text{star}}(v; K_o) | v \text{ is a vertex of } K_o\}$, where $\mathring{\text{star}}(v; K_o) = |K_o| - \cup\{\sigma \in K_o | v \notin \sigma\}$. By 6.2.1, there exists a finite sequence of proper moves $h_1, \ldots, h_r$, each supported by some element of α $h_r: M \to M$, with $h = h_1 \circ \ldots \circ h_r$. If h keeps the boundary fixed, we may assume each h_i also,

We are going to complete the proof by showing that each h_i can be extended to Q. So suppose that $\text{supp}\, h_i \subseteq \mathring{\text{star}}(v; K_o)$, v a vertex.

<u>Case 1:</u> $v \notin \partial K$. Then h_i is the identity on $\text{link}(v; K_o)$. Moreover $(\overline{\text{star}}(v; K), \overline{\text{star}}(v; K_o))$ is a proper unknotted ball pair, and its boundary is the sphere pair $(\text{link}(v; K), \text{link}(v; K_o))$. We may extend h_i to a p.l. homeomorphism of $\overline{\text{star}}(v; K_o) \cup \text{link}(v; K)$ by defining it to be the identity on $\text{link}(v; K)$. By Lemma 4, this map extends to a p.l. homeomorphism of

$\overline{\text{star}}(v; K)$ into itself, which we then extend to all of Q by the identity outside $\overline{\text{star}}(v; K)$.

<u>Case 2.</u> $v \in \partial K$. Assume for the moment that $(\overline{\text{star}}(v; K), \overline{\text{star}}(v; K_o))$ is unknotted. Then by the same argument as in Case 1, we may extend $h_i | \overline{\text{star}}(v; K_o)$ to a homeomorphism of $\overline{\text{star}}(v; K)$ which is the identity on link(v; K). This homeomorphism extends to $\text{link}(v; K) \cup \overline{\text{star}}(v; K)$ by the identity outside star(v; K), and so we get a homeomorphism of $\partial(\overline{\text{star}}(v; K))$ into itself which agrees with h_i on $\overline{\text{star}}(v; K)$ and is the identity on link(v; K). But h_i is the identity on $\text{link}(v; K_o)$ and is defined on $\overline{\text{star}}(v; K_o)$ (whose boundary is $\text{link}(v; K_o) \cup \overline{\text{star}}(v; K_o)$). Hence by the lemma quoted in Case 1, we may extend h_i to $\overline{\text{star}}(v; K)$, getting a homeomorphism which is the identity on $|\text{link}(v; K)| \supseteq \text{Fr}_K |\overline{\text{star}}(v; K)|$. Now extend to all of Q by the identity outside $\overline{\text{star}}(v; K)$.

To prove that $(\text{star}(v; K), \text{star}(v; K_o))$ is unknotted, we simply observe that it is the cone on the sphere pair $(\text{link}(v; K), \text{link}(v; K_o))$ which is unknotted because it is the boundary of the ball pair $(\text{link}(v; K), \text{link}(v; K_o))$.

Remarks: 1) k can be chosen to be the identity outside of an arbitrary neighborhood of M.

2) It is clear that if k is constructed as in the proof of Lemma 6.5, then k is isotopic by moves to the identity and so ambient isotopic to the identity.

3) We also proved that the boundary pair of a locally unknotted pair is locally unknotted.

§3. Uniqueness of Boundary Collars and Construction of Compatible Collars for Proper Manifold Pairs.

Let $M \subseteq Q$ be compact PL manifolds, with $M \cap \partial Q = \partial M$. Then the boundary collars $c_1 : \partial M \times I \longrightarrow M$ and $c_2 : \partial Q \times I \longrightarrow Q$ are said to be <u>compatible</u> if c_1 is the restriction of c_2 to $\partial M \times I$. In this section we see how to obtain compatible collars in general and, given a collar $c_1 : \partial M \times I \longrightarrow M$, we can extend it to a collar of c_2. In the process we prove the uniqueness of collars up to ambient isotopy. These results will be used to help prove the general isotopy extension theorem.

<u>Theorem 6.6.</u> If (Q, M) is proper pair of compact manifolds and is a locally unknotted pair, then there exist compatible boundary collars of M and of Q.

<u>Remark.</u> The reader will observe from the proof to follow that it would suffice to assume that the pair (Q, M) is <u>locally unknotted</u> at the boundary; i.e. every point in the boundary of M has a neighborhood in Q, V, such that $(V, V \cap M)$ is an unknotted proper ball pair. One would need a variant of Lemma 5.4. The details are left to the reader.

<u>Proof.</u> Let $Q^+ = (Q \times 0) \cup (\partial Q \times I)$ and let $M^+ = (M \times 0) \cup (\partial M \times I)$. We will construct a PL homeomorphism $Q^+ \longrightarrow Q$ carrying M^+ into M, which sends $\partial Q \times 1 \longrightarrow \partial Q$ by mapping $(x, 1)$ onto x.

Let $K_0 \subseteq K$ triangulate $M \subseteq Q$. Let K' be the barycentric first derived. Let $A_1, \ldots, A_N$ be the simplices of ∂K in order of decreasing dimension.

Let A_i^* be the dual cell of A_i in K and let $A_i^\#$ be its dual cell in ∂K. If $A_i \in K_o$, let $A_{i,o}^*$ and $A_{i,o}^\#$ be the dual cells of A_i in K_o and ∂K_o, respectively.

We are going to construct homeomorphisms $(A_i^* \times 0) \cup (A_i^\# \times I) \longrightarrow A_i^*$ which, if $A_i \in K_o$, send $(A_{i,o}^* \times 0) \cup (A_{i,o}^\# \times I)$ onto $A_{i,o}^*$.

Let $B_i = (A_i^* \times 0) \cup (A_i^\# \times I)$. Let $B_{i,o} = (A_{i,o}^* \times 0) \cup (A_{i,o}^\# \times I)$ if $A_i \in K_o$. Let $C_i = \mathrm{cl}\,(\partial A_i^* - A_i^\#)$ and $c_{i,o} = \mathrm{cl}(\partial A_{i,o}^* - A_{i,o}^\#)$ if $a_i \in K_o$. (See the section on dual cells, Chapter I.)

<u>Claim:</u> If $A_i \in \partial K_o$, then $(B_i, B_{i,o})$ is an unknotted ball pair.

The following picture indicates the situation:

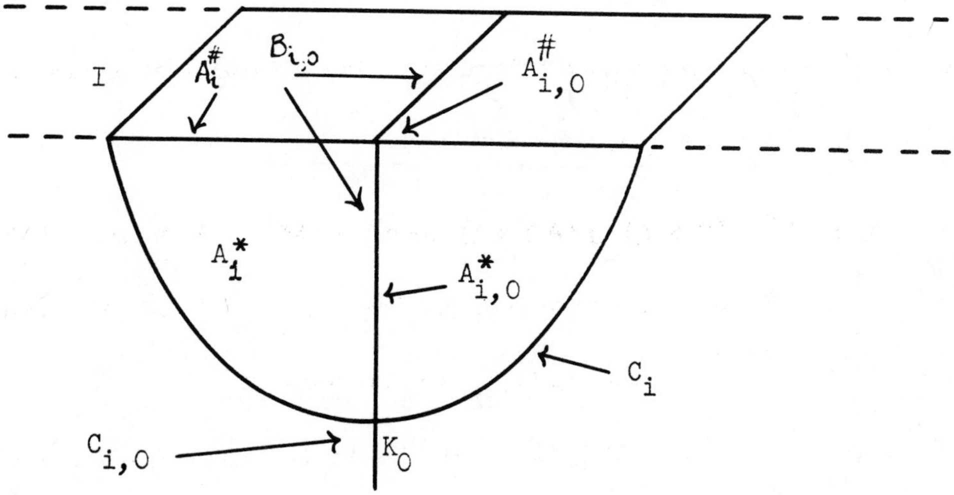

To prove the claim, we use the pseudo-radial projection $p: A_i^* \longrightarrow \hat{A}_i \, \mathrm{link}(A_i; K)$. Under this map, $A_{i,o}^*$ is carried onto $\hat{A}_i . \mathrm{link}(A_i; K_o)$. Let $F_1 = (C_i, C_{i,o})$ a proper ball pair. Under p (see the section on dual cells), this pair becomes the pair $(\mathrm{link}(A_i; K), \mathrm{link}(A_i; K_o))$, an unknotted ball pair. The pair $\partial F_1 = (\partial C_i, \partial C_{i,o}) \simeq (\mathrm{link}(A; \partial K), \mathrm{link}(A; \partial K_o))$ is also unknotted.

Let $F_2 = (A_i^{\#}, A_{i,o}^{\#})$; under p it is carried onto $\hat{A}. p(\partial F_1)$, also an unknotted pair. Therefore $F_2 \times I$ is unknotted. Let $F_3 = (F_2 \times 1) \cup (\partial F_2 \times I)$, an unknotted pair because there is a p.l. homeomorphism $(F_2 \times 1) \cup (\partial F_2 \times I) \longrightarrow v. \partial F_2$. (To see this, embed the first pair in $v. \partial F_2$ suitably and use a pseudo-radial projection, as in the following picture:

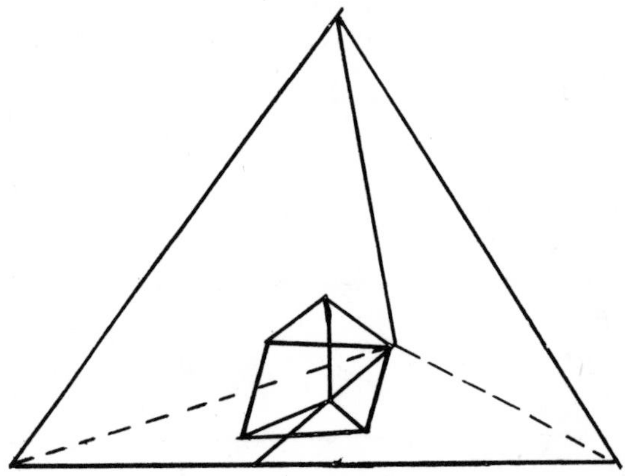

The identity $\partial F_2 \longrightarrow \partial F_2$ extends to homeomorphisms

$h_1 : F_1 \longrightarrow a(\partial F_2)$

$h_2 : F_2 \longrightarrow b(\partial F_2)$,

$h_3 : F_3 \longrightarrow c(\partial F_3)$;   note that $\partial F_1 = \partial F_2 = \partial F_3$.

Extending homeomorphisms defined on boundaries by these maps, we get homeomorphisms

$h_4 : (A_i^*, A_{i,o}^*) \longrightarrow ab(\partial F_2)$

$h_5 : F_2 \times I \longrightarrow (bc) . \partial F_2$.

Finally, $h_4 \cup h_5 : (B_i, B_{i,o}) \longrightarrow (ab\partial F_2 \cup bc\partial F_2) \cong ac(\partial F_2)$ is a homeomorphism. This proves the claim.

Now we define inductively a sequence of p. l. homeomorphisms $k_i : (A_i^* \times 0) \cup (A_i^\# \times I) \longrightarrow A_i^*$ with the following properties:

1) $k_i(x, 1) = x$ if $x \in \partial Q$;

2) $k_i(x, 0) = x$ if $x \in A_i^* - A_i^\#$;

3) If $A_i \in K_o$, then k_i maps $(A_{i,o}^* \times 0) \cup (A_{i,o}^\# \times I)$ onto $A_{i,o}^*$;

and

4) If $A_i < A_j$ ($\Longrightarrow i \geq j$ and $A_j^* \subseteq A_i^*$), then $k_j = k_i | (A_j^* \times 0) \cup (A_j^\# \times 1)$.

Having defined k_j for $j \leq i-1$, we define $k_i | \partial B_i$ by conditions 1), 2) and 4), and then extend it to all of B_i to satisfy 3), if it applies, by using the "claim." Having defined the k_i, we define $c : Q^+ \longrightarrow Q$ by extending k_N, by the identity on $(Q \times 0) - \bigcup_{i-1}^{N} (A_i^* \times 0)$, to all of Q^+. Clearly c is the desired homeomorphism.

To solve the problem of extending a boundary collar on the smaller manifold of a manifold pair, we first must consider the question of comparing boundary collars of a manifold.

Lemma 6.7. Let $K_o \subseteq K$ be finite simplicial complexes. Consider a p.l. embedding $c: K \times [0, \varepsilon] \longrightarrow K \times I$ with $c(x,0) = (x,0)$, $x \in K$. Suppose that $c|K_o \times [0,\varepsilon]$ is level preserving. Then there exists $0 < \delta < \varepsilon$ and $h: K \times I \longrightarrow K \times I$, a p.l. homeomorphism, such that:

1) $h \circ c|K \times [0,\delta]$ is level preserving; and

2) h is ambient isotopic to the identity keeping $(K \times \partial I) \cup c(K_o \times [0,\varepsilon])$ fixed.

Proof. Let α and β be subdivisions such that α contains triangulations of $K \times 0$ and $K \times [0,\varepsilon]$, and $c: \alpha(K \times [0,\varepsilon]) \longrightarrow \beta(K \times I)$ is simplicial. Let $\delta > 0$ be such that no vertices of α and β have a level t such that $0 < t \leq \delta$ and such that $c(K \times [0,\delta] \cap (K \times 1) = \emptyset$. Now choose first derived subdivisions α' and β' of α and β, using the following starring points:

1) $\hat{\sigma}$ has level δ if $\mathring{\sigma}$ has any points of level δ ;

2) If $\sigma \in \alpha(K_o \times 0)$, $\widehat{c\sigma} = c(\hat{\sigma})$;

3) If $\sigma \in \alpha(K_o \times [0, \ ])$, $\widehat{c\sigma} = c\hat{\sigma}$; and

4) $\hat{\sigma}$ arbitrary otherwise .

Note that 3) and 1) are consistent because σ is level preserving on $K \times [0, \mathcal{E}]$. Now define $c' : \alpha'(K \times [0, \mathcal{E}]) \longrightarrow \beta'(K \times I)$ to be the simplicial map defined by $c'(\hat{\sigma}) = \widehat{c\sigma}$. Then c' is a simplicial embedding which is level-preserving on $K \times [0, \delta]$ and agrees with c on $K_o \times [0, \mathcal{E}]$.

Now let β'' be a first derived subdivision of β such that $c: \alpha'(K \times [0, \mathcal{E}]) \longrightarrow \beta''(K \times I)$ is simplicial; it is clear that such a subdivision exists, and that we may choose β'' such that

1) $\beta''(K \times 1) = \beta'(K \times 1)$ and $\beta''(K \times 0) = \beta'(K \times 0)$; and

2) $\beta''(c(K_o \times [0, \mathcal{E}])) = \beta'(c(K_o \times [0, \mathcal{E}]))$.

Then let $h: \beta''(K \times I) \longrightarrow \beta'(K \times I)$ be the natural simplicial homeomorphism between two first deriveds of the same complex. Then $h \circ c = c'$ on all of $K \times [0, \mathcal{E}]$, clearly. Moreover, by moving one vertex at a time, it is easy to see that h is ambient isotopic to 1 by moves keeping $(K \times \partial I) \cup c(K_o \times [0, \mathcal{E}])$ fixed.

<u>Lemma 6.8.</u> If c_1 and c_2 are boundary collars in M, then there exists $\delta > 0$ and an ambient isotopy H of M, fixed in ∂M, such that $c_2^{-1} H_1 c_1 | \partial M \times [0, \delta]$ is defined and level preserving. (M = compact PL manifold.)

Proof. Let $\mathcal{E} > 0$ be such that $c_1(\partial M \times [0, \mathcal{E}]) \subseteq \operatorname{Im} c_2$. Then there exists an ambient isotopy H' of $\partial M \times I$, fixed $\partial M \times \partial I$, and $\delta < \mathcal{E}$, such that $H'_1 \circ c_2^{-1} \circ (c_1 | \partial M \times [0, \delta])$ is level preserving. Define H_t on $c_2(\partial M \times I)$ by $H_t = c_2 H'_t c_2^{-1}$. Since H'_t is the identity on $\partial M \times 1$, we may extend H_t to all of M by the identity where it is not already defined.

Lemma 6.9. If c is a boundary collar of M and $0 < \delta < 1$, then there exists an ambient isotopy H of M, fixed on ∂M, such that $H_1 c(x, t) = c(x, \delta t)$, all $(x, t) \in \partial M \times I$.

Proof. Let $M_1 = \operatorname{cl}(M - \text{Image } c)$, a PL manifold. Let $c_1\colon \partial M_1 \times I \longrightarrow M_1$ be a boundary collar. Define $c_2\colon \partial M \times [0, 2] \longrightarrow \partial M$ by

$$c_2(x, t) = c(x, t) \qquad 0 \leq t \leq 1 .$$

$$c_2(x, t) = c_1(c(x, 1), t-1), \qquad 1 \leq t \leq 2 .$$

Then c_2 is a well-defined embedding, since $c_1(c(x, 1), 0) = c(x, 1)$.

Let $\alpha\colon [0, 2] \times I \longrightarrow [0, 2] \times I$ be a PL ambient isotopy with $\alpha | (0 \times I) \cup (2 \times I) = \text{identity}$ and $\alpha_1(t) = \delta t$ if $0 \leq t \leq 1$. Now define $h\colon M \times I \longrightarrow M \times I$ by

$$h[c_2(x, s), t] = [c_2(x, p\alpha(s, t)), t]$$

$h(y, t) = (y, t)$ for all $y \in \operatorname{cl}(M - \operatorname{Im} c_2)$. Here $p\colon [0, 2] \times I \longrightarrow [0, 2]$ is projection on the first coordinate. Observe that h is well-defined as $[c_2(x, p\alpha(2, t)), t] = [c2(x, 2), t]$; and $h[c_2(x, 0), t] = [c_2(x, 0), t] = [x, t]$, so $h | \partial M \times I = \text{identity}$. The map h is piecewise linear, for in $\operatorname{Im} c_2 \times I$ its first coordinate is just the composite:

$$\text{Im } c_2 \times I \xrightarrow{c_2^{-1} \times 1} \partial M \times [0, 2] \times I \xrightarrow{1 \times p, \alpha} \partial M \times [0, 2] \xrightarrow{c_2} M$$

To show h is a homeomorphism, suppose that $h(c_2(x, s), t) = h(c_2(x', s'), t')$. Then $t = t'$. Therefore $x = x'$ and $p, \alpha(s, t) = p, \alpha(s', t')$. As α is a level preserving homeomorphism, this implies that $s = s'$. So h is one-one, and h is clearly onto.

To complete the proof, we just note that if $0 \leq t \leq 1$, $h(c(x, t), 1) = h(c_2(x, t), 1) = (c_2(x, p\alpha(t, 1)), 1) = (c_2(x; \delta t), 1) = (c(x; \delta t), 1)$.

Lemma 6.10. Let c_1 and c_2 be boundary collars of M, with $\text{Im } c_1 = \text{Im } c_2$, and suppose in addition that $c_2^{-1} c_1 : \partial M \times I \longrightarrow \partial M \times I$ is level preserving. Then there exists an ambient isotopy h of M, fixed on ∂M, such that $h_1 \circ (c_1 | \partial M \times [0, 1/2]) = c_2 | \partial M \times [0, 1/2]$.

Proof. Let $\alpha = c_2^{-1} c_1 : \partial M \times I \longrightarrow \partial M \times I$. We may write $\alpha(x, t) = (\alpha_t x, t)$. Let $\beta : I \times I \longrightarrow I$ be a p.l. map such that $\beta(t, 0) = t$,

$$\beta(t, 1) = \begin{cases} 0 & 0 \leq t \leq 1/2 \\ 2t - 1, & \frac{1}{2} \leq t \leq 1 \end{cases},$$

$\beta(1, s) = 1$, $\beta(0, s) = 0$ for $0 \leq s \leq 1$.

Now define $H_s : \partial M \times I \longrightarrow \partial M \times I$ by putting $H_s(x, t) = (\alpha_{\beta(t, s)}(x), t)$. Then H_s defines an ambient isotopy of $\partial M \times I$; for if $H_s(x, t) = H_s(x', t')$, then $t = t'$ and $\alpha_{\beta(t, s)}(x) = \alpha_{\beta(t, s)}(x)$ implies $x = x'$.

The ambient isotopy defined by H_s is a p.l. map because it is the composite of p.l. maps.

Define $h: M \times I \longrightarrow M \times I$ by $h(c_1(x,t),s) = (c_2H_s(x,t),s)$, $h(y,s) = (y,s)$ if $y \in cl(M - \text{Im } c_1)$. Then h is a well-defined p.l. homeomorphism, as $c_2H_s(x,1) = c_2(\alpha_{\beta(1,s)},1) = c_1(x,1)$. Now $h(c_1(x,t),0) = (c_2H_0(x,t),0) = (c_2(\alpha_t(x),t),0) = (c_1(x,t),0)$; so h_0 = identity. Moreover, if $t \leq \frac{1}{2}$, $h(c_1(x,t),1) = (c_2(\alpha_{\beta(t,1)}(x),t),1) = (c_2(\alpha_0(x),t),1) = (c_2(x,t),1)$. Finally, if $t = 0$, $h(c_1(x,t),s) = (c_2(x,t),s) = (c_1(x,t),s) = (x,s)$, so h fixes the boundary.

Theorem 6.11. (Uniqueness of Boundary Collars). If c_1 and c_2 are two boundary collars of M, then there exists an ambient isotopy h of M, fixed on ∂M, with $h_1c_1 = c_2$.

Proof. By 6.8 and 6.9, there exist ambient isotopies H and K of M, fixed on ∂M such that if $c_1' = H_1c_1$ and $c_2' = K_1c_2$, then $\text{Im } c_1' = \text{Im } c_2'$ and $(c_2')^{-1}c_1'$ is level preserving. By 5.10, we may suppose after another ambient isotopy that we also have $c_1' = c_2'$ on $\partial M \times [0, 1/2]$. Now apply 6.9, again, with $\delta = 1/2$.

Corollary 6.12. Let (Q, M) be a locally unknotted compact proper manifold pair. Given a boundary collar c_1 on M, there exists a collar c_2 of Q, compatible with c_1.

Proof. By Theorem 6.6, there exist collars c and c' of M and Q respectively, which are compatible. By Theorem 6.11, there exists a p.l. homeomorphism $h: M \longrightarrow M$, ambient isotopic to the identity, which keeps

∂M fixed, such that $hc = c_1$. By the weak Isotopy Extension Theorem, Lemma 6.5, there exists a p.l. homeomorphism $k: Q \to Q$, fixed on ∂Q, with $k(M) = M$ and $k|M = h$. Put $c_2 = k\, c'$.

4. The Isotopy Extension Theorem.

Definition. Let M and Q be P.L. manifolds. An isotopy $F: M \times I \to Q \times I$ is said to be proper if $F^{-1}(\partial Q \times I) = \partial M \times I$. It is called locally unknotted if in addition, for all $0 \leq s \leq t \leq 1$, the following proper manifold pair is locally unknotted: $(Q \times [s,t], F(M \times [s,t]))$. F is always locally unknotted if it is proper and $\dim Q - \dim M \geq 3$.

Theorem 6.12 (Isotopy Extension Theorem): Let $F: M \times I \to Q \times I$, M compact, be a proper locally unknotted isotopy. Then there exists an ambient isotopy H of Q such that

$$F = H\,(F_o \times 1_I).$$

Furthermore, if $F|\partial M \times I = (F_o|\partial M) \times 1_I$, then we may choose H so that $H|\partial Q \times I = \text{identity}$.

Remarks: 1) 6.12 may be generalized as follows: Call F allowable if $F^{-1}(\partial Q \times I) = N \times I$, where N is an (m-1)-manifold, m = dim M, in ∂M (possibly $\emptyset$). One can define the notion of locally unknotted for allowable isotopies by defining the notion of unknotted for certain types of non-proper ball pairs. One can prove that if $\dim Q - \dim M \geq 3$, all allowable isotopies are locally unknotted, and one can prove an isotopy extension theorem for such isotopies.

2) If $q-m \geq 3$, one can prove the corresponding theorem for isotopies $F: K \times 1 \longrightarrow Q \times 1$ where K is a polyhedron and $F^{-1}(\partial Q \times 1) = K_o \times 1$, K_o a subpolyhedron of K.

Unsolved Problem. Find a definition of locally unknotted for isotopies of polyhedra in manifolds which would make the theorem work for codimension < 3.

3) One can also generalize by replacing I by I^n. We shall do this later in section 5.

To prove 6.12, we start by proving a restricted version in a special case.

Lemma 6.12.1. Let $F: M \times I \longrightarrow Q \times I$ be a proper locally unknotted isotopy, Q and M compact. Suppose $F|\partial M \times I = (F_o|\partial M) \times 1$. Then ther exists $\varepsilon > 0$ and a P. L. homoemorphism $h: Q \times [0, \varepsilon] \longrightarrow Q \times [0, \varepsilon]$, level preserving, such that

1) $h|\partial Q \times [0, \varepsilon] =$ identity.

2) $h(F_o x, t) = F(x, t)$ for all $(x, t) \in M \times [0, \varepsilon]$.

Proof. Let $c: (\partial(M \times I)) \times I \longrightarrow M \times I$ be a boundary collar. Let c_1 and c_2: $\partial(Q \times I) \times I \longrightarrow Q \times I$ be boundary collars such that the following diagrams commute:

(1)
$$\begin{array}{ccc} \partial(M \times I) \times I & \xrightarrow{\quad c \quad} & M \times I \\ \Big\downarrow (F_o \times 1) \times 1 & & \Big\downarrow F_o \times 1_I \\ \partial(Q \times I) \times I & \xrightarrow{\quad c_1 \quad} & Q \times I \end{array}$$

$$(2) \qquad \begin{array}{ccc} \partial(M \times I) \times I & \xrightarrow{\ c\ } & M \times I \\ \Big\downarrow {\scriptstyle F \times I} & & \Big\downarrow {\scriptstyle F} \\ \partial(Q \times I) \times I & \xrightarrow{\ c_2\ } & Q \times I \end{array}$$

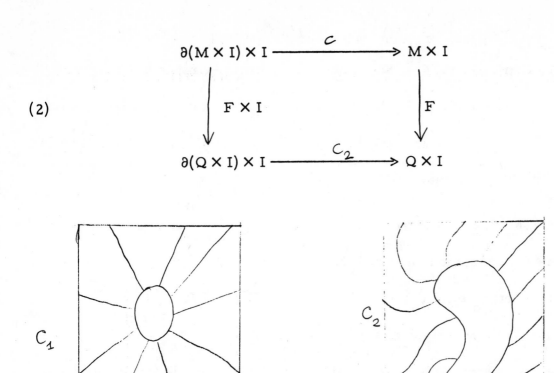

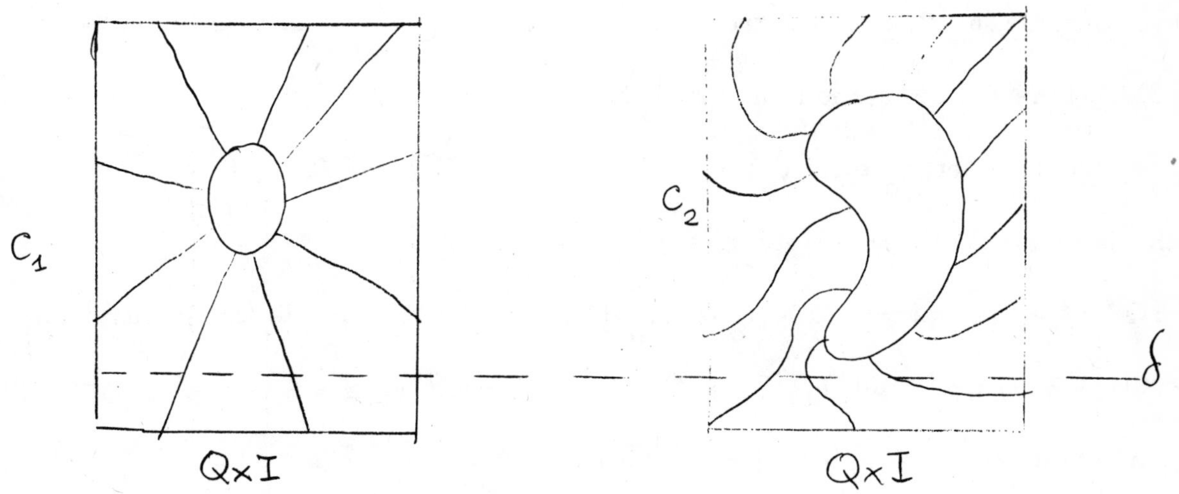

This is possible because $(Q, F_o(M))$ is a proper locally unknotted manifold pair, and $(Q \times I, F(M \times I))$ is a locally unknotted proper manifold pair.

Now choose $\delta > 0$ such that $Q \times [0, \delta] \subset c_1([(Q \times 0) \cup (\partial Q \times I)] \times I)$. This is possible because the set on the right is a neighborhood of $Q \times 0$ in $Q \times I$ and because Q is compact.

Define $h: Q \times [0, \delta] = Q \times I$ by putting $h = c_2 \; (c_1^{-1} | Q \times [0, \delta])$. Clearly, h is the identity on $(Q \times 0) \cup (\partial Q \times [0, \delta])$, since c_1 and c_2 are boundary collars of $Q \times I$. Moreover, $h \; (F_o \times 1_{[0, \delta]}) = F | Q \times [0, \delta]$, by (1) and (2) and the fact that $(F_o \times 1) | \partial M \times I = F | \partial M \times I$. In particular,

h is level preserving on $(F_o(M) \times [0,\delta]) \cup (\partial Q \times [0,\delta])$. Hence by Lemma 6.1, there exists $0 < \varepsilon < \delta$ and a p.l. homeomorphism $h' : Q \times I \longrightarrow Q \times I$ such that $h'\, h$ is level preserving and h' is the identity $(Q \times \partial I) \cup h(F_o(M) \times [0,\varepsilon]) \cup (\partial Q \times [0,\varepsilon])$. The map $h'\, h$ satisfies the requirements of the lemma.

<u>Lemma 6.12.2.</u> Theorem 6.12 holds in the case Q is compact and $F \mid \partial M \times I$ is the constant isotopy $F_o \times 1$.

<u>Proof.</u> Let $t_o \in I$, $t_o \neq 0$ or 1. Then by Lemma 6.12.1, applied in both directions, there exists $\varepsilon = \varepsilon(t_o) > 0$ and

$h_{t_o} : Q \times [t_o - \varepsilon, t_o + \varepsilon] \longrightarrow Q \times [t_o - \varepsilon, t_o + \varepsilon]$ such that h_{t_o} is the identity on $\partial Q \times [t_o - \varepsilon, t_o + \varepsilon]$ and $h_{t_o}(F_{t_o} x, t) \mid F(x,t)$ for $t_o - \varepsilon \leq t \leq t_o + \varepsilon$. Similarly we may find $h_o : Q \times [0, \varepsilon(0)] \longrightarrow Q \times [0, \varepsilon(0)]$ and $h_1 : Q \times [1 - \varepsilon(1), 1] \longrightarrow Q \times [1 - \varepsilon(1), 1]$ with similar properties. The open sets in I of the form $(t_o - \varepsilon(t_o), t_o + \varepsilon(t_o))$, $[0, \varepsilon(0))$, and $(1 - \varepsilon(1), 1]$ cover I, and this covering has a Lesbesgue number α. Choose numbers $0 = t_o = s_o < s_1 < \ldots < s_{r-1} < s_r = 1$, such that $s_i - s_{i-1} < \alpha$.

Now we define inductively a sequence of maps $H^{(i)} : Q \times [0, s_i] \longrightarrow Q \times [0, s_i]$ as follows: let $H^{(0)} = $ identity. Suppose that $H^{(i-1)}$ has been defined and has the property that $H^{(i-1)} \mid \partial Q \times [0; s_{i-1}]$ is the identity, and $H^{(i-1)}(F_o x, t) = F(x,t)$ if $(x,t) \in M \times [0, s_{i-1}]$. Then there exists $k : Q \times [s_{i-1}, s_i] \longrightarrow Q \times [s_{i-1}, s_i]$ which is level preserving, which is the identity on $\partial Q \times [s_{i-1}, s_i]$, and which satisfies $k(F_{t_o} x, t) = F(x,t)$ for $s_{i-1} \leq t \leq s_i$ and for some t_o. Now define $H^{(i)}$ by putting

$$H_t^{(i)} = H_t^{(i-1)} \quad \text{if } 0 \leq t \leq s_{i-1}$$

and

$$H_t^{(i)} = k_t \, k_{s_{i-1}}^{-1} \, H_{s_{i-1}}^{(i-1)} \quad \text{for } s_{i-1} \leq t \leq s_i \, .$$

The definitions agree for $t = s_{i-1}$. $H^{(i)}$ is a P.L. homeomorphism of $Q \times [0, s_i]$ onto itself, as shown by alternative definition

$$H^{(i)}(x, t) = k \, (k_{s_{i-1}}^{-1} \times 1) \, (H_{s_{i-1}}^{(i-1)} \times 1)(x, t), \quad s_{i-1} \leq t \leq s_i \, .$$

Clearly $H^{(i)}$ is the identity on $\partial Q \times [0, s_i]$. If $s_{i-1} \leq t \leq s_i$, then we have

$$H_t^{(i)}(F_o x) = k_t k_{s_{i-1}}^{-1} H_{s_{i-1}}^{i-1} (F_o x) = k_t k_{s_{i-1}}^{-1} F_{s_{i-1}} x = k_t F_{t_o}(x) = F_t(x).$$

The lemma is thus proved by putting $H = H^{(r)}$.

<u>Lemma 6.12.3.</u> Let Q be a compact manifold. Suppose that h is an ambient isotopy of ∂Q. Then there exist an ambient isotopy of Q extending h.

<u>Proof.</u> Let $c: \partial M \times I \longrightarrow M$ be a boundary collar. Let $\phi: I^2 \longrightarrow I$ be a p.l. map with

$$\phi(0, t) = t \quad \text{for all } t$$

$$\phi(1, t) = 0 \quad \text{for all } t$$

$$\phi(s, 0) = 0 \quad \text{for all } s.$$

Define $k: Q \times I \longrightarrow Q \times I$ by

$$k_t \, c(x, s) = c(h_{\phi(s, t)} x, s) \quad x \in \partial M, \ s \text{ and } t \text{ in } I$$

and $k_t(y) = y$ if $y \in cl(Q - \text{Im } c)$. Note that $c(h_{\phi(1,t)}x, s) = c(x, s)$. It is not hard to see that k is an ambient isotopy extending h.

Lemma 6.12.4. Suppose that Q and M are compact and that $F: M \times I \longrightarrow Q \times I$ is an isotopy which is proper and locally unknotted. Then there exists an ambient isotopy H of Q such that $F = H\,(F_o \times 1)$.

Proof. By 6.12.2, there exists $h: \partial Q \times I \longrightarrow \partial Q \times I$, an ambient isotopy, with $h\,(F_o \times 1) = F|\partial M \times I$. Let k be an ambient isotopy of Q extending h. Let $F' = k^{-1}F: M \times I \longrightarrow Q \times I$. Then F' is a locally unknotted proper isotopy whose restriction to ∂M is a constant isotopy. By 6.12.2, there exists an ambient isotopy k' of Q with k' fixed on ∂Q and $k'(F'_o \times 1) = F'$. Let $H = kk'$.

Remark: The proof shows that if one is given an ambient isotopy h of ∂Q such that $h\,(F_o \times 1) = F$ on $\partial M \times I$, then H may be chosen to extend h. For we had $H|\partial Q \times I = h|\partial Q \times I$ in the proof.

Proof of Theorem 6.12. By the lemmas already proven, it suffices to consider the case in which Q is not compact. Let $P_1: Q \times I \longrightarrow Q$ be the projection onto the first co-ordinate. Let Q^* be a regular neighborhood of $P_1\ F(M \times I)$ meeting ∂Q regularly. Let $Q_1 = Q^* \cap \partial Q$ and let $Q_2 = cl(\partial Q^* - Q_1)$, both $(q-1)$-manifolds.

Now, $F|\partial M \times I: \partial M \times I \longrightarrow Q_1 \times I$, since F is proper. Q_1 is compact. If $F|\partial M \times I$ is a constant isotopy, define $\alpha: Q_1 \times I — Q_1 \times I$ to be the identity; otherwise by lemma 6.12.2 let α be such that

$\alpha(F_0 \times 1 | \partial M \times I) = F | \partial M \times I$ and such that $\alpha | \partial Q_1 \times I$ is the identity.

Let $h: \partial Q^* \times I \longrightarrow \partial Q^* \times I$ be defined by $h | Q_1 \times I = \alpha$ and $h | Q_2 \times I =$ identity. By the remark following lemma 6.12.4, we can extend h to an ambient isotopy $k: Q^* \times I \longrightarrow Q^* \times I$ with $k(F_0 \times 1) = F$. Now extend k to all of Q by putting $k =$ identity on $cl(Q - Q^*) \times I$.

5. The n-isotopy Extension Theorem.

Definition. An n-isotopy is a P. L. embedding $F: M \times I^n \longrightarrow Q \times I^n$ which is level-preserving ; i.e., the following diagram commutes:

$$\begin{array}{ccc} M \times I^n & \xrightarrow{\;F\;} & Q \times I^n \\ & {\scriptstyle P_2}\searrow \quad \swarrow{\scriptstyle P_2} & \\ & I^n & \end{array}$$

where P_2 = projection on the 2nd factor $(I^n = I \times \ldots \times I \subset E^n)$.

An ambient n-isotopy is a level preserving P. L. homeomorphism $H: Q \times I^n \longrightarrow Q \times I^n$ such that $H(x, 0, \ldots, 0) = (x, 0, \ldots, 0)$.

An n-isotopy $F: M \times I^n \longrightarrow Q \times I^n$ is called proper if $F^{-1}(\partial Q \times I^n) = \partial M \times I^n$. A proper n-isotopy is called locally unknotted if, for any simplex Δ linearly embedded in I^n, $(Q \times \Delta, F(M \times \Delta))$ is a locally unknotted manifold pair.

If $F: M \times I^n \longrightarrow Q \times I^n$ is an n-isotopy and if $x \in I^n$, then F_x is defined by $F(z, x) = (F_x z, x)$.

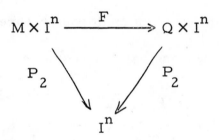

Theorem 6.13. Let $F: M \times I^n \longrightarrow Q \times I^n$, M and Q P.L. manifolds, M compact, be an n-isotopy which is proper and locally unknotted. Then there exists an ambient n-isotopy H of Q with $H(F_o \times 1) = F$. If $F_t | \partial M = F_o | \partial M$ for all $t \in I^n$, then we can insist that $H | \partial Q \times I^n$ be the identity. (Note : $0 = (0, 0, \ldots, 0) \in I^n$).

Remarks: 1) Let an allowable n-isotopy $F: M \times I^n \longrightarrow Q \times I^n$ be an n-isotopy such that $F^{-1}(\partial Q \times I^n) = N \times I^n$, N a manifold in ∂M of dim(m-1), m = dim M. Then one can prove an analogous theorem to 5.13 for allowable n-isotopies.

2) One also can prove an analogous theorem for isotopies of complexes into manifolds, provided one has codimension at least 3.

Lemma 6.14. Let $F: M \times I^n \longrightarrow Q \times I^n$ be a proper n-isotopy, locally unknotted and fixed on ∂M, i.e., $F_t | \partial M = F_o | \partial M$ for all t. If M and Q are compact then there is a P.L. homeomorphism $H: Q \times I^n \longrightarrow I^n$ such that $H | \partial Q \times I$ = identity, $H(Q \times A) = Q \times A$ for every face A of the cube I^n, and $H(F_o \times 1) = F$.

Proof. By induction on n. Suppose $h: Q \times I^{n-1} \longrightarrow Q \times I^{n-1}$ is a P.L. homeomorphism, equal to the identity on $Q \times I^{n-1}$ and sending $Q \times A$ to $Q \times A$ for each face of A of I^{n-1}, and with $h(F_o \times 1) = F | M \times I^{n-1}$. Then define $h': Q \times I^n \longrightarrow Q \times I^n$ by $h' = h \times 1$. Let $F' = (h')^{-1} F: M \times I^n \longrightarrow Q \times I^n$ and regard this as a 1-isotopy with the last coordinate of I^n as parameter.

Let $A_1, \ldots, A_r$ be the faces of I^{n-1} in order of increasing dimension (with $A_r = I^{n-1}$). Then, by the remark following 6.12.4 we can define inductively **PL** homeomorphisms $k_i: Q \times A_i \times I \to Q \times A_i \times I$, level-preserving on the last coordinate such that

1. $k_i | \partial Q \times A_i \times I =$ identity,
2. if $A_i < A_j$, $k_i = k_j | Q \times A_i \times I$, and
3. $k_i(F_o x, s, t) = F'(x, s, t)$ for all $x \in M$, $s \in A_i$, $t \in I$.

Then $k = h'k_r: Q \times I^n \to Q \times I^n$ is a PL homeomorphism satisfying all the required conditions.

Definition. Identifying I^r with the face of I^{r+1} having the last coordinate zero we define a primary simplex of I^n as a n-simplex linearly embedded in I^n with a vertex at 0, a 1-face in I^1, a two face (2-face) in I^2, etc. Thus a primary simplex will be of the form $(0, v_1, v_2, \ldots, v_n)$ where $v_i \in I^i$.

Lemma 6.15. Let $F: M \times I^n \to Q \times I^n$ be a proper locally unknotted n-isotopy, fixed on ∂M, M and Q being compact. Then there is a primary simplex Δ in I^n and a PL homeomorphism $H: Q \times \Delta \to Q \times \Delta$ commuting with projection onto Δ, with $H | \partial Q \times \Delta =$ identity and $H(F_o \times 1) = F | M \times \Delta \to Q \times \Delta$.

Proof. Let $k: Q \times I^n \to Q \times I^n$ be a PL homeomorphism given by Lemma 6.14. Let α and β be triangulations of $Q \times I^n$ such that $k: \alpha(Q \times I^n) \to \beta(Q \times I^n)$ is simplicial and the projections $\alpha(Q \times I^n) \to I^n$, $\beta(Q \times I^n) \to I^n$ are linear. Now choose constants $\delta_o, \delta_1, \ldots, \delta_n$ as follows:

Choose $\delta_o > 0$ such that, for any simplex σ in $\alpha(Q \times I^n)$ or $\beta(Q \times I^n)$, <u>either</u> $d(0, p_2\sigma) = 0$ <u>or</u> $d(0, p_2\sigma) > \delta_o$.

Now suppose that σ is a simplex of $\alpha(Q \times I^n)$ or $\beta(Q \times I^n)$ having a vertex x_o in $Q \times 0$ and a vertex x_j in $Q \times I^j - Q \times I^{j-1}$ for each $j < i$. Let $x'_j = p_2 x_j$ for each j. Let $A(p_2\sigma, I^i)$ [minimum angle between I^i and $(x'_o x'_1 \ldots x'_{i-1} y)$ for $y \in p_2\sigma$]. Choose $\delta_i > 0$ such that, for all such σ, <u>either</u> $A(p_2\sigma, I^i) = 0$ <u>or</u> $A(p_2\sigma, I^i) > \delta_i$. Now let Δ be the simplex $(0, v_1, v_2, \ldots, v_n)$ in I^n where $v_i \in I^i - I^{i-1}$, for each i, $d(0, v_i) = \delta_o$, and $\text{angle}(0 v_1 v_2 \ldots v_{j-1} v_i, I^j) = \delta_j$ for all $j \leq i$. As a result of the way we have chosen the δ_i, if σ is any principal simplex of $\alpha(Q \times I^n)$ or $\beta(Q \times I^n)$ such that $p_2\sigma \cap \Delta \neq \emptyset$, then $p_2\sigma \supset \Delta$, and $Q \times v_n$ meets $\text{Int}\,\sigma$. Moreover, for each i, σ meets I^i in a face, σ_i say, and $Q \times v_i$ meets $\text{Int}\,\sigma_i$.

Now choose first derived subdivisions α' and β' of α and β such that, if if $\hat{\sigma}$ denotes the subdivision point of σ, then

1. $\hat{\sigma} \in Q \times v_i$ if $Q \times v_i$ meets $\text{Int}\,\sigma$,

and 2. $\widehat{k\sigma}$ $k(\hat{\sigma})$ if $\sigma \in F(M \times I^n) \cup \partial Q \times I^n$.

Note that these two requirements are compatible since k is level-preserving on $F(M \times I^n)$ and $\partial Q \times I^n$.

Now let $k' \colon \alpha'(Q \times I^n) \longrightarrow \beta'(Q \times I^n)$ be the induced simplicial map. Then we still have k' a PL homeomorphism, equal to the identity on $\partial Q \times I^n$, and with $k'(F_o \times 1)$ F. Moreover, k' is level-preserving on $Q \times \Delta$. For let x be a vertex of $\alpha'(Q \times I^n)$ lying in $Q \times \Delta$. Then $x \in Q \times 0$ or $Q \times v_j$ for some j. But $k'x$ must also lie in the same set, and so $p_2 k'x = p_2 x$.

But k' is simplicial and so we may join linearly to get $p_2k'y = p_2y$ for all points y in $Q \times \Delta$.

Lemma 6.16 (A covering theorem): Let $\mathcal{H}$ be the group of rotations, reflections, and translations of R^n. Suppose that for each $h \in \mathcal{H}$ we are given a primary simplex $\sigma(h)$. Then there is a finite set $h_1, h_2, \ldots, h_r$ of elements of $\mathcal{H}$ such that $I^n \subset \bigcup_{i=1}^{r} h_i(\sigma(h_i))$.

Definition. An r-flag in R^n is a set of oriented affine subspaces $[A_o \subset A_1 \subset A_2 \subset \ldots \subset A_r]$, where $\dim(A_i) = i$. An r-wedge on this r-flag is a set of the form $\{x \in R^n \mid d(x, A_o) < \delta_o, \measuredangle(A_o x, A_1) < \delta_1, \ldots, \measuredangle(A_{r-1}x, A_r) < \delta_r\}$ where $\delta_o, \delta_1, \ldots, \delta_r$ are positive constants and $\measuredangle$ denotes angle between oriented subspaces.

We shall show by induction on decreasing r that, given any r-flag in R^n, there is an r-wedge on it that may be covered by finitely many simplexes of the form required in the lemma. Since an 0-wedge is simply a spherical neighbourhood, the compactness of I^n will complete the proof of the lemma.

To start the induction, consider an (n-1)-wedge $[A_o \subset \ldots \subset A_{n-1}]$. There are two possible orthonormal coordinate systems having this wedge as $[0, 0x_1, 0x_1x_2, \ldots, 0x_1x_2\ldots x_{n-1}]$, one being simply the reflection of the other in $x_n = 0$. For each of these coordinate systems we have a primary simplex and we can choose an (n-1)-wedge contained in the union of these two simplexes; see figure:

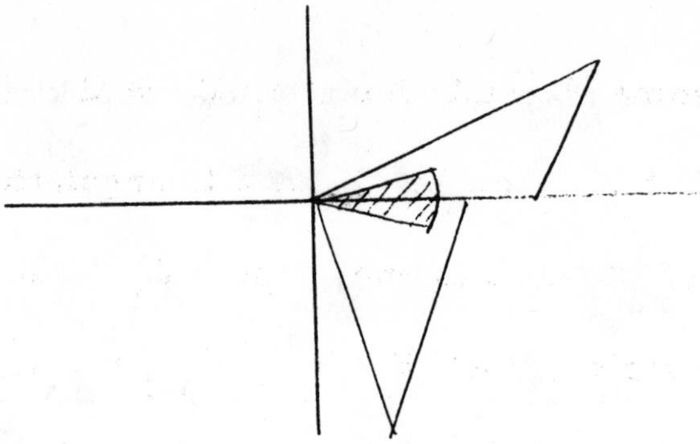

<u>The inductive step.</u> Let $F = [A_o \ \ldots \ A_r]$ be an r-flag. Let $\mathcal{S}$ be the set of oriented $(r+1)$-spaces through A_r. $\mathcal{S}$ is naturally isomorphic to the set of unit vectors orthogonal to A_r, which is an $(n-r-1)$-sphere. Now for each $B \in \mathcal{S}$, let W_B be a wedge on the flag $[A_o \subset A_1 \subset \ldots \subset A_r \subset B]$ given by the inductive hypothesis, and suppose that W_B is determined by the constants $(\delta_o^B, \delta_1^B, \ldots, \delta_{r+1}^B)$. Then the set $\{B' \in \mathcal{S} \mid \measuredangle(B, B') < \delta_{r+1}^B\}$ is a neighbourhood of B in $\mathcal{S}$. But $\mathcal{S}$ is compact, and so we can choose a finite set $B_1, B_2, \ldots, B_s$ such that the corresponding neighbourhoods cover $\mathcal{S}$. Let W be the wedge on F determined by the constants $(\delta_o, \delta_1, \ldots, \delta_r)$ where $\delta_i = \min(\delta_i^{B_j})$, $j = 1, 2, \ldots, s$. Then $W \subset \bigcup_{j=1}^{s} W_{B_j}$.

Proof of Theorem 6.13 (The n-isotopy extension theorem): First consider the special case when Q is compact. By reflection in the subspaces x_j = integer, we may assume that $F: M \times I^n \rightarrow Q \times I^n$ is the restriction of a PL embedding $F: M \times R^n \rightarrow Q \times R^n$, commuting with projection on R^n, and with $F_t | \partial M = F_o | \partial M$ for all $t \in R^n$. Now by Lemmas 6.15 and 6.16 there are a finite number of simplexes Δ_i in R^n, covering I^n, and PL homeomorphisms $k_i: Q \times \Delta_i \rightarrow Q \times \Delta_i$ commuting with projection onto the second factor, such that $k_i | \partial Q \times \Delta_i$ is the identity and

$k_i(\alpha_i \times 1) = F|M \times \Delta_i$ for some PL embedding $\alpha_i: M \longrightarrow Q$. (In fact, $\alpha_i = F_t$ for t = a vertex of Δ_i.) Now let K be a triangulation of I^n such that 1) each simplex of K_i lies in one of the Δ_i, and 2) K collapses simplicially to the origin. Let $K = K_p \searrow K_{p-1} \searrow \ldots \searrow K_o$ = the origin, be the simplicial collapse. We define inductively level-preserving PL homeomorphisms $h_i: Q \times K_i \longrightarrow Q \times K_i$ such that $h_i|\partial Q \times K_i$ = identity and $h_i(F_o \times 1) = F$ on $M \times K_i$. Start with h_o = identity. Suppose h_{i-1} is defined. Let $K_i = K_{i-1} + aA + A$. Let $\rho: aA \longrightarrow aA$ be a PL retraction. Suppose that $aA \subset \Delta_j$. Then define $h_i: Q \times K_i \longrightarrow Q \times K_i$ by $h_i(x,t) = (h_{i,t}x, t)$ where

$$h_{i,t} = \begin{cases} h_{i-1,t} & \text{if } t \in K_{i-1} \\ k_{j,t}(k_{j,\rho t})^{-1}h_{i-1,\rho t} & \text{if } t \in aA \end{cases}$$

One may readily check that this is a PL homeomorphism, equal to the identity on $\partial Q \times K_i$. Moreover, if $x \in M$, $t \in aA$,
$h_i(F_o x, t) = k_{j,t}(k_{j,\rho t})^{-1}F_{\rho t}(x) = k_{j,t}\alpha_j(x) = F_t(x)$.

Putting $H = h_p: Q \times I^n \longrightarrow Q \times I^n$ gives the required ambient n-isotopy. The extension to the case when Q is not compact is more or less identical to the argument when $n = 1$ and so will be omitted.

Chapter VII. Engulfing

0. Introduction.

Suppose X is a closed subspace of the PL manifold Q^q. Then we may pose the question: Is there a q-ball B in Q with $X \subset B$? Some uses for the answers to this question are in proving embedding theorems (See Chapter VIII) and in proving a weak generalized Poincare conjecture in dimensions ≥ 5 and a variant of the h-cobordism theorem (see 5).

We approach this question by considering the following two related questions:

(A) If U is open in Q and X is a compact PL subspace of Q, is there a PL homeomorphism $h: Q \longrightarrow Q$ with $X \subset hU$?

(B) If C and X are compact PL subspaces of Q, is there a compact subspace C' of Q with $X \subset C'$ and $C' \searrow C$? What can we insist about the dimension of $(C'-C)$?

1. Preliminary Results.

Lemma 7.1. Suppose that $X_o \subset X$ are compact PL subspaces of Q, and suppose Y is a closed PL subspace of Q such that $X \cap (\partial Q \cup Y) \subset X_o$. Assume that $X \searrow X_o$ and let $U \supset X_o$ be open in Q. Then there exists a PL homeomorphism $h: Q \longrightarrow Q$ with compact support, which is the identity on $\partial Q \cup Y \cup X_o$, such that $X \subset h(U)$.

Picture:

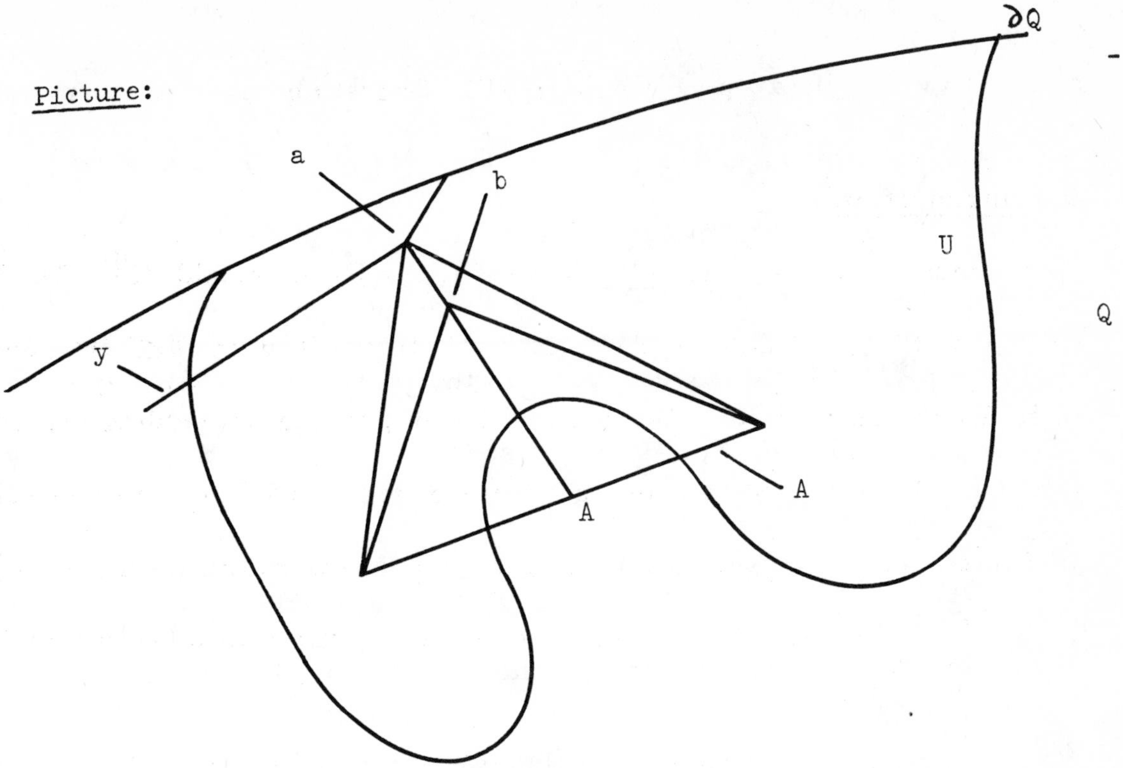

Proof. Let J be a triangulation of Q containing triangulations K_o, K, and L of X_o, X, and Y, respectively. We may assume that $K \overset{s}{\searrow} K_o$.

Let $K = K_r \overset{es}{\searrow} K_{r-1} \overset{es}{\searrow} \cdots \overset{es}{\searrow} K_o$. Then $K_i \searrow K_{i-1}$ and $|K_i| \cap (|\partial J| \cup |L|) \subset |K_{i-1}|$. Hence it suffices by induction to prove the lemma for K_i, K_{i-1}, and Y. So we may as well suppose $K = K_1 \overset{es}{\searrow} K_o$.

Let $K = K_o + aA + A$. Then $a\dot{A} \subset U$. Let $\hat{A}$ be the barycenter of A. Let $b \neq a$ be a point of $a\hat{A}$ close enough to a so that $ab\dot{A} \subset U$. Let $R = \text{link}(A; J)$. Since $A \not\subset \partial J$, R is a PL sphere of dimension q-dim A-1. Since $\dim A \leq q-1$, $R \neq \emptyset$. Therefore there is a PL homeomorphism $\alpha: R \longrightarrow \{a, c\}.S$, S a sphere of dimension q-dim A-2 ($S = \emptyset$ is possible). Define a PL homeomorphism $\beta: A.R \longrightarrow A.(a \cup c).S = (a \cup c).\hat{A}.\dot{A}.S$ by letting $\beta|\dot{A}$ = identity and $\beta|R = \alpha$ and extending linearly.

Now let $\gamma': (a \cup c).A \longrightarrow (a \cup c).A$ be a PL homeomorphism such that $\gamma'(a) = a$, $\gamma'(b) = \hat{A}$, and $\gamma'(c) = c$. Then let $\gamma: (a \cup c)\hat{A}.\dot{A}.S \longrightarrow (a \cup c).\hat{A}.\dot{A}.S$ be a PL homeomorphism such that $\gamma|(a \cup c)\mathring{A} = \gamma'$ and $\gamma|\dot{A}.S = \text{identity}$. Then let $\delta: \overline{\text{star}}(A; J) \longrightarrow \overline{\text{star}}(A; J)$ be defined by $\delta = \beta^{-1}\gamma\beta$. Then $\delta(ab\dot{A}) = a\hat{A}.\dot{A} = aA$. Moreover, δ is the identity on $\dot{A}.R$. So if we put $h|\,\text{star}(A; J) = \delta$ and $h = \text{identity}$ elsewhere, then $h|\,|K_o| = \text{identity}$ and $h(U) \supset |K|$.

<u>Definition.</u> If $K = K_o + aA + A$ is an elementary simplicial collapse $K \overset{es}{\searrow} K_o$, then $\dim(aA)$ is called the <u>dimension</u> of the collapse.

<u>Lemma 7.2:</u> If $K \overset{s}{\searrow} K_o$, then we can rearrange the elementary simplicial collapses $K \overset{s}{\searrow} K_o$ to be in order of decreasing dimension.

<u>Proof.</u> Suppose $K_2 = K_1 + aA + A$ and $K_1 = K_o + bB + B$ are two simplicial collapses, and $\dim B > \dim A$. Then $a\dot{A} \subset K_o$. So $K_o + aA + A$ is a subcomplex of K_2. Moreover, $K_2 = (K_o + aA + A) + bB + B$. So $K_2 \overset{es}{\searrow} (K_o + aA + A) \overset{es}{\searrow} K_o$ is in order of decreasing dimension.

<u>Lemma 7.3.</u> If $X, Y \subseteq Z$ are polyhedra and if $Z \searrow X$, then there exists $T \subset Z$, a polyhedron, such that $Y \cup X \subset T$, $Z \searrow X \cup T \searrow X$, and $\dim T \leq \dim Y + 1$.

<u>Proof.</u> Let $K, L \subset J$ triangulate $X, Y \subset Z$. Choose subdivisions $K', L' \subset J'$ so that $J' \overset{s}{\searrow} K'$, and let $J' = K'_r \overset{es}{\searrow} \dots \overset{es}{\searrow} K'_o$ be elementary simplicial collapses in order of decreasing dimension. Let $i \leq r$ be the least integer such that $K'_i \supset L'$. We may suppose $i \neq 0$, as if $i = 0$ there

is nothing to prove. Let $K'_i = K'_{i-1} + aA + A$. Then $A \subset L'$, as otherwise $L' \subset K'_{i-1}$. In particular, the collapse $K_i \searrow K_{i-1}$ has dimension $\leq$ (dim L+1). So if $T = \mathrm{cl}|K'_i - K'_o| = |\overline{K'_i - K'_o}|$, dim $T \leq$ dim $L+1$ and $Z \searrow X \cup T \searrow X$.

3. Engulfing Theorems, Type (A).

Definition. A topological pair (X, A) is n-connected, $n \geq 0$, if every point of X may be joined by a path to some point of A and if $\pi_i(X; A) = 0$ for $1 \leq i \leq n$. [If A is not connected, we insist the condition holds for any base point in A.]

Theorem 7.4. Let U be an open subset of the PL manifold Q^q. Assume $\partial Q = \emptyset$. Let $X \subset Q$ be a compact PL subspace of Q, and let $Y \subset U$ be a closed PL subspace of Q. Let $j = \dim X$, $s = \dim Y$, suppose that (Q, U) is k-connected, and suppose that $j \leq q-3$, $s \leq q-3$, and $t \leq k$. Then there exists a PL homeomorphism $h: Q \longrightarrow Q$, which is the identity on Y, such that $X \subset h(U)$.

Proof. We let k and s be fixed and proceed by induction on j. So given j, assume the result for $j-1$.

Because of the connectivity assumptions on (Q, U), we can construct a map $\phi: X \times I \longrightarrow Q$ such that $\phi(x, 1) = x$ all x, and $\phi(X \times 0) \subset U$, as follows: Let K triangulate X, $K^j = j^{th}$ skeleton. Define ϕ_o on $(K^{(o)} \times I)$ $(K \times 1)$ by $\phi(x, 1) = x$ and $\phi(v, t) = \varphi_v(t)$, where φ_v is a path from v to a point in U. Suppose that $\phi_{j-1}: (K^{(j-1)} \times I) \cup (K \times 1) \longrightarrow Q$, $j \leq \dim K$, has been defined so that $\phi_{j-1}(K^{(j-1)} \times 0) \subset U$ and $\phi_{j-1}(x, 1) = x$, all x. For each j-simplex Δ of $K^{(j)}$, ϕ_{j-1} is defined on $(\Delta \times 1) \cup (\dot{\Delta} \times I)$, a retract of $\Delta \times I$. Hence there exist $f_\Delta : \Delta \times I \longrightarrow Q$ extending $\phi_{r-1} | (\Delta \times 1) \cup (\dot{\Delta} \times I)$. Let $g_\Delta = (f_\Delta)_o$. Then $g_\Delta : (\Delta, \dot{\Delta}) \longrightarrow (Q, U)$. Since dim $\Delta \leq k$, let $H_\Delta : \Delta \times I \longrightarrow Q$ be a homotopy of $g_\Delta = (H_\Delta)_o$, relative $\dot{\Delta}$ such that $H_\Delta(x, 1) \in U$ for all $x \in \Delta$. Then if $x \in \Delta \in K^{(j)}$ and if $t \in I$, define

$$\phi_j(x, t) = \begin{cases} f_\Delta(x; 2t-1) & 1/2 \leq t \leq 1 \\ H_\Delta(x; 1-2t) & 0 \leq t \leq 1/2 \end{cases} .$$

Then $\phi_j : K^{(j)} \times I \longrightarrow Q$ is a well-defined map, $\phi_j(K^{(j)} \times 0) \subset U$, and $\phi_j(x, 1) = x$. Finally, put $\phi = \phi_j$, where $j = \dim K$.

By the lemmas of Chapter IV we can assume, after a small homotopy of ϕ relative $X \times 1$ that ϕ is also a non-degenerate PL map (Lemmas 4.2 and 4.4).

Now let L be a triangulation of $X \times I$, containing triangulations L_o and L_1 of $(X \times 0)$ and $(X \times 1)$ respectively, such that $\phi : L \longrightarrow Q$ can be made simplicial by suitably triangulating Q. Then ϕ embeds each simplex of L. Let L' be a subdivision of L such that $L' \overset{s}{\searrow} L'_o$ = induced subdivision of L_o. By Lemma 4.7, $\phi \simeq \phi$ (rel $X \times 1$), where ϕ' is a PL map which embeds each simplex of L and which satisfies the following:

1) If $\sigma, \tau \in L' - L'_1$, $\dim(\phi'\sigma) \cap (\phi'\tau) \leq \dim \sigma + \dim \tau - q$;

2) For all $\sigma \in L' - L'_1$, $\dim (\phi\sigma) \cap Y \leq \dim \tau + s - q$;

3) For all $\sigma \in L' - L'_1$, $\tau \in L'_1$, $\dim(\phi'\sigma \cap \phi'\tau) \leq \dim\sigma + \dim\tau - q$.

Now let $L' = R_n \overset{es}{\searrow} \cdots \overset{es}{\searrow} R_o = L'_o$. Let $R_i^{(j)}$ = j-skeleton of R_i, each i. By induction on i, we are going to find PL homoemorphisms $h_i: Q \longrightarrow Q$, fixed on Y, with $\emptyset'(R_i^{(j)}) \subset h_i U$. This will complete the proof for if we take $i = n$ then $X \subset \emptyset'(X \times 1) \subset \emptyset(R_n^{(j)}) \subset h_i(U)$. Since $\emptyset'(R_o) \subset U$, let h_o = identity. Suppose h_{i-1} is defined. Then let $V = h_{i-1}(U)$. Let $R_i = R_{i-1} + aA + A$. Let Z be a polyhedron such that
$(\emptyset'|aA)^{-1}(Y \cup \emptyset' R_{i-1}^{(j)}) = a\dot{A} \cup Z$, By 1) and 2) above,
$\dim Z \leq \max(j+1+s-q, j+1-j-q) \leq j-2$. By 7.3, there exists a polyhedron T such that $aA \searrow a\dot{A} \cup T \searrow a\dot{A}$, $Z \subset T \cup a\dot{A}$, and $\dim T \leq j-1$. Therefore $\emptyset'(R_{i-1}^{(j)} + aA + A) \searrow \emptyset'(R_{i-1}^{(j)} \cup T)$ by a collapse "not crossing Y"; i.e., a collapse in which no points of Y are disturbed.

Now we are going to use the main inductive hypothesis to engulf $\emptyset'[R_{i-1}^{(j)} \cup T]$. $\dim \emptyset'(T) \leq j-1$. $Y \cup \emptyset'(R_{i-1}^{(j)}) \subset V$. So letting $\emptyset'(T)$ play the role of X in the theorem, and $Y \cup \emptyset'(R_{i-1}^{j})$ the role of Y, there exists a PL homeomorphism $\alpha: Q \longrightarrow Q$, fixed on $Y \cup \emptyset'(R_{i-1}^{(j)})$, with $\emptyset' T \subset \alpha V$. Now by Lemma 7.1, there exists a PL homeomorphism $\beta: Q \longrightarrow Q$ such that β is fixed on $Y \cup \emptyset'(R_{i-1}^{(j)} \cup T)$ and $\emptyset'(R_{i-1}^{(j)} \cup aA \cup A) \subset (\beta\alpha V)$. Now $R_i^{(j)} \subseteq R_{i-1}^{(j)} + aA + A$. So put $h_i = \beta\alpha h_{i-1}$. Then $\emptyset R_i^{(j)} \subset h_i U$. This completes the proof.

<u>Remarks:</u> We can insist that h have compact support. In fact, in view of the fact that the homeomorphism of 7.1 could have been taken to be isotopic to the identity by moves, the same is true of h.

Corollary 7.5. Let X, Y, Q, U satisfy all the hypotheses of Theorem 7.4 except that X is merely a closed PL subspace of Q. Suppose that $X - X \cap U$ is compact. Then there exists h (with compact support) a homeomorphism of Q, such that $X \subset h(U)$.

Proof. Let $X_o \subset X$ be a compact PL subspace of Q (or X) containing $X - X \cap U$. Then $X - X_o \subset U$. But $X' = X_o$, $Y' = Y \cup cl(X - X_o)$. Let $h: Q \longrightarrow Q$ be a PL homeomorphism with compact support, such that $h|Y' =$ identity and $h(U) \supset X$. Then $h(U) \supset X_o \cup (X - X_o) = X$.

Corollary 7.6. Let $U \subset Q^q$ be an open subset of the PL manifold Q, $\partial Q \neq \emptyset$. Let X be a compact PL subspace of Q, Y a closed PL subspace of X, with $\dim X = r \leq q-3$, $\dim Y = s \leq q-3$. Assume (Q, U) is k-connected $k \geq r$, and assume $Y \subset U$ and $X \cap \partial Q \subset U$. Then there exists a PL homeomorphism (with compact support) $h: Q \longrightarrow Q$, with $h|\partial Q \cup Y =$ identity, such that $X \subset h(U)$.

Proof. $X' = X - X \cap \partial Q$ and $Y' = Y - Y \cap \partial Q$ are closed PL subspaces of $Q - \partial Q$. $U' = U - U \cap \partial Q$ is open in $Q - \partial Q$. The pair $(Q - \partial Q, U')$ is q-connected; to see this suppose

$f: (D^q; S^{q-1}) \longrightarrow (Q - \partial Q, U - \partial Q \cap U)$ is homotopic rel S^{q-1}, to a map of D^q into U. Then by using a boundary collar, one can push the homotopy slightly off the boundary without disturbing it on S^{q-1}, getting a homotopy H of f such that $H_1(D^q) \subset U - (\partial Q) \cap U$.

Now let $h': Q - \partial Q \longrightarrow Q - \partial Q$ be a PL homeomorphism such that $h'(U') \supset X'$ and h has compact support. Define $h: Q \longrightarrow Q$ by extending h' to be the identity on ∂Q.

Remark. This corollary could have been included in Theorem 7.4 using almost the same proof.

4. Engulfing Theorems, Type (B)

Theorem 7.7. Let C and X be compact PL subspaces of the PL manifold Q^q, $\partial Q = \emptyset$, with (Q, C) a t-connected pair. Let $r = \dim X$, and suppose $C \searrow Y$, whoere Y is a closed PL subspace of dimension s. Then if $r \leq q-3$, $s \leq q-3$, and $r \leq t$, there is a compact PL subspace C' of Q such that $C \cup X \subset C' \searrow C$ and $\dim(C'-C) \leq r+1$.

Proof. Let $X_1 = cl(X - X \cap C)$; assume $X_1 \neq \emptyset$. Then $\dim(X_1 \cap C) \leq r-1$. Hence by Lemma 7.3, there exists a compact PL Y_1 in Q such that $C \searrow Y \cup Y_1$, $X_1 \cap C \subset Y \cup Y_1$, and $\dim Y_1 \leq r$. Therefore $C \cup X = C \cup X_1 \searrow Y \cup Y_1 \cup X_1$, by Lemma 2.

Let N be a regular neighborhood of Y in Q, and let U = Int. N. The inclusions $Y \subset C$ and $Y \subset U$ are both homotopy equivalences; therefore (Q, U) is t-connected. By Theorem 7.4, there is a PL homeomorphism $h: Q \longrightarrow Q$ such that $h|Y$ = identity and $X_1 \cup Y_1 \subset h(U)$. So $X_1 \cup Y_1 \cup Y \subset h(U)$. By 7.1, there is a PL homeomorphism $k: Q \longrightarrow Q$ with $k|Y \cup Y_1 \cup X_1$ = identity and $C \cup X \subset khU$. Since $kh|Y$ = identity, khN is a regular neighborhood of Y. In particular, $khN \searrow Y$. But $C \searrow Y$ and $C \subset \text{Int } khN$. So by Lemma 5.1 (on factoring collapses), $khN \searrow C$. So by Lemma 7.3 again, $khN \searrow C' \searrow C$, where $X \subset C'$ and $\dim(C'-C) \leq \dim X + 1$.

Lemma 7.8. Suppose that C and X are compact PL subspaces of Q^q, $C \searrow C \cap \partial Q$. Assume that $(Q, \partial Q)$ is r-connected, $\dim X = r$, and $r \leq q-3$. Then there exists C' in Q, a compact PL subspace, such that $C \cup X \subset C' \searrow (C' \cap \partial Q) \cup C$, and $\dim(C'-C) \leq r+1$.

Proof. Let N be a derived neighborhood of ∂Q in Q. Let $U = \text{Int}_Q N$. Then (Q, U) is r-connected. Now, as in the proof of 7.7, $C \cup X \searrow (C \cap \partial Q) \cup Y$, where $\dim Y \leq r$. So, by Corollary 7.6, there is a PL homeomorphism $h: Q \to Q$ with $h|\partial Q =$ identity, $Y \subset hU$, $h^{-1}Y \subset U \subset N$. Now $(C \cap \partial Q) \cup (h^{-1}Y)$ is compact, and so there is a compact polyhedron P in ∂Q such that $(C \cap \partial Q) \cup (h^{-1}Y) \subset V = \text{Int}_Q N'$, where N' is the derived neighborhood of P in Q. By Lemma 7.1, there is a PL homeomorphism $k: Q \to Q$, fixed on $\partial Q \cup Y$ with $C \cup X \subset khV \subset khN'$. Now khN' is a regular neighborhood of P in Q and $P \cup C \searrow P$, $P \cup C \subset \text{Int}_Q khN'$. So, by Lemma 5.1, khN' is a regular neighborhood of $P \cup C$ in Q. So, by Lemma 7.3, $khN' \searrow P \cup C \cup T \searrow P \cup C$, where $X \subset T$ and $\dim T \leq r+1$. $C' = C \cup T \searrow C \cup (T \cap \partial Q) \searrow (C \cup T) \cap \partial Q$.

5. Applications of Engulfing.

Definition. If Q is an open manifold (i.e., Q is not compact and $\partial Q = \emptyset$), Q is called 1-connected at ∞ if given $C \subset Q$, C compact, there is a $C' \subset Q$, compact, such that $C \subset C'$ and $(Q-C')$ is 1-connected.

Theorem 7.9 (Stallings): Let Q be open, $(q-3)$-connected PL manifold which is 1-connected at ∞. Suppose $q = \dim Q \geq 5$. Then Q is PL homeomorphic to E^q, Euclidean space of dimension q.

Proof. We shall prove that if $C \subset Q$ is compact, then C is contained in the interior of a PL q-ball contained (as a PL subspace) in Q. This is sufficient: it implies that $Q = \bigcup_{i=1}^{\infty} B_i$, where $B_i \subset \operatorname{Int} B_{i+1}$ are all q-balls. By the annulus theorem, $\operatorname{cl}(B_{i+1} - B_i)$ is PL homeomorphic to $\partial B_i \times I$. Moreover, E^q is also such a union of balls, and so it is clear how to define a PL homeomorphism of Q onto E.

So let $C \subset Q$ be any compact subset of Q. Let $C' \supset C$ be another compact subset, so that $(Q-C')$ is 1-connected. Let $V = Q-C'$.

Let J be a triangulation of Q. Let J_1 be the $(q-3)$-skeleton of J. Let J_2 be the subcomplex of J' consisting of all simplices of J' which do not meet (i.e., have no faces in) J_1', where J' = barycentric first derived of J. A general simplex of J' is of the form $\sigma = \hat{A}_1 \ldots \hat{A}_r$, $A_1 < \ldots < A_r \in J$. If σ does not meet J_1', then $\dim A_i \geq q-2$, $1 \leq i \leq r$. Therefore $r \leq 3$. So $\dim J_2 \leq 2$.

Now, J_1' is full in J', so there is a linear map $\phi: J' \longrightarrow I$, such that $\phi(J_2) = 1$ and $\phi^{-1}(0) = J_1'$. If D is any compact subset of Q not meeting J_2, then there exists $0 < \varepsilon < 1$ such that $\phi(D) \subset [0, \varepsilon]$. But $\phi^{-1}[0, \varepsilon]$ is a derived neighborhood of J_1 in J. In fact, if D is compact, D is contained in a derived neighborhood of a finite subcomplex of J_1. Therefore there are compact PL subspaces Z and Z_0 of Q (can take Z to be a q-manifold) such that $D \subset Z \searrow Z_0$ and $\dim Z_0 \leq q-3$.

$J_2 - (J_2 \cap V)$ is compact, and $\dim J_2 \leq 2 \leq q-3$ because $q \geq 5$. Since V is one- connected and Q is $(q-3)$-connected, $q \geq 5$, (Q, V) is 2-connected. Hence by Corollary 7.5, there is a PL homeomorphism $h: Q \longrightarrow Q$, such that $|J_2| \subset hV$.

In particular, $Q-hV = h(Q-V)$ is compact and does not meet J_2. Hence, we may take $D = Q-hV$; so, $Q-hV \subset Z \searrow Z_0$, $\dim Z_0 \leq q-3$.

Now let U be the interior of a PL q-ball contained in Q. Then (Q, U) is certainly $(q-3)$-connected. Therefore there is a $k: Q \longrightarrow Q$ such that $Z_0 \subset kU$, by Theorem 7.4. By Lemma 7.1, there exists a $k': Q \longrightarrow Q$ with $Z \subset k'kU$. Therefore $Q-hV \subset k'kU$, and so $Q-V \subset h^{-1}k'k(U)$. But $C \subset C' = Q-V \subset h^{-1}k'k(U) \subset h^{-1}kk(\overline{U})$, a PL q-ball.

<u>Corollary 7.10</u>. (Weak Generalized Poincare Conjecture): Let M^m be a closed (= compact without boundary) PL manifold, $m \geq 5$. Assume M is $[m/2]$-connected. Then there is a topological homeomorphism of M onto the sphere S^m.

Proof. By Poincare duality, M is $(m-1)$-connected. (1-connected implies orientable.) Therefore M is a homology sphere. Moreover, by excision $H_i(M, M\text{-pt.}) = 0$, for $i < m$, $H_i(M\text{-pt.}) = 0$, all $0 < i \leq m-2$. As $\pi_2(M, M\text{-pt.}) = 0$, (by general position), $\pi_1(M\text{-pt}) = 0$. Therefore, M-pt. is $(m-2)$-connected.

If $C \subset M$-pt. is compact, there is a regular neighborhood N of pt. in M not meeting C. $C' = cl(M-N)$ is compact in M-pt. $(M\text{-pt})-C' = N\text{-pt.}$ But N is a m-ball, so N-pt. is homotopy equivalent to S^{m-1}, and $\pi_1(S^{m-1}) = 0$. Therefore M-pt. is 1-connected at ∞. Therefore by Theorem 7.9, M is topologically equivalent to the one point compactification of E^m, which is S^m.

We conclude this chapter with a type of h-cobordism theorem.

Theorem 7.11. Let W be a compact PL q-manifold with $q \geq 5$. Suppose $\partial W = M_1 \cup M_2$, where M_1, M_2 are disjoint $\overline{q-1}$ manifolds. Suppose that (W, M_1) is r-connected, (W, M_2) is s-connected, where $r \leq q-3$, $s \leq q-3$, $r+s+1 = q$. Then $W-M_2 \cong M_1 \times [0,\infty)$, $W-M_1 \cong M_2 \times [0,\infty)$, and $\text{Int } W \cong M_1 \times R \cong M_2 \times R$.

Proof. It suffices to prove the first statement of the conclusion. Let $Q = W-M_2$. We will show that if C is compact, $C \subset Q$, then C is contained in the interior of a regular neighborhood of M_1 in Q. From this it follows that $Q = \bigcup_1^\infty N_i$, where each N_i is a regular neighborhood of M_1 and $N_i \subset \text{Int } N_{i+1}$. Then, since $cl(N_{i+1} - N_i)$ is PL homeomorphic to $(Fr_Q N_i) \times I$ by the generalized annulus theorem, and since by uniqueness of regular neighborhoods and the existence of boundary collars for Q, $Fr_Q N_i \simeq M_1$, we have $cl(N_{i+1} - N_i) \simeq M_1 \times I$. Using this PL homeomorphism, it is clear how to define inductively PL homeomorphisms $h_N: \bigcup_{i=1}^{N} N_i \to M_1 \times [0, N]$ such that $h_N = h_{N+1}$ where both are defined. Clearly the h_N define the required homeomorphism. So let $C \subset Q$ be compact. Let N be a regular neighborhood of M_1 in Q, and let $U = Int_Q N$. Let N' be a regular neighborhood of M_2 in W such that $N' \cap C = \emptyset$, and let $V = Int_Q(N' - M_2)$. Then the inclusion $M_1 \to U \simeq M_1 \times [0, 1)$ is a homotopy equivalence, so (Q, U) is ∞-connected. A similar sort of argumant, but using a boundary collar of M_2, shows that (Q, V) is also ∞-connected.

Let $J_o \subset J$ be a triangulation of $M_1 \subset Q^q$. Let $J_1 = J_o \cup J^{(r)}$, $J^{(r)}$ = r-skeleton of J. Let J_2 consist of those simplices of J' which do not meet J_1. As in the proof of 7.9, $\dim J_2 \leq q-r-1 = s$.

By the engulfing theorem, Corollary 7.5, ($J_2 - J_2 \cap V$ is compact) there exists a PL homeomorphism $h: Q \to Q$, with $|J_2| \subset hV$. $h(C) \subset h(Q-V) = Q-hV$; therefore $h(C) \cap |J_2| = \emptyset$. Hence, since J_1' is full in J', h(C) is contained in a derived neighborhood of a finite subcomplex of J_1 (see page 17, 2nd complete paragraph). We may suppose that the subcomplex of J_1 is of the form $M_1 \cup Y$, where $\dim Y \leq r$. Then if Z is the regular neighborhood $h(C) \subset Z \searrow M_1 \cup Y$. By Corollary 7.6, there is a PL homeomorphism $k: Q \to Q$, with $M_1 \cup Y \subset kU$. By Lemma 7.1, there is a PL homeomorphism $k': Q \to Q$ with $Z \subset k'kU$. So $hC \subset k'kU$. Therefore

C $h^{-1}k'kU$ Int($h^{-1}k'kN$), and the latter is a regular neighborhood of M_1 in Q.

<u>Note.</u> In fact, Poincare duality and the Hurewicz theorem ensures that the inclusions M_1 W, M_2 W, are homotopy equivalences.

Chapter VIII -- Some Embedding Theorems

1. An Embedding Theorem Relative the Boundary

Theorem 8.1. Let M^m and Q^q be connected P. L. manifolds, M compact. Let $f:(M, \partial M) \longrightarrow (Q, \partial Q)$ be continuous, and suppose that $f|\partial M$ is a P. L. embedding. If M is $(2m-q)$-connected and Q is $(2m-q+1)$-connected, and if $q-m \geq 3$, then $f \simeq f'$ (rel ∂M), where f' is a P. L. embedding.

Proof. By the general position theorems of Chapter IV, $f \simeq g$ (rel ∂M), where g is a P. L. map, $\dim S_2(g) \leq 2m-q$, and $g(\text{Int } M) \subseteq \text{Int } Q$.

We can suppose that $S_2(g) \subseteq \text{Int } M$. For let $\alpha: M \longrightarrow (M \times 0) \cup (\partial M \times I)$ and $\beta: Q \longrightarrow (Q \times 0) \cup (\partial Q \times I)$ be P. L. homeomorphisms such that $\alpha(x) = (x, 1)$ if $x \in \partial M$ and $\beta(y) = (y, 1)$ if $y \in \partial Q$. Then let g' be the following composite:

$$M \xrightarrow{\alpha} (M \times 0) \cup (\partial M \times I) \xrightarrow{g \times 1} (Q \times 0) \cup (\partial Q \times I) \xrightarrow{\beta^{-1}} Q.$$

Then $S_2(g') = (\alpha^{-1}|M \times 0)(S_2(g) \times 0)$, so $S_2(g') \subseteq \text{Int } M$ and $\dim S_2(g') \leq 2m-q$. But we can choose β so that there is a homotopy $F_t: (Q \times 0) \cup (\partial Q \times I) \longrightarrow Q$ such that for all t, $F_t|\partial Q \times 1 = \beta^{-1}|\partial Q \times 1$, $F_0 = \beta^{-1}$, $F_1|Q \times 0$ is a P. L. homeomorphism of $Q \times 0$ onto Q, and $F_1(x, t) = x$, all $x \in \partial Q$ and $t \in I$. This can be seen by adjoining a boundary collar for $Q^* = \text{cl}(Q - \beta(\partial Q \times I))$ to the collar $\beta|\partial Q \times I$ and then expanding the inner collar at the expense of the outer one. Similarly for suitable α, there is a homotopy $G_t: M \longrightarrow (M \times 0) \cup (\partial M \times I)$ with $G_0 = \alpha$, $G_t(x) \in x \times I$ for all $x \in \partial M$, and G_1 a P. L. homeomorphism of M onto $M \times 0$ such that $G_1(x) = (x, 0)$.

Then $g' = F_0 \circ (g \times 1) \circ G_0 \simeq F_1 \circ (g \times 1) \circ G_0 \simeq F_1 \circ (g \times 1) \circ G_1$ and each homotopy is relative ∂M. But the last map may also be written in the form $k.g.h$, where k and h are P. L. homeomorphisms of Q and M respectively, which are the identity maps on ∂Q and ∂M.

So we may assume $S_2(g) \subseteq \text{Int } M$. Dim $S_2(g) \leq 2m-q \leq m-3$. Int M is as connected as M, and so there is a collapsible compact P. L. subspace C of Int M, with $S_2(g) \subseteq C$ and $\dim C \leq 2m-q+1$, by the Engulfing Theorem 7. By the same theorem, there exists a collapsible P. L. subspace D of Int Q such that $g(C) \subseteq D$ and $\dim D \leq 2m-q+2$. By general position theorems, there exists a P. L. homeomorphism $h: Q \longrightarrow Q$, fixed on $g(C)$, so that

$$\dim((hD-gC) \cap g(M)) \leq (2m-q+2) + m-q = 3m-2q+2 \leq 2m-q-1.$$

So if $D' = hD$, $g^{-1}D' = C \cup X$, where X is a compact P. L. subspace of M, and $\dim X \leq 2m-q-1$.

Let $C_1 = C$, $D_1 = D'$, $X_1 = X$, and suppose by induction we have found collapsible P. L. subspaces $C_i \subseteq \text{Int } M$ and $D_i \subseteq \text{Int } Q$, and $X_i \subseteq \text{Int } M$, such that $S_2(g) \subseteq C_i$, $(g')^{-1}D_i = C_i \cup X_i$, $\dim X_i \leq 2m-q-i$ $(\leq m-3)$. Then by the Engulfing Theorem 7. there is a compact P. L. subspace $C_{i+1} \subseteq \text{Int } M$ with $C_i \cup X_i \subseteq C_{i+1} \searrow 0$, and $\dim(C_{i+1}-C_i) \leq \dim X_i+1$. By the same theorem, there is a P. L. subspace D'' of Int Q such that $D_i \cup g'(C_{i+1}) \subseteq D'' \searrow 0$, and $\dim(D'' - D_i) \leq \dim X_i + 2$. By the General Position Theorem, there exists a P. L. homeomorphism $k: Q \longrightarrow Q$ with $k|D_i \cup g'(C_{i+1}) = \text{identity}$ and $\dim[k(D''-D_i \cup g(C_{i+1}))] \cap g(M) \leq \dim X_i + 2 + m-q \leq \dim X_i - 1$, since $m-q \leq -3$. Let $D_{i+1} = kD''$.

For k large enough, $X_k = \emptyset$, as $2m-q-k < 0$. So we get $g^{-1}D_k = C_k \supseteq S_2(g)$. Now let K and L triangulate M and Q respectively, with C_k and D_k triangulated as subcomplexes (some large k, now fixed), and with $g: K \longrightarrow L$ simplicial. Since g is non-degenerate, it carries barycenters to barycenters, and so if K'' and L'' are barycentric 2nd derived subdivisions, then $g: K'' \longrightarrow L''$ is simplicial. Let $N_1 = N(S; K'')$ and $N_2 = N(T; L'')$, where S and T are subcomplexes of K'' and L'' respectively triangulating C_k and D_k respectively. Then by uniqueness of regular neighborhoods, N_1 is an m-ball in Int M and N_2 is a q-ball in Int Q. Also, $N_1 = q^{-1}N_2$, as $S = q^{-1}T$ and q is simplicial. As $S_2(g) \subsetneq \text{Int } N_1$, $g|cl(M-N_1)$ embeds $cl(M-N_1)$ piecewise linearly in $cl(Q-N_2)$ and embeds ∂N_1 piecewise linearly in ∂N_2.

Now $g|\partial N_1$ extends to a P.L. embedding of N_1 into N_2, f', say. We may extend f' to all of N by putting $f' = g$ on $cl(M-N_1)$. Then f' is a P.L. embedding. Since N_2 is a ball, $f'|N_1 \simeq g|N_1$ (rel. ∂N_1). Therefore $f' \simeq g$ (rel ∂M). This completes the proof.

Note. The hypothesis that M be compact can be removed provided we insist that f be a proper map, i.e., f^{-1}(compact) = compact, and $S_2(f)$ is compact.

Corollary 8.1.1. If $k \leq m-3$, a closed, k-connected m-manifold can be embedded in E^{2m-k}.

Corollary 8.1.2. If Q^q is k-connected, then every element of $\pi_r(Q)$ can be represented by an embedded sphere provided that $r \leq \min(q-3, \frac{q+k-1}{2})$.

2. An Embedding Theorem Modulo the Boundary

Theorem 8.2. Let M^m be a compact P. L. manifold, Q^q a P. L. manifold, and let $f:(M, \partial M) \longrightarrow (Q, \partial Q)$ be a continuous map. Then if $(M, \partial M)$ is $(2m-q)$-connected and $(Q, \partial Q)$ is $(2m-q+1)$-connected, and if $q-m \geq 3$, then $f \simeq f'$ via a homotopy of pairs, $(M\times I, \partial M\times I) \longrightarrow (Q, \partial Q)$, with f' a P. L. embedding.

Corollary 8.2.1. If $(Q, \partial Q)$ is k-connected, an element of $\pi_r(Q, \partial Q)$ may be represented by a properly embedded disk, provided that $r \leq (q-3, \frac{q+k-1}{2})$.

Proof of Theorem 8.2. By the results on General Position (Chapter IV), and by the Homotopy Extension Property for polyhedral pairs, $f \simeq f_1$ via a homotopy of pairs, where $f_1|\partial M$ is a non-degenerate P. L. map. Again by General Position, $f_1 \simeq f_2$ via a homotopy fixed on ∂M, where f_2 is a P. L. map with $f_2(\text{Int } M) \subseteq \text{Int } Q$ and where $f_2|\text{Int } M$ is in general position. In particular, $\dim(S_2(f_2) \cap \text{Int } M) \leq 2m-q$.

Write f for f_2, and let $X_o = \text{cl}(S_2(f) - S_2(f) \cap \partial M)$. By the Engulfing Theorem 7. , there exists a compact P. L. subspace C of M such that $X_o \subseteq C \searrow C \cap \partial M$ and $\dim C \leq (2m-q) + 1$. By the same theorem, there exists a compact P. L. subspace D of Q such that $f(C) \subsetneq D \searrow D \cap \partial Q$ and $\dim D \leq 2m-q+2$. By General Position, there exists a P. L. homeomorphism $h: Q \longrightarrow Q$, fixed on $f_2 C \cup \partial Q$, such that $\dim[(hD - (fC) \cup \partial Q) \cap fM] \leq (2m-q+2) + m-q \leq 2m-q-1$. Therefore, $f^{-1}(hD) = C \cup X \cup Y$, where $\dim X \leq 2m-q-1$ (because f is non-degenerate) and $Y \subsetneq \partial M$.

Letting $C = C_1$, $hD = D_1$, $X = X_1$, $Y = Y_1$, we can define inductively $C_i, X_i, Y_i \subsetneq M$ and $D_i \subsetneq Q$ such that $X_o \subsetneq C_i \searrow C_i \cap \partial M$, $D_i \searrow D_i \cap \partial Q$, and $f^{-1}(D_i) = C_i \cup X_i \cup Y_i$, where $Y_i \subsetneq \partial M$ and $\dim X_i \subsetneq 2m-q-i$. The inductive step combines the first step and the inductive argument used in Theorem 8.1. (At each step, the Y_i's are ignored.)

Assume now that Q is compact. Let K and L triangulate M and Q respectively so that $f: K \longrightarrow L$ is simplicial and C_k and D_k are triangulated as subcomplexes, where k is an integer such that $X_k = \emptyset$. Then $S_2 f \subsetneq C_k \cup \partial M$, $C_k \searrow C_k \cap \partial M$, $D_k \searrow D_k \cap \partial Q$, $f^{-1} D_k = C_k \cup Y_k$, so that $f^{-1}(D_k \cup \partial Q) = C_k \cup \partial M$. Let $N_1 = N(\partial M \cup C_k; K'')$ and $N_2 = N(\partial Q \cup D_k; L'')$, where K'' and L'' are 2nd derived subdivisions so that $f: K'' \longrightarrow L''$ is still simplicial. Then $f^{-1} N_2 = N_1$. Moreover, $N_1 \searrow \partial M \cup C_k \searrow \partial M$ and $N_2 \searrow D_k \cup \partial Q \searrow \partial Q$, so by uniqueness of regular neighborhoods and existence of boundary collars, $N_1 \cong \partial M \times I$ and $N_2 \cong \partial Q \times I$. In fact, N_1 and N_2 may be realized as the images of boundary collars in M and Q respectively. Using these collars and adjoining to each a second "inner collar", we may construct homotopies $F_t : M \longrightarrow M$ and $G_t : Q \longrightarrow Q$ with the following properties: F_o = identity, F_1 is a P. L. homeomorphism $M \longrightarrow \overline{M - N}$, $F_t(\partial M) \subseteq N_1$ all t; G_o = identity, G_1 maps $cl(Q-N_2)$ homeomorphically onto Q and carries N_2 into ∂Q, and $g_t(\partial Q) = \partial Q$ for all t.

Let $f_3 = G_1 \circ f \circ F_1 \simeq G_1 \circ f \circ F_o \simeq G_o \circ f \circ F_o = f$. These homotopies are all homotopies of pairs $(M, \partial M)$ in $(Q, \partial Q)$; i. e., $G_1 f F_t(\partial M) \subseteq g_1 f N_1 \subseteq G_1 N_2 = \partial Q$ and $G_t f F_o(\partial M) \subseteq G_t(\partial Q) \subseteq \partial Q$. Clearly, f_3 is the required P. L. embedding.

It remains to consider the case in which Q is not compact. Choose the C's and D's as above, and let Q^* be a regular neighborhood of $f_2 M \cup D_k$ in Q meeting ∂Q regularly. Let $P_1 = Q^* \cap \partial Q$, $P_2 = Fr\, Q^*$. Then $D_k \searrow D_k \cap P_1$ and $f_2(\partial M) \subseteq P_1$. Let K and L triangulate M and Q^* so that $f: K \longrightarrow L$ is simplicial and C_k and D_k are triangulated as sub-complexes. Let K" and L" be barycentric 2nd derived subdivisions. Let $N_1 = N(C_k \cup \partial M; K")$, $N_2 = N(D_k \cup P_1; L")$. Then as $f: K" \longrightarrow L"$ is simplicial, $f^{-1}(N_2) = N_1$. Also, $f^{-1}(P_2) = \emptyset$.

Now, $N_2 \searrow P_1 \cup D_k \searrow P_1$, so N_2 is a regular neighborhood of P_1 in Q^*. Also, $N_2 \cap P_2$ is a regular neighborhood of ∂P_2 in P_2 (as it is a derived neighborhood). As in the compact case, we want to use uniqueness of regular neighborhoods to conclude that $(N_2; N_2 \cap P_2) \cong (P_1 \times I, \partial P_1 \times I)$. (We still have $N_1 \cong \partial M \times I$, of course.)

Let $C_1: \partial Q^* \times I \longrightarrow Q^*$ be a boundary collar. Let $C_2: \partial P_2 \times I \longrightarrow P_2$ be a boundary collar. Let $C_3: \partial(P_1 \times I) \times I \longrightarrow P_1 \times I$ be a boundary collar. Let $\varepsilon > 0$ be such that $P_1 \times [0, \varepsilon] \subsetneq C_3([(P_1 \times 0) \cup (\partial P_1 \times I)] \times I)$. Define $c: P_1 \times [0, \varepsilon] \longrightarrow Q^*$ to be the following composite

$$P_1 \times [0, \varepsilon] \xrightarrow{c_3^{-1}} [(P_1 \times 0) \cup (\partial P_1 \times I)] \times I \xrightarrow{(c_1 \cup c_2) \times \text{id.}} \partial Q^* \times I \xrightarrow{c_1} Q^*.$$

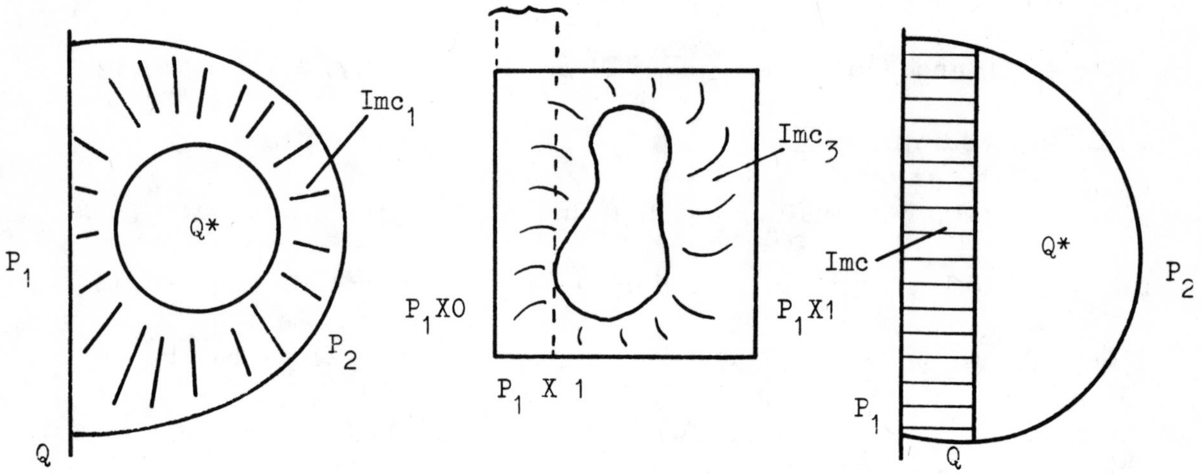

Then it follows from results in the sections of Chapter IV on uniqueness of regular neighborhoods that there exists a P. L. homeomorphism

$(N_2; N_2 \cap P_2) \cong (P_1 \times [0, \varepsilon], \partial P_1 \times [0, \varepsilon]) \cong (P_1 \times [0, 1], \partial P_1 \times [0, 1])$.

Now define $f_3: M \longrightarrow Q^*$ by letting f_3 be the composite with P. L. homeomorphisms:

$$M \xrightarrow{\alpha} cl(M - N_1) \xrightarrow{f} cl(Q^* - N_2) \xrightarrow{\beta} Q^*.$$

As in the compact case, we can choose α and β so that $f \cong f_3$ via a homotopy of pairs, $(M, \partial M) \longrightarrow (Q^*; P_1) \subseteq (Q, \partial Q)$. This completes the proof.

Note. A separate argument for the compact case would have been unnecessary, had we developed the regular neighborhood theory for regular neighborhoods of non-compact P. L. subspaces of a P. L. space.

3. Embedding into a non-bounded manifold.

Definition. Let $f: X \longrightarrow Y$ be a continuous map of topological spaces. Then $B(f)$, the branch locus of f, consists of all those points of X no neighborhood of which is embedded by f.

Suppose $f: M \longrightarrow Q$, M compact, is a non-degenerate P. L. map of P. L. manifolds (or spaces). Then $B(f)$ is a P. L. subspace of M, $B(f) \subseteq S_2(f)$, and $\dim B(f) \lneqq \dim S_2(f)$. For let K and L triangulate M and Q respectively, with $f: K \longrightarrow L$ simplicial. If $x \in B(f)$, let $x \in \mathring{\sigma}$, $\sigma \in K$. Then the open star $\mathring{st}(Q; K)$ contains points y, z, $y \neq z$, with $f(y) = f(z)$. Suppose $y \in \mathring{\tau}_1$ and $z \in \mathring{\tau}_2$, where $\sigma < \tau_1$ and $\sigma < \tau_2$. Then $\tau_1 \neq \tau_2$ because f is non-degenerate. But $f\tau_1 = f\tau_2$ because f is simplicial. Also, neither τ_1 nor τ_2 equals σ, because f is non-degenerate. Therefore $\sigma \subseteq B(f)$ and τ_1 and τ_2 are contained in $S_2(f)$.

Theorem 8.3. Let M^m be a compact P. L. manifold, $\partial M \neq \emptyset$. Let Q^q be a P. L. manifold without boundary. Suppose that $q-m \geq 2$ and $(M, \partial M)$ is $(2m-q-1)$-connected. Then if $f: M \longrightarrow Q$ is a continuous map, f is homotopic to a P. L. embedding, f'.

Proof. Let f be homotopic to f_1, where f_1 is non-degenerate and $\dim S_2(f_1) \leq 2m-q$. Let K and L be triangulations of M and Q respectively, so that $f_1 : K \longrightarrow L$ is simplicial. Let K' be a first derived subdivision of K with each simplex starred at $\hat{\sigma}$ so that if $\dim \sigma_1 \geq 1$, $f_1\sigma_1 = f_1\sigma_2$, then $f_1\hat{\sigma}_1 \neq f_2\hat{\sigma}_2$.

Now let K_o be the 2m-q-1 skeleton of K, and let K_1 be the simplices of K' which do not meet $|K_o|$. Then $K_1 = \{\hat{\sigma}_1 \ldots \hat{\sigma}_r | \sigma_1 < \ldots < \sigma_r$ and $\dim \sigma_1 \geq 2m-q\}$. Therefore $K_1 \cap S_2(f_1) = \{\hat{\sigma} | \sigma \in S_2(f_1)$ and $\dim \sigma = 2m-q\}$. Hence $K_1 \cap B(f) = \emptyset$ so there exists a neighborhood U of $|K_1|$ in $|K|$ such that $f_1 | U$ is an embedding, because $f | K_1$ is an embedding and each point of K_1 has a neighborhood embedded by f.

Now M-U is a compact set not meeting K_1. Hence there is a derived neighborhood N_1 of K_o such that $M-U \subseteq N_1 \setminus K_o$.

Now let $c: \partial M \times I \longrightarrow M$ be a boundary collar. Then $(M, c(\partial M \times [0,1)))$ is (2m-q-1)-connected, and so, from engulfing theorems [Chapter 7], there is a P. L. homeomorphism $h: M \longrightarrow M$ with $N_1 \subset h(\text{Im } c)$. So $\overline{M - h(\text{Im } c)} \subset U$. But $M \cong \overline{M - h(\text{Im } c)}$ by a homeomorphism homotopic to the identity. Composing with $f_1 | \overline{M-h(\text{Im } c)}$ gives the required embedding.

Chapter IX: Concordance and Isotopy

1. Introduction.

Definition. A proper concordance of M in Q is a P.L. embedding $F: M \times I \longrightarrow Q \times I$ with $F^{-1}(Q \times 0) = M \times 0$, $F^{-1}(Q \times 1) = M \times 1$, $F^{-1}(\partial Q \times I) = \partial M \times I$. F is a concordance between F_0 and F_1, where $F(x, t) = (F_t x, t)$, $t = 0, 1$. F is said to be fixed on the boundary if $F | \partial M \times I = (F_0(\partial M) \times 1$.

Definition. Two proper embeddings f and g are said to be (properly) concordant if there exists a concordance between them.

In this chapter we consider the question of when concordance implies isotopy. For example, concordance does not in general imply isotopy when the codimension (dim Q - dim M) is two. For example, the "slice knots" of classical knot theory are precisely the knots cobordant to the trivial knot.

The main positive results that we shall prove are the following two about a proper concordance F of M in Q fixed on the boundary, M compact.

Theorem 9.1. If dim Q - dim $M \geq 3$, then there exists an ambient isotopy H of $Q \times I$, fixed on $\partial(Q \times I)$, such that $H_1 \circ F$ is level preserving.

Theorem 9.2. If dim Q - dim $M \geq 3$, then there exists an ambient isotopy H of $(Q \times I)$, fixed on $(Q \times 0) \cup (\partial Q \times I)$, such that $H_1 \circ F = F_0 \times 1$.

2. Relative Second Derived Neighborhoods.

Let $K_o \subseteq K_1 \subseteq K_2$ be finite simplicial complexes. Then let $N(K_1 - K_o; K_2) = \{\sigma \in K_2 \mid \sigma < \tau$ for some simplex τ meeting $K_1 - K_o\}$. This subcomplex is called the simplicial neighborhood of K_1 mod K_o in K_2.

Let $K_1' \subseteq K_2'$ be first derived. Let K_2^* be obtained from K_2' by starring the simplices of $K_2' - K_1'$ in order of decreasing dimension. We may obtain a second derived K'' from K_2^* by starring all the simplices of K_1^* $(= K_1')$ in order of decreasing dimension. If $A \in K_2^* - K_1^*$, $\text{link}(A; K_2^*) \cap K_1^* = \emptyset$ or a single simplex. So the same is true of $\text{link}(A; K_2^*) \cap (\overline{K_1^* - K_o^*})$, as $\overline{K_1^* - K_o^*} = (\overline{K_1 - K_o})^*$ is full in K_2^*. Moreover, $|N(K_1^* - K_o^*; K_2^*)| = |N(K_1'' - K_o''; K_2'')|$.

Lemma 9.3. Suppose that $K_o \subseteq K_1 \subseteq K_2$, K_i full in K_{i+1}, $i = 1, 2$. Suppose that if $A \in K_2 - K_1$, $\text{link}(A; K_2) \cap (\overline{K_1 - K_o})$ is $\emptyset$ or a single simplex. Then $N = N(K_1 - K_o; K_2) \searrow (\overline{K_1 - K_o})$.

Proof. Let $\{A_i\}$ be the simplices of N not meeting $K_1 - K_o$, in order of decreasing dimension. For each i, $\text{link}(A_i; K_2) \cap (\overline{K_1 - K_o})$ = a single simplex C_i which meets $K_1 - K_o$. By fullness $N = \bigcup_i A_i C_i$. Let $N_j = (\overline{K_1 - K_o}) \cup (\bigcup_{j \geq i} A_j \cdot C_j)$. Then $\text{cl}(N_i - N_{i+1}) = A_i \cdot C_i$. $(A_i C_i) \cap N_{i+1} \supseteq \dot{A}_i C_i$. $(A_i C_i) \cap (N_{i+1}) \subseteq (A_i C_i) \cap (\overline{K_1 - K_o}) \cup \left(\bigcup_{j \geq i+1} (A_i C_i \cap A_j C_j)\right)$ $\subseteq \dot{A}_i C_i$. So $(A_i C_i) \cap (N_{i+1}) = \dot{A}_i C_i$. So $N_i \searrow N_{i+1}$. Therefore $N \searrow \overline{K_1 - K_o}$.

Lemma 9.4. With the conditions of Lemma 9.3, suppose K_1 and K_2 a-re manifolds and $K_o \subseteq \partial K_1$. Then $N(K_1 - K_o; K_2)$ is a manifold of the same dimension as K_2.

Proof. By induction on the dimension of K_2. Let $N = N(K_1 - K_o; K_2)$, and let $A \in N$. If A meets $K_1 - K_o$, then $\text{link}(A; N) = \text{link}(A; K_2)$, a sphere or ball.

Suppose $A \cap (K_1 - K_o) = \emptyset$. Then $\text{link}(A; N) = N[\text{link}(A; K_2) \cap K_1 - \text{link}(A; K_2) \cap K_o; \text{link}(A; K_2)]$. For $\sigma \in \text{Link}(A; N) \Longleftrightarrow \sigma A \in N \Longleftrightarrow \sigma < \rho$, $A\rho \in K_2$ and $\rho \cap (K_1 - K_o) \neq \emptyset \Longleftrightarrow$ $\sigma \in N[L \cap K_1 - L \cap K_o; L \cap K_2]$, $L = \text{link}(A; K_2)$.

Now $L \cap K_o \subseteq L \cap K_1 \subseteq L$ satisfy the hypotheses of this lemma. For certainly each of these complexes is full in the next. If $B \in L$, $\text{link}(B; L) \cap (L \cap (\overline{K_1 - K_o})) = \text{link}(B, L) \cap (\overline{K_1 - K_o}) = \text{link}(AB; K_2) \cap (K_1 - K_o) = \emptyset$ or a single simplex. If $A \in K_o$, then $L \cap K_1 = \text{link}(A; K_1)$ is a submanifold of the manifold L and $L \cap K_o \subseteq \text{link}(A; \partial K_1)$ is contained in the boundary. If $A \notin K_1$, $L \cap K_1 = L \cap (\overline{K_1 - K_o})$, as $K_o \subseteq \partial K_1$, so $L \cap K_1 = \rho$, a single simplex. Since A is a face of a simplex meeting $K_1 - K_o$, $\rho \cap K_o$ is a subcomplex of ρ not equal to ρ and so lies in $\partial\rho$.

Therefore by induction $\text{link}(A; N)$ is a manifold of the appropriate dimension. By Lemma 9.3, $\text{link}(A; N) \searrow L \cap (\overline{K - K_o}) = \rho \searrow 0$ if $A \notin K_1$. If $A \in K_o$, $\text{link}(A; N) \searrow \text{link}(A; N) \cap (\overline{K - K_o}) = \text{link}(A; K_1) \searrow 0$. So $\text{link}(A; N)$ is a collapsible manifold and so is a P. L. ball.

3. The Main Lemma.

Lemma 9.5. Let $F: B^m \times I \longrightarrow Q^q \times I$, B^m and m-ball, be a proper concordance which is fixed on the boundary. Suppose $q-m \geq 3$. Let U be an open neighborhood of $F_o B^m$ in Q. Then there exists an ambient isotopy H of $(Q \times I)$, fixed on $(Q \times 0) \cup (\partial Q \times I)$, such that $H_1 \circ F(B^m \times I) \subseteq U \times I$.

Picture:

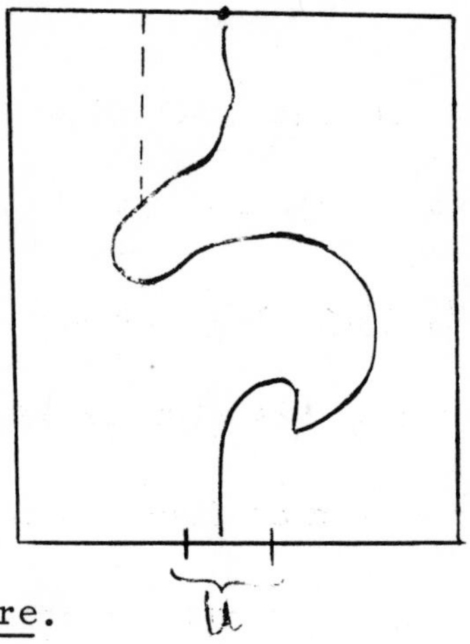

Before.

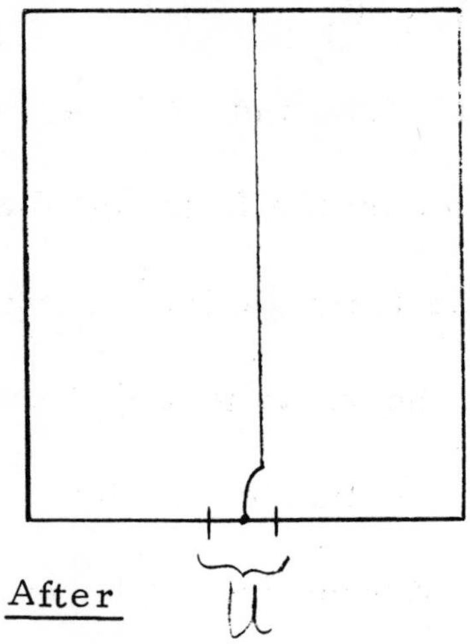

After

The main idea is to construct "walls" (dotted line) and then to push the concordance back behind the walls. That is, we find W_i such that $Fr\, W_i$ is not overshadowed by W_i and use these to "push the concordance back" until it eventually looks like the 2nd picture.

Proof.of Lemma 9.5. From the chapters on General Position and Sunny Collapsing, there is a P. L. homeomorphism $h: Q \times I \longrightarrow Q \times I$, level preserving and ambient isotopic to 1 by an arbitrarily small ambient isotopy, such that $hF(B \times I)$ sunny collapses to $hF((B \times 0) \cup (\partial B \times I))$. Let $X = hF(B^m \times I)$, $X_o = hF((B^m \times 0) \cup (\partial B \times I))$. We may assume by choosing h near enough to 1 that there is a neighborhood V of $F_o B^m$ in Q such that $X_o \subseteq V \times I \subseteq h(U \times I)$.

Let $K_o \subseteq K$ be triangulations of $X_o \subseteq X$ and let J be a triangulation of Q such that the inclusion embeds K linearly in $J \times I$ and such that there is a sequence $K = K_r \searrow^{es} K_{r-1} \searrow^{es} \cdots \searrow^{es} K_o$ with shadow $K_i \cap |K| \subseteq K_{i-1}$.

Let αK and βJ be subdivisions such that if $p_i : Q \times I \longrightarrow Q$ is projection on the first coordinate, then $p_1 | K: \alpha K \longrightarrow \beta J$ is simplicial. It follows from the last section of Chapter V, already quoted, that h above may be chosen so that $p_1 | K$ is non-degenerate; this also follows directly from the sunny collapse. So let $\alpha'' K$ and $\beta'' J$ be 2nd derived subdivisions with $p_1 | K: \alpha'' K \longrightarrow \beta'' J$ still simplicial. Let $\tau : Q \times I \longrightarrow I$ be projection on the 2nd coordinate. Let $\psi_i : \alpha'' K \longrightarrow \mathbb{R}_+$ be the linear map defined by setting $\psi_i(v) = 0$ if v is a vertex of $\alpha'' K_i$ and $\psi_i(v) = 1 + \tau(v)$ if v is a vertex of $\alpha'' K - \alpha'' K_i$. Then $\psi_i^{-1}(0) = \alpha'' K_i$, as $\alpha'' K_i$ is full in $\alpha'' K$. In particular, $\psi_o^{-1}(0) \subseteq V \times I$. Hence there exists $0 < \varepsilon < 1$ such that $\psi_o^{-1}[0, \varepsilon] \subseteq V \times I$.

Let $W_i = \psi_i^{-1}[0, \varepsilon]$. Then W_i is a derived neighborhood of $\alpha'' K_i$ in $\alpha'' K$. $W_r = W = X$. (See picture following this proof.)

Claim: Shadow(W_i) $\cap$ W $\subseteq$ $\mathrm{Int}_W W_i$.

Suppose $x \in W_i$, $y \in W$, and x overshadows y. Choose $\sigma, \tau \in \alpha''(K)$, $x \in \mathring{\sigma}$ and $y \in \mathring{\tau}$. Then $p_1\sigma = p_1\tau$, and $\sigma \neq \tau$ because $p_1|K$ is non-degenerate. Let $\sigma = \rho\sigma_1$, $\rho \in \alpha''K_i$, $\sigma_1 \cap \alpha''K_i = \emptyset$. Let $\tau = \rho'\tau_1$, where $p_1\rho' = p_1\rho$ and $p_1\tau_1 = p_1\sigma_1$. Since shadow $K_i \cap K \subseteq K_{i-1} \subseteq K_i$, $\rho' \in \alpha''K_i$. For each vertex v of σ_1, $\psi_i(v)$ is not less than the value of ψ_i or the vertex v' of τ_1 with $p_1v' = p_1v$. Moreover, $\psi_i(v) > \psi_i(v')$ unless $v = v'$. Therefore $\psi_i(x) > \psi_i(y)$ unless $\sigma_1 \neq \tau_1$. So it suffices to show that $\sigma_1 \neq \tau_1$.

If $A \in \alpha''K - \alpha''K_i$, then link(A; $\alpha''K$) $\cap$ $\alpha''K_i \neq \emptyset$ or the first derived B' of a single simplex B of $\alpha'K_i$. So as $p_1|K$ embeds B', no point of B' overshadows any other. Therefore if $\sigma_1 = \tau_1$, $\rho = \rho'$ and so $\sigma = \tau$, a contradiction.

Notation: If $S \subseteq J \times I$, let $\overset{\frown}{S} = S \cup$ {pts. lying above pts. of S}.

Let $Y_i = W_i \cup \overline{\mathrm{Fr}_W W_i}$. $Y_o \subset V \times I$. $Y_r = W_r = X$. We are going to throw Y_i onto Y_{i-1}. Suppose $K_i = K_{i-1} + A + aA$. Let $N = N(\alpha''(aA) - \alpha''(a\dot{A}); \alpha''K)$. Outside N, $\psi_i = \psi_{i-1}$. N is an (m+1)-manifold and $N \searrow aA$.

Consider $\overset{\frown}{N}$. (See 2nd picture following this proof.) Then $\overset{\frown}{N} \searrow \overset{\frown}{N} \cap (Q \times I) \cong p_1N = N[p_1(a\dot{A}) - p_1(aA); p_1(\alpha''K)] \searrow p_1(aA)$. Since p_1 embeds Aa, this shows that $\overset{\frown}{N} \searrow 0$.

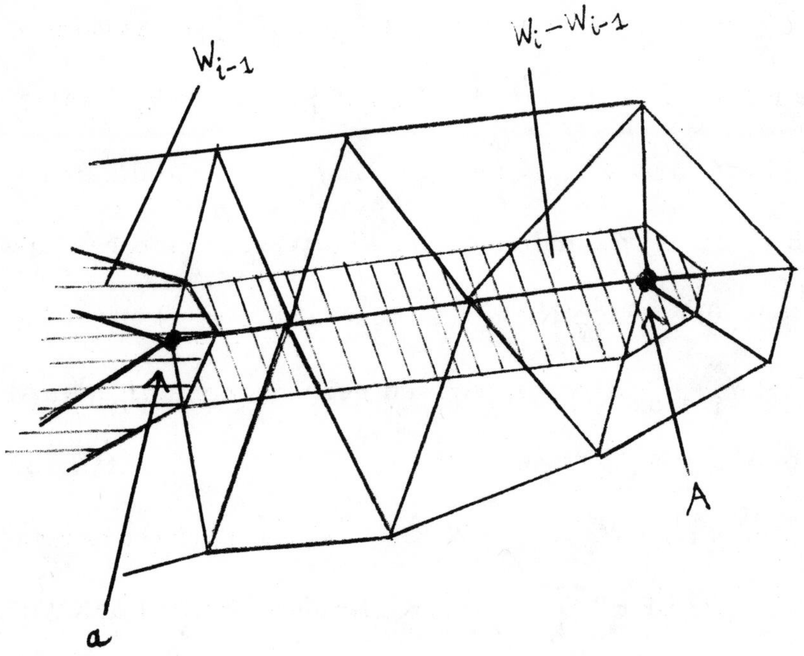
W_{i-1}
$W_i - W_{i-1}$
A
a

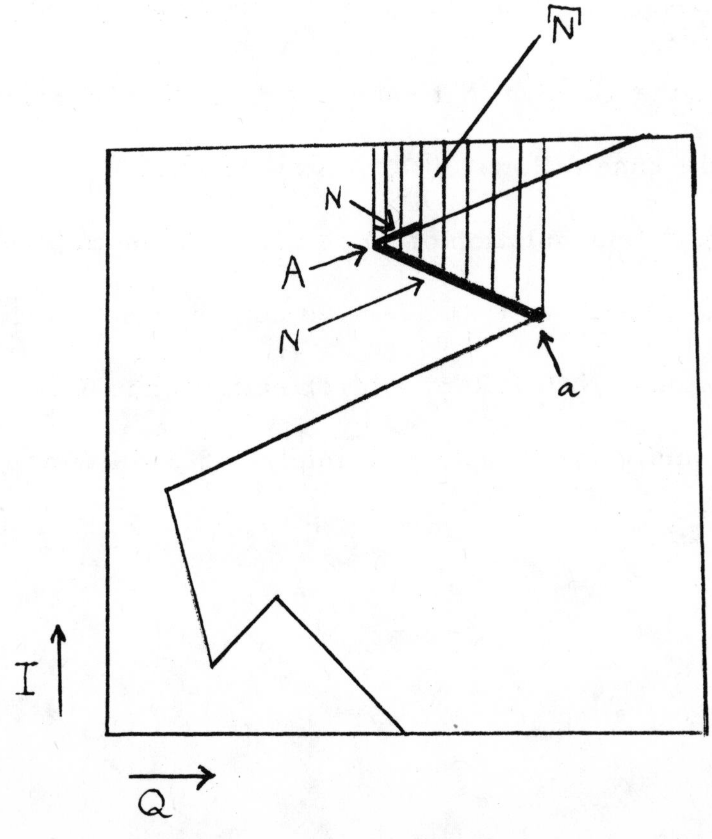
$\overline{N}$
N
A
N
a
I
Q

$W_i \cap N$ is a derived neighborhood of $\alpha''(aA)$ in N, an (m+1)-ball. Similarly, $W_{i-1} \cap N$ is a derived neighborhood of $\alpha''(aA)$ in N and so is an $\overline{m+1}$-ball.

Now $\partial(W_i \cap N) = (Fr\, W_i \cap N) \cup [W_i \cap N \cap (Q \times 1)] \cup [W_i \cap Fr_W N]$. If $A \in Q \times 1$, $\partial N = [N \cap (Q \times 1)] \cup Fr_W N$, $N \cap (Q \times 1)$ = a derived neighborhood of either A mod $\dot{A}$ or of aA mod $a\dot{A}$ in $W \cap (Q \times 1)$. So $N \cap (Q \times 1)$ is an n-ball. If $A \notin Q \times 1$, $\partial N = Fr_W N$. In either case $Fr_W N$ is an m-manifold. $W_i \cap Fr\, N = W_{i-1} \cap Fr\, N$ = a derived neighborhood of $\alpha''(aA)$ in $Fr\, N$ = an m-ball. So $W_i \cap N \searrow [(Fr\, W_i) \cap N] \cup [W_i \cap N \cap (Q \times 1)]$. So

$$
\begin{aligned}
Y_i \cap \overline{N} &= (W_i \cup \overline{Fr_W W_i}) \cap \overline{N} \searrow \overline{Fr\, W_i \cap N} \cup W_i \cap N \cap (Q \times 1) \\
&\searrow [\overline{Fr\, W_i \cap N} \cap (Q \times 1)] \cup [W_i \cap N \cap (Q \times 1)] \\
&\cong p[Fr\, W_i \cap N \cup W_i \cap N \cap (Q \times 1)] \\
&= \text{an n-ball} \searrow 0.
\end{aligned}
$$

Similarly $Y_{i-1} \cap \overline{N} \searrow Y_{i-1} \cap \overline{N} \cap (Q \times 1) \searrow 0$.

Let us assume for the moment that each Y_i is an (m+1)-manifold. That this is actually the case follows (Cor. 9.6.1).

Subdivide $J \times I$ (J = triangulation of Q) so that $\overline{N}$, the K_i, etc., ... are all subcomplexes. Let R be a 2nd derived neighborhood of $\overline{N}$ in this subdivision. Then because $\overline{N} \searrow 0$, R is a (q+1)-ball. Since $\overline{N} \cap (Q \times 1) \searrow 0$, and since we may assume $Q \times 1$ was a subcomplex of $J \times I$, $R \cap (Q \times 1)$ is also a ball, of dim q.

$R \cap Y_i$ is a 2nd derived neighborhood of $Y_i \cap \overline{N}$ in Y_i, and so is an (m+1)-ball, by uniqueness of regular neighborhoods. Similarly, $(R \cap Y_i) \cap (Q \times 1)$ is an m-ball. Similarly, $R \cap Y_{i-1}$ is an (m+1)-ball and $(R \cap Y_{i-1}) \cap (Q \times 1)$ is an m-ball. Also, $Y_i \cap \mathrm{Fr}\, R = Y_{i-1} \cap \mathrm{Fr}\, R$ because $\psi_i = \psi_{i-1}$ outside of N.

But $q-m \geq 3$. Therefore all of the following ball pairs are unknotted: $[R \cap Y_i \cap (Q \times 1) \subseteq R \cap (Q \times 1)]$, $[R \cap Y_i \subseteq R]$, $[R \cap Y_{i-1} \cap (Q \times 1) \subseteq R \cap (Q \times 1)]$, $[R \cap Y_{i-1} \subseteq R]$. Moreover, $Y_i \cap \mathrm{Fr}\, R$ is a face of $Y_i \cap R$ and $Y_i \cap \mathrm{Fr}\, R \cap (Q \times 1)$ is the boundary of $Y_i \cap R \cap (Q \times 1)$. Hence we may find an ambient isotopy of R, fixed on $\mathrm{Fr}\, R = \mathrm{cl}(\partial R - R \cap (Q \times 1))$, throwing $R \cap Y_i$ onto $R \cap Y_{i-1}$. Extending by the identity outside of R, we get an ambient isotopy H_i of $Q \times I$, fixed on $(Q \times 0) \cup (\partial Q \times I)$, which throws Y_i onto Y_{i-1}.

Hence by induction there is an ambient isotopy H of $Q \times I$, fixed on $(Q \times 0) \cup (\partial Q \times I)$, with $H_1 X \subseteq X_0 \subseteq V \times I$. Recall that $X = h \circ F(B^m \times I)$. Define H' by $H'_t = h^{-1} H_t h$. Then H' is the required ambient isotopy.

<u>Lemma 9.6</u>. If N is a submanifold of $Q \times I$ with $p_1 | N$ an embedding and $N \cap (Q \times 1) \subseteq \partial N$, then $\overline{N}$ (= N and points lying above N) is a manifold.

<u>Proof.</u> By induction on dim N. If dim N = 0, this lemma is clear. Now suppose $x \in \overline{y}$, $y \in N - \mathbf{N} \cap (Q \times 1)$. Then there exists a closed P. L. ball V of y in N with $V \cap (Q \times 1) = \emptyset$. Then $\overline{V}$ is P. L. homeomorphic to $V \times I$. So $\overline{N}$ is a manifold near x; i.e., there is a neighborhood of x in

$\overline{N}$ which is P. L. homeomorphic to a ball. Say, on the other hand, $x \in N \cap (Q \times 1)$. Triangulate $\overline{N}$ so that $p_1 | \overline{N}: \overline{N} \to Q$ is simplicial for some triangulation of Q. Then $\text{link}(x; \overline{N}) = \overline{\text{link}(x; N)}$. Link(x; N) is a ball meeting $Q \times 1$ in a subset of its boundary. So by induction, $\overline{\text{link}(x; N)}$ is a manifold. But $\overline{\text{link}(x; N)} \searrow \text{link}(x; N) \searrow 0$, and so is a ball. So $\overline{N}$ is a manifold.

Corollary 9.6.1. Let $X \subseteq Q \times I$ be a properly embedded manifold. Let $K \subseteq X$ be a polyhedron. Let W be a derived neighborhood of K in X, with $(\text{shadow } W) \cap X \subseteq \text{Int}_X W$. Then $W \cup \overline{\text{Fr}_X W}$ is a manifold.

Proof. If $N = \text{Fr}_X W$, then $p_1 | N: N \to Q$ is an embedding. $\partial N = N \cap \partial X \supseteq N \cap (Q \times 1)$. Therefore $\overline{N}$ is a manifold. Clearly, $N \subseteq \partial \overline{N}$. So $W \cup \overline{\text{Fr}_X W}$ is the union of two manifolds of the same dimension which meet in a submanifold, of one lower dimension, contained in the boundary of each.

Therefore it is a manifold.

4. Proof of Theorems 9.1 and 9.2.

Theorem 9.2. Let $F: M^m \times I \longrightarrow Q^q \times I$ be a proper concordance, fixed on ∂M, M compact and $q-m \geq 3$. Then there is an ambient isotopy H of $Q \times I$, fixed on $(Q \times 0) \cup (\partial Q \times I)$, such that $H_1 \circ F = F_0 \times \mathrm{id}$.

Proof. By induction on dim Q. Let K triangulate M. Let $\{A_i\}_1^N$ be the simplices of $K - \partial K$, in order of increasing dimension. Let K $K_i = \overline{A_1 \cup \dots \cup A_i}$ (= these simplices and all their faces). We shall define ambient isotopies $h^{(i)}$ of $Q \times I$, fixed on $(Q \times 0) \cup (\partial Q \times I)$, such that $h_1^{(i)} F$ is fixed on a neighborhood of K_i.

Suppose that h is defined. $F' = h^{(i-1)} \circ F: M \times I \longrightarrow Q \times I$ is fixed on a neighborhood U of K_{i-1} and on ∂M. Triangulate $M \times I$, $Q \times I$, and Q so that $M \times I \xrightarrow{F'} Q \times I \xrightarrow{p_1} Q$ are simplicial, and so that $K_{i-1} \times I$ and $A_i \times I$ are triangulated as subcomplexes of $M \times I$.

Now $(p_1 \circ F')(K_{i-1} \times I) = F_0'(K_{i-1})$. Let N_1 and N_2 be 2nd derived neighborhoods of $A_{i-1} \times I$ in $M \times I$ and of $F_0'(K_{i-1})$ in Q, respectively, such that $N_1 \subseteq U \times I$ and $N_1 = (p_1 \circ F')^{-1} N_2$. Then clearly $N_1 = N_3 \times I$, where $N_3 = (F_0')^{-1} N_2$.

Let $M^* = \mathrm{cl}(M - N_3)$, and let $Q^* = \mathrm{cl}(Q - N_2)$. Let $F^* = F' | M^* \times I: M^* \times I \longrightarrow Q^* \times I$. $A_i \cap N_3$ is a derived neighborhood of ∂A_i in A_i, because of the ordering of the A_i. Put $B = A_i \cap M^* = \overline{A_i - A_i \cap N_3}$, a ball.

Let V be a regular neighborhood of F_oB in Q^*. By Proposition 9.5, there exists an ambient isotopy k of $Q^* \times I$, fixed on $(Q^* \times 0) \cup (\partial Q^* \times I)$, such that $k_1 F(B \times I) \subseteq (\text{Int } V) \times I$. By uniqueness of regular neighbourhoods V is a q-ball. By the unknotting of balls, there exist an ambient isotopy k' of $V \times I$, fixed on $(V \times 0) \cup (\partial V \times I)$, such that $k_1' k_1 F' | B \times I = F_o \times \text{id} | B \times I$. We may extend k' to all of $Q^* \times I$ by letting it be constantly the identity outside $V \times I$. Put

$$F'' = k_1' k_1 F^* : M^* \times I \longrightarrow Q^* \times I.$$

Now triangulate to make $M^* \times I \xrightarrow{F''} Q^* \times I \xrightarrow{p_1} Q$ simplicial, with $B \times I$ triangulated as a subcomplex. Subdivide so that F'' and p are simplicial and let N_4 be the 2nd derived neighborhood of F_oB in Q^*. Let $N_5 = (p_1 F'')^{-1} N_4$. Let $N_6 = (F_o^{-1} N_4) \times I$. $N_7 = F_o^{-1}(N_4)$ is a derived neighborhood of B in M^*, and so N_6 is a derived neighborhood of $B \times I$ in $M^* \times I$. So is N_5.

Lemma 9.7. There is an ambient isotopy k'' of $M^* \times I$, fixed on $(M^* \times 0) \cup (\partial M^* \times I)$, such that $k_1'' N_5 = N_6$.

(Proof postponed until later.)

Proof of 9.2 continued. Let k'' be as in Lemma 9.7. By the isotopy extension theorem, there exists an ambient isotopy k''' of $Q^* \times I$, fixed on $(Q^* \times 0) \cup (\partial Q^* \times I)$, so that $k_1''' F'' N_5 = F'' N_6$.

Put $F''' = (k_1''')^{-1} F''$. Then $(p_1 F''')^{-1} N_4 = N_6 = N_7 \times I$. Consider $F''' | Fr_{M^*} N_7 \times I$. Then the image of this map is contained in $(Fr_{Q^*} N_4) \times I$, as in fact $N_7 = F_o^{-1}(N_4)$. Moreover, $\partial(Fr_{M^*}N_7) = (Fr_{M^*}N_7) \cap \partial M^*$. Therefore we are in the situation in which the inductive hypothesis applies to give us an ambient isotopy $k^{(4)}$ of $(Fr_{Q^*}N_4) \times I$, fixed on the bottom and sides, such that $k_1^{(4)}F'''|Fr_{M^*}N_7 \times I = F_o \times id|Fr_{M^*}N_7 \times I$. The $k^{(4)}$ extends to all of $Q^* \times I$ to an ambient isotopy also called $k^{(4)}$, fixed on $(Q^* \times 0) \cup (\partial Q^* \times I)$.

By the unknotting of balls, there exists an ambient isotopy $k^{(5)}$ of $Q^* \times I$, fixed on $(Q^* \times 0) \cup (\partial Q^* \times I) \cup (Q^* - N_4) \times I$, so that $k_1^{(5)} \circ k_1^{(4)}F'''|N_7 \times I = (F_o \times id)|N_7 \times I$. This completes the proof of the inductive step because the relation of ambient isotopic is an equivalence relation.

To start the induction put $q = 3$, $m = 0$. Then a simple version of the same proof work: there are no neighborhoods in which to straighten out the concordance, and so an inductive hypothesis is not necessary.

Proof of Lemma 9.7. N_5 is a derived neighborhood of $B \times I$ in $M^* \times I$. $N_7 = N_5 \cap (M^* \times 0)$, $N_6 = N_7 \times I$, $N_5 \cap (\partial M^* \times I) = N_6 \cap (\partial M^* \times I)$. Now let $\alpha: M^* \times I \longrightarrow M^* \times I$ be a P. L. homeomorphism throwing $(M^* \times 0) \cup (\partial M^* \times I)$ onto $M^* \times 0$. αN_5 and αN_6 are regular neighborhoods of αB, meeting the boundary regularly. Let $N_8 = \alpha N_5 \cap (M^* \times 0) = \alpha N_6 \cap (M^* \times 0)$. By the uniqueness of regular neighborhoods, there is an ambient isotopy H of $M^* \times I$ such that $H_1(\alpha N_5) = N_8 \times I$. Let H' be the ambient isotopy of $M^* \times I$ defined by $H'_t = [H_t|(M^* \times 0)] \times 1$. Then

$H'_1(N_8 \times I) = (N_8 \times I)$ and $(H')^{-1}H$ is an ambient isotopy fixed on $M^* \times 0$. Similarly, we may throw αN_6 onto $N_8 \times I$, keeping $M^* \times 0$ fixed. Composing these two isotopies and conjugating with α gives an ambient isotopy of $M^* \times I$, fixed on $(M^* \times 0) \cup (\alpha M^* \times I)$, throwing N_5 onto N_6.

Theorem 9.1. Suppose $F: M^m \times I \longrightarrow Q^q \times I$ is a proper concordance fixed on ∂M, M compact, $q-m \geq 3$. Then there exists an ambient isotopy H of $Q \times I$, fixed on $\partial(Q \times I)$, such that $H_1 F$ is level preserving.

Proof. By 9.2, there exists an ambient isotopy K of $Q \times I$, fixed on $(Q \times 0) \cup (\partial Q \times I)$, with $K_1 F = F_0 \times \mathrm{id}$. Let k be the ambient isotopy of Q defined by $K_t(x, 1) = (k_t x, 1)$. Let $\phi: I^2 \longrightarrow I$ be a P. L. map with $\phi(s, 1) = s$, $\phi(1, t) = t$, $\phi(s, 0) = \phi(0, t) = 0$ for all $s, t \in I$. Define $K': (Q \times I) \times I \longrightarrow (Q \times I) \times I$ by putting $K'(x, s, t) = (k_{\phi(s,t)}(x), s, t)$. Then K' is the identity on $(\partial Q \times I \times I) \cup (Q \times 0 \times I) \cup (Q \times I \times 0)$. $K'_0: Q \times I \longrightarrow Q \times I$ is the identity. K'_t agrees with K_t on $Q \times 1$. Define $H: Q \times I \times I \longrightarrow Q \times I \times I$ by $H = (K')^{-1}K$. Then H is fixed on $\partial(Q \times I)$ and $H_1 F = (K'_1)^{-1} K_1 F = (K'_1) F_0 \times \mathrm{id}$ is certainly level preserving.

5. Extensions.

In this section we quote without proof two further results along these lines. The first follows from what we have already shown, the second can be proven using a result on unknotting of cones quoted at the end of the chapter on Sunny Collapsing and Unknotting.

9.7. If $F: M^m \times I \to Q^q \times I$ is a proper concordance and if $q-m \geq 3$ and M is compact, then there is a ambient isotopy H of $Q \times I$, fixed on $Q \times 0$, with $H_1 F = F_o \times id$, and an ambient isotopy K_1 fixed on $Q \times \partial I$, with $K_1 F$ level preserving.

9.8. If $K_o \subseteq K$ are polyhedra and $f: K \times I \to Q^q \times I$ is a concordance with $f^{-1}(Q \times 0) = K \times 0$, $f^{-1}(Q \times 1) = K \times 1$, $f^{-1}(\partial Q \times I) = K_o \times I$, and if $\dim K \leq q-3$ and $\dim K_o \leq q-4$, then there exists an ambient isotopy H of $Q \times I$, fixed on $Q \times 0$, with $H_1 F = F_o \times id$. If F is fixed on K_o, then one can insist that H be fixed on $\partial Q \times I$.

Chapter X: Some Unknotting Theorems

1. An Unknotting Theorem Keeping the Boundary Fixed.

Theorem 10.1. Let M^m and Q^q be compact P.L. manifolds, and let $f, g: M \to Q$ be two proper P.L. embeddings. Suppose that f is homotopic to g relative ∂M. Then if $q-m \geq 3$, M is $(2m-q+1)$-connected, and Q is $(2m-q+2)$-connected, then f and g are ambient isotopic keeping ∂Q fixed.

Proof. Let $F: M \times I \to Q \times I$ be a (level-preserving) homotopy of f to g. $F|\partial M \times I = (f \times id)|\partial M \times I$. Now, $(M \times I)$ is $q(m+1)-(q+1) = 2m-q+1$ connected, and $Q \times I$ is $q(m+1)-(q+1)+1$ connected. Hence by the embedding theorem 8.1 , F is homotopic relative $\partial(M \times I)$ to $F': M \times I \to Q \times I$, a proper embedding. Therefore F' is a proper concordance of f to g, fixed on ∂M. By Theorem 9.2, there is an ambient isotopy H of $Q \times I$, fixed on $(Q \times 0) \cup (\partial Q \times I)$, with $H_1 F' = F'_0 \times id$. Then $H|(Q \times 1) \times I$ is an ambient isotopy, fixed on $\partial(Q \times 1)$, throwing g onto $f = [H|Q \times 1 \times I]_1 \circ g$.

Corollary 10.1. Any k-connected closed manifold M unknots in E^{2m-k+1}; i.e., any two embeddings of M in E^{2m-k} are isotopic, if $k \leqslant m-2$.

Corollary 10.1.2: If Q is k-connected, then the elements of $\pi_r(Q)$ can each be represented by a unique isotopy class of embedded spheres, provided that

$$r \leq \min(q-3, \frac{q+k-2}{2}).$$

2. An Unknotting Theorem Moving the Boundary

Theorem 10.2. If $f, g: M^m \longrightarrow Q^q$ are proper P. L. embeddings, M compact, f, g homotopic as maps of pairs $(M, \partial M) \longrightarrow (Q, \partial Q)$; and if $q-m \geq 3$, $(M, \partial M)$ is $(2m-q+1)$-connected, and if $(Q, \partial Q)$ is $(2m-q+2)$-connected, then f and g are ambient isotopic.

Note: As in 10.1, it suffices to show that f and g are properly concordant. Unfortunately, we have not proved an appropriate embedding theorem; we need to alter a homotopy to an embedding keeping $M \times \partial I$ fixed.

Proof. Let $F: M \times I \longrightarrow Q \times I$ be a (level preserving) homotopy of f to g, with $F_t(\partial M) \subseteq \partial Q$ for all t. We may assume that there is $\varepsilon > 0$, so that $F_t = F_o$ for $t \leq \varepsilon$ and $F_t = F_1$ for $t \geq 1-\varepsilon$. Applying general position first to $\partial M \times [\varepsilon, 1-\varepsilon]$ in $\partial Q \times [\varepsilon, 1-\varepsilon]$ and then to $M \times [\varepsilon, 1-\varepsilon]$ in $Q \times [\varepsilon, 1-\varepsilon]$ (this also uses the well-known homotopy extension property for polyhedra), we get a proper P. L. map $F': M \times I \longrightarrow Q \times I$, with the following properties:

1) $F'(x,t) = \begin{cases} (fx, t) & t \leq \varepsilon \\ (gx, t) & t \geq \varepsilon \end{cases}$

2) $S_2(F') \subseteq M \times [\varepsilon, 1-\varepsilon]$.

3) $\dim[S_2(F') \cap (\partial M \times I)] \leq 2m-q$

4) $\dim(S_2 F') \leq 2(m+1) - (q+1) = 2m-q+1$.

Now $(M \times \text{Int } I, \partial(M \times \text{Int } I))$ is $(2m-q+1)$-connected and $(W \times \text{Int } I, \partial(Q \times \text{Int } I))$ is $(2m-q+2)$-connected. Notice that S_2F' is a compact polyhedron in $M \times \text{Int } I$. By an argument we have used several times (see Engulfing Theorem 7.8 and the embedding theorem 8.2) there exist polyhedra C and D in $M \times \text{Int } I$ and $Q \times \text{Int } I$, respectively, such that $S_2 F' \subseteq C \searrow C \cap (\partial M \times \mathring{I})$, $D \searrow D \cap (\partial Q \times \text{Int } I)$, and $(F')^{-1} D = C$.

Triangulate so that F' is simplicial and $S_2(F'), C, D, C \cap (\partial M \times I)$, and $D \cap (\partial M \times I)$ are all subcomplexes. Take 2nd deriveds keeping F' simplicial. Let N_2 = 2nd derived neighborhood of D in $Q \times I$. Let $N_1 = (F')^{-1} N_2$, a 2nd derived neighborhood of C in $M \times I$. Then $F' | \text{cl}(M \times I - N_1) \longrightarrow \text{cl}(Q \times I - N_2)$ is a proper embedding. To complete the proof it suffices to find P. L. homeomorphisms $h: \text{cl}(M \times I - N_1) \longrightarrow M \times I$ and $k: \text{cl}(Q \times I - N_2) \longrightarrow Q \times I$ with $h | M \times \partial I = \text{id}$ and $k | Q \times \partial I = \text{id}$. For then $kF'h^{-1}$ is a proper concordance from f to g. Now $N_1 \searrow C \searrow C \cap (\partial M \times I)$. So N_1 is a regular neighborhood of $C \cap (\partial M \times I)$, meeting the boundary regularly. Let $N_3 = N_4 \cap (\partial M \times I)$. Let $c: \partial(M \times I) \times I \longrightarrow M \times I$ be a boundary collar. Then $c(N_3 \times I)$ is also a regular neighborhood of $C \cap (\partial M \times I)$, regular at the boundary. $c(N_3 \times I) \searrow c[(N_3 \times 1) \cup (\partial N_3 \times I)]$. So, by the uniqueness of regular neighborhoods, $N \searrow Fr(N)$. Let N_4 be a derived neighborhood of N_1. Then $M \times I$ and $\text{cl}(M \times I - N)$ are both regular neighborhoods of $\text{cl}(M \times I - N_4)$. So there is a P. L. homeomorphism $M \times I \longrightarrow \text{cl}(M \times I - N)$ which is the identity outside N_2.

A similar argument works for Q.

<u>Corollary 10.2.2.</u> If $(Q, \partial Q)$ is k-connected, an element of $\pi_r(Q, \partial Q)$ is representable by a <u>unique</u> isotopy class of properly embedded r-balls, provided that $r \leq \min(q-3, \frac{q+k-2}{2})$.

3. Unknotting in a Manifold without Boundary

Theorem 10.3. Say M^m is compact, $\partial M \neq \emptyset$, $\partial Q^q = 0$. Let $f, g: M \longrightarrow Q$ be P.L. embeddings, $f \simeq g$, $q-m \geq 3$. Suppose $(M, \partial M)$ is $(2m-q)$-connected. Then f and g are ambient isotopic.

Unfortunately, we cannot prove this theorem based only on preceding results because we did not prove a concordance implies isotopy theorem for concordances of a bounded manifold in a non-bounded manifold. Modulo this gap, the proof of 10.3 proceeds as follows:

Let $F: M \times I \longrightarrow Q \times I$ be a (level-preserving) homotopy of f to g. As in the proof of 10.2, we may assume that F is a P.L. map in general position and $S_2 F \subsetneq M \times \text{Int } I$, $(\dim S_2 F = 2m-q+1)$. Let $|K| = M \times I$ and $|Q| = Q \times I$ be triangulations such that $F: K \longrightarrow Q$ is simplicial. Let K' be a first derived of K such that $\dim \sigma \geq 1$ and $F\sigma = F\tau \Rightarrow F\hat{\sigma} \neq F\hat{\tau}$. Let $K_1 \subsetneq K$ be the 2m-q skeleton. Let L be the "dual skeleton" of K_1' in K, together with the top and bottom; i.e., the simplices of K' not meeting K_1', together with $(M \times 0) \cup (M \times 1)$ which we assume to be a subcomplex. Then F' embeds a neighborhood of L, U say, (see proof of embedding theorem 8.3). Engulf K_1 to $\partial M \times I$; i.e., let C be a polyhedron containing K_1 which collapses to $C \cap (\partial M \times I)$, with $C \subsetneq M \times \text{Int } I$. Let N be a derived neighborhood of C in $\partial M \times \mathring{I}$. Then then there exists a homeomorphism, fixed in $M \times \partial I$, $M \times I \cong \text{cl}(M \times I - N)$, a compact set not meeting K_1. Hence $\text{cl}(M \times I - N)$ is contained in a regular neighborhood of L not meeting K_1 (see proof of Theorem 7.9), $\tilde{N}$. On the other hand, U contains a regular neighborhood $\overline{N}$ of L. So $\overline{N} \cong \tilde{N}$, via a homeomorphism which leaves L pointwise fixed. Hence by compositing F with homeomorphisms, we get a concordance F' between f and g. Now apply the unproved concordance $\Longrightarrow$ isotopy theorem to deduce that f and g are ambient isotopic.

Chapter XI: Obstructions to Embedding and Isotopy

1. Linking Numbers.

If S^p, S^q are disjoint spheres in the sphere S^{p+q+1}, the linking number of S^p and S^q in S^{p+q+1} is defined to be equal to the degree of the map $S^p \longrightarrow S^{p+q+1} - S^q$, this latter being a homology p-sphere by Alexander duality. We shall only use the linking number reduced modulo 2 in this chapter, and so will not have to worry about signs and orientations.

Lemma 11.1. Let M, N, W be compact connected P. L. manifolds with dim W = dim M + dim N. Suppose that $\partial W = \bigcup_1^r S_j^{m+n-1}$, $\partial M = \bigcup_1^r S_j^{m-1}$, $\partial N = \bigcup_1^r S_j^{n-1}$ and suppose $f: M \longrightarrow W$, $g: N \longrightarrow W$ are proper P. L. maps in general position with $fS_j^{m-1} \subset S_j^{m+n-1}$, $gS_j^{n-1} \subset S_j^{m+n-1}$ for each j. Suppose $fM \cap gN = \emptyset$, and let L_j = linking number of fS_j^{m-1}, gS_j^{n-1} in S_j^{m+n-1} (mod 2). If $H^m(W, \partial W) = H^{m+1}(W, \partial W) = 0$, then $\sum L_j = 0$.

Proof. Consider the following commutative diagrams, all homology and cohomology having $\mathbb{Z}_2$ coefficients.

$$\begin{array}{ccc}
\sum_j H_{m-1}(S_j^{m-1}) & \xrightarrow{f_*} & \sum_j H_{m-1}(S_j^{m+n-1} - gS_j^{n-1}) \\
\Big\downarrow i_1 & & \Big\downarrow i_2 \\
H_{m-1}(M) & \xrightarrow{f_*} & H_{m-1}(W - gN)
\end{array}$$

$$\begin{array}{ccccc}
H_{m-1}(W - gN) & \overset{\cap w}{\underset{\cong}{\longleftarrow}} & H^{n+1}(W, \partial W \cup gN) & \overset{\delta}{\underset{\cong}{\longleftarrow}} & H^n(gN, g\partial N) = \mathbb{Z}_2 \\
\uparrow i_* & & \uparrow \delta & & \uparrow \delta \\
H_{m-1}(\partial W - g\partial N) & \overset{\partial w}{\underset{\cong}{\longleftarrow}} & H^m(\partial W, g\partial N) & \overset{\delta}{\underset{\cong}{\longleftarrow}} & H^{n-1}(g\partial N)
\end{array}$$

The left-hand isomorphism being given by Lefshetz duality and the right-hand ones from the exact cohomology sequences of $\partial W \subset N \cup \partial W \subset W$ and $\partial N \subset \partial W$. Now the right-hand vertical arrow maps the generator of $H^{n-1}(gS_j^{n-1})$ onto the generator of $H^n(gN, g\partial N)$ for each j. So the generator of $H_{m-1}(S_j^{m+n-1} - gS_j^{n-1})$ maps onto the generator of $H_{m-1}(W - gN)$ for each j. So in the first diagram, if ξ_j generates $H_{m-1}(S_j^{m-1})$, $\sum L_j = i_2 f_* \sum \xi_j = f_* i_1 \sum \xi_j = 0$ since $i_1 \sum \xi_j$ is a boundary.

<u>Intersections.</u> Let M^m, N^n, W^{m+n} be P. L. manifolds. Let $f: M \longrightarrow W$, $g: N \longrightarrow W$ be proper P. L. maps in general position. If $x \in fM \cap gN$, we can define an intersection number $\ell(x)$ as equal to the linking numbers (mod 2) of link(x, fM) and link(x, gN) in link(x, Q).

<u>Lemma 11.2.</u> If $M \cong N \cong S^n$, $W \cong S^{2n}$ and $fM \cap gN = \{x_1, x_2, \ldots, x_k\}$, then $\sum \ell(x_i) = 0$.

<u>Lemma 11.3.</u> If $M \cong N \cong B^n$, $W \cong B^{2n}$ and $fM \cap gN = \{x_1 \ldots x_k\}$, then $\sum \ell(x_i)$ = linking number of $f\partial M$, $g\partial N$ in ∂W.

<u>Proof.</u> Triangulate and remove the stars of the points $x_1, x_2, \ldots, x_k$. Applying Lemma 11.1 now gives the required result.

2. An Obstruction to Embedding and Isotopy.

Let $f: M^m \longrightarrow Q^q$ be a proper P. L. map in proper general position; i. e., $f|\partial M: \partial M \longrightarrow \partial Q$ is also in general position. Assume M is compact, and $m < q-1$. Triangulate M and Q, getting K and L such that $f: K \longrightarrow L$ is simplicial, and $K_o \subseteq K$ a full subcomplex triangulating $S_2 f$. Let K' and L' be formed by starring at the barycenters the simplices of $K-K_o$ and $L-fK_o$, in order of decreasing dimension. Then $f: K' \longrightarrow L'$ is still simplicial.

If $\sigma \in K_o$ is a $(2m-q)$-simplex, then there exists a unique $\sigma' \in K_o$, $\sigma' \neq \sigma$, with $f\sigma = f\sigma'$, as the triple points have dimension $3m-2q < 2m-q$. Let $S_1 = \text{link}(\sigma; K')$, $S_2 = \text{link}(\sigma'; K')$, $\Sigma = \text{link}(f\sigma; L')$, $\dim S_1 = m-(2m-q) - 1 = g-m-1 = \dim S_2$. Dim $\Sigma = 2(q-m) - 1$. Now, since $\dim \sigma = 2m-q = \dim \sigma'$, f embeds S_1 and S_2. Moreover, $S_1 \cap S_2 = \emptyset$. For if $\tau \in S_1 \cap S_2$, $\sigma\tau$ and $\sigma'\tau \in K'$ implies $\sigma, \sigma' \in \text{link}(\tau; K')$. But $\text{link}(\tau; K') \cap |K_o| =$ a single simplex ρ. Since f embeds ρ, this means $\sigma = \sigma'$, a contradiction.

Now, define $\emptyset_f(\sigma) =$ linking number of fS_1 and fS_2 in Σ, mod 2; i. e., $\emptyset_f(\sigma) \in Z_2$.

<u>Definition.</u> $$c(f) = \sum_{\substack{\sigma \in K_o \\ \dim \sigma = 2m-q}} \emptyset_f(\sigma) \cdot \sigma \in C_{2m-q}(M) \otimes Z_2 .$$ If $\dim K_o < 2m-q$, $c(f) = 0$.

Now, $c(f)$ is defined with respect to triangulations of M and Q. Let $\partial f = f|\partial M$ and let $c(\partial f)$ be defined with respect to the induced triangulation.

Lemma 11.4. $\partial c(f) = c(\partial f)$.

Proof. Suppose $\tau \in K_o$ and $\dim \tau = 2m-q-1$. Assume $\tau \notin \partial M$, and that there exist $\tau' \neq \tau$ and $f\tau' = f\tau$. Let $S_1 = \mathrm{link}(\tau; K')$, $S_2 = \mathrm{link}(\tau'; K')$, $\Sigma = \mathrm{link}(f\tau; L')$, $\dim S_1 = \dim S_2 = q-m$, $\dim \Sigma = 2(q-m)$. S_1, S_2, and Σ are spheres, and $S_1 \cap S_2 = \emptyset$, as above.

Let $g = f| S_1 \cup S_2$. Then $g(S_1) \cap g(S_2)$ consists entirely of vertices, for otherwise $\dim S_2 f > 2m-q$. Moreover, each point of intersection y determines a pair of vertices x and x' in S and S', respectively, such that $x\tau$ and $x'\tau'$ are in $S_2 f$. Conversely, if $\tau < \sigma \in S_2 f$, let x be vertex of σ not in τ. Then if σ' is a simplex such that $f\sigma = f\sigma'$, $\tau < \sigma'$ because, as $m < q-1$, the triple points of f have dimension at most $2m-q-2$. Thus the simplices $\sigma \in S_2 f$ such that $\tau < \sigma$ correspond to intersection points of gS_1 and gS_2.

Now say $x \in X_1$ and $x\tau \in S_2 f$. Then $\phi_f(x\tau)$ linking number of $f(\mathrm{link}(x\tau; K'))$ and $f(\mathrm{link}(x'\tau'; K'))$ in $\mathrm{link}(f(x\tau; L')$, where $x' \in S_2$ is the unique point such that $f(x') = f(x)$. But $\mathrm{link}(\tau x; K') = \mathrm{link}(x; S_1)$ and $\mathrm{link}(\tau' x'; K') = \mathrm{link}(x'; S_2)$ and $\mathrm{link}(f(x\tau); L') = \mathrm{link}(fx; \Sigma)$, as f is simplicial. Therefore $\phi_f(x\tau) = \phi_g(x)$.

Let $x_1, \ldots, x_q$ be the vertices of S_1 mapped by g to intersection points of $g(S_1)$ and $g(S_2)$. Then $\sum_{\substack{\sigma > \tau \\ \sigma \in S_2 f}} \phi_f(\sigma) = \sum_{i=1}^{q} \phi_g(x_i) =$ sum of the linking numbers (mod 2) of link$(y_i; gS_1)$ and link$(y_i; gS_2)$ in link$(y_i; \Sigma)$, $y_i = f(x_i)$. Since g is in general position (its double points are of dimension zero and it has no triple points), Lemma 11.3 implies that this sum is congruent to zero modulo 2.

Now, for $\tau \in K_o$, dim $\tau = 2m-q-1$, suppose there is no τ' with $f\tau = f\tau'$ but $\tau \neq \tau'$. Then suppose $\tau < \sigma$ and $\sigma \in S_2f$. Then there exists σ' such that $f\sigma = f\sigma'$ but $\sigma \neq \sigma'$. Since f embeds σ and σ', σ' has a face τ' such that $f\tau = f\tau'$. Therefore $\tau = \tau'$. Therefore if $\sigma_1, \ldots, \sigma_p$ are simplices of S_2f having τ as a face, p is even and we may suppose $f(\sigma_i) = f(\sigma_{i+1})$ for $i \equiv 1(2)$. By definition, $\phi_f(\sigma_i) = \phi_f(\sigma_{i+1})$, $i \equiv 1(2)$, $i \leq p-1$. So $\sum_{\substack{\sigma > \tau \\ \sigma \in S_2f}} \phi_f(\sigma) \equiv 0 \pmod 2$ in this case also.

Now suppose $\tau \in K_o$ and $\tau \in \partial M$ and there exists τ' such that $f\tau = f\tau'$, $\tau \neq \tau'$, and $\tau \in \partial M$. Let $B_1 = \text{link}(\tau; K')$, $B_2 = \text{link}(\tau'; K')$, $(q-m)$-balls. Let $B = \text{link}(f\tau; L')$, a $2(q-m)$-ball. Since τ is a principal simplex of $S_2(f) \cap \partial M$, ∂B_1 and ∂B_2 are embedded disjointly in ∂B. An argument similar to that for the first case, using Lemma 11.3 instead of Lemma 11.2 shows that $\sum_{\substack{\sigma > \tau \\ \sigma \in S_2f}} \phi_f(\sigma)$ = linking number of ∂B_1 and ∂B_2 in ∂B = $\phi_{\partial f}(\tau)$ (all modulo 2). Now $\partial c(f) = \sum_{\tau} \left(\sum_{\sigma > \tau} \phi_f(\sigma) \right) \cdot \tau$ where we sum only over simplexes of $S_2(f)$. But

$$\sum_{\sigma > \tau} \phi_f(\sigma) = 0 \text{ if } \tau \notin S_2(\partial f)$$
$$= \phi_{\partial f}(\tau) \text{ if } \tau \in S_2(\partial f).$$

So $\partial c(f) = c(\partial f)$. So $c(f)$ represents an element $\alpha(f) \in H_{2m-q}(M, \partial M; \mathbb{Z}_2)$ if ∂f is an embedding, $c(f)$ gives an element $\bar{\alpha}(f) \in H_{2m-q}(M; \mathbb{Z}_2)$.

Lemma 11.5. $\alpha(f)$ and $\bar{\alpha}(f)$ do not depend on the choice of triangulation.

Proof. Suppose $f: K \to L$ is simplicial, K_o is full in K with $|K_o| = S_2(f)$ and K', L' are obtained from K, L as above. Let σ be a $(2m-q)$-simplex of fS_2f. Now suppose αK: βL are subdivisions of K, L and $f: \alpha K \to \beta L$ is still simplicial, and let $\alpha' K, \beta' L$ be obtained by starring simplexes not in K_o, fK_o. Then pseudo-radial projection assures us that there is a P. L. homeomorphism $\text{link}(\sigma_1, \beta' L) \longrightarrow \text{link}(\sigma, L')$ sending $\text{link}(\sigma_1, f\alpha' K) \longrightarrow \text{link}(\sigma_1, fK')$. So $\phi_f(\sigma_1) = \phi_f(\sigma)$. Thus each principal simplex occurs with the correct coefficient and gives rise to the same homology class.

Lemma 11.6. If $f, g: M^m \to Q^q$, $m \leq q-2$, are proper P. L. maps in proper general position, and if $f \cong g$ as maps $(M, \partial M) \to (Q, \partial Q)$, then $\alpha(f) = \alpha(g)$. If $f|\partial M$ is an embedding and $f \cong g$ (rel ∂M), then $\bar{\alpha}(f) = \bar{\alpha}(g)$.

Proof. Let $F: M \times I \longrightarrow Q \times I$ be a level preserving homotopy between f and g. $F|M \times \partial I$ is in general position. Therefore, let $G: M \times I \to Q \times I$ be a P. L. map in proper general position which agrees with F on $M \times \partial I$.

Triangulate so that $M \times 0$, $M \times 1$, and $\partial M \times I$ are subcomplexes and G is simplicial. So $\partial c(F) = c(\partial F) = c[F|M \times 0] + c[F|M \times 1] + c(F|\partial M \times I)$.

Let $p_*: C(M \times I) \times Z_2 \longrightarrow C(M) \times Z_2$ be the map induced by projection, where C = simplicial chains with respect to this triangulation. Then $\partial p_* c(F) = c(f) + c(g) + p_*(c(F | \partial M \times I))$. The last is in $C(\partial M)$. Therefore $\alpha(f) = \alpha(g)$.

In the event that $F | \partial M \times I$ is $(f | \partial M) \times 1$, one may suppose G also has this property. Then $c(G | \partial M \times I) = 0$, so $\partial p_* c(G) = c(f) + c(g)$.

Note: In view of this lemma, we may view α as a map $\pi[(M, \partial M), (Q, \partial Q)] \longrightarrow H_{2m-q}(M; \partial M; Z_2)$.

Definition. Now suppose that $\partial M = \emptyset$ and $Q = E^q$. Then let $f, g: M \longrightarrow E^q$ be two embeddings of M in E^q. Then there is always a homotopy of f and g. Let $F: M \times I \longrightarrow E^q \times I$ be a P. L. homotopy of f and g in general position. Then $F | \partial(M \times I)$ is an embedding, so $\overline{\alpha}(F) \in H_{2m-q+1}(M \times I; Z_2)$ is defined. If F' is another homotopy of f and g, then $F \cong F'$ (rel $\partial(M \times I)$), so $\overline{\alpha}(F) = \overline{\alpha}(F')$. Let $p: M \times I \longrightarrow M$ be projection onto the first coordinate. Then define

$$d(f, g) = p_* \overline{\alpha}(F) \in H_{2m-q+1}(M; Z_2).$$

We call d(f, g) the "difference class" between f and g.

Lemma 11.7. If f and g are concordant, $d(f, g) = 0$.

Proof. Let F be a homotopy of f and g and G a concordance. Then $F \cong G$ (rel $\partial(M \times I) = M \times \partial I$). Therefore $\alpha(F) = \alpha(G) = 0$.

Lemma 11.8. If $h: M \longrightarrow E^q$ is an embedding, then

$$d(f, g) + d(g, h) = d(f, h).$$

Proof. Let $F: f \cong g$. Let $G: g \cong h$. Define $H: f \cong h$ by

$$H(x,t) = \begin{cases} F(x, 2t) & 0 \leq t \leq \frac{1}{2} \\ G(x; 2t-1) & \frac{1}{2} \leq t \leq 1 \end{cases} .$$

Then it is not hard to see that $\overline{\alpha}(H) = \overline{\alpha}(F) + \overline{\alpha}(G)$.

Remark. Say $f: M^m \to Q^q$ is a proper P. L. map in proper general position, and $2m-q = 0$. Then $\overline{\alpha}(f)$ is defined, since $2(m-1) - (q-1) = -1$, and $\overline{\alpha}(f) \in H_o(M; Z_2)$. However, it is clear from the definition that $\sum_{\sigma \in S_2 f} \phi_f(\sigma) = 0 \pmod 2$, M is triangulated with f simplicial. Therefore we may view $\overline{\alpha}(f) \in \tilde{H}_o(M; Z_2)$. Similarly, if $f, g: M^m \to E^q$ are embeddings $\partial M = \emptyset$ and $2m-q+1 = 0$, $d(f,g) \in \tilde{H}_o(M; Z_2)$. Note that this is consistent with the fact that M connected implies that M can be embedded in E^{2m} and any two embeddings of M in E^{2m+1} are isotopic.

3. Obstruction to Isotopy of Embeddings of a Manifold in Euclidean Space.

Suppose $f_o: M^m \to E^q$ is an embedding, M compact, $\partial M = \emptyset$. Then if $g: M \to E^q$ is an embedding, $d(f_o, g) \in H_{2m-q+1}(M; Z_2)$ depends only upon the isotopy class of g. For $d(f_o, f) = d(f_o, g) + d(g, f)$, and if g and f are isotopic, $d(g, f) = 0$. Then $g \to d(f_o, g)$ defines a map of isotopy classes of embeddings of M^m into E^q into $H_{2m-q+1}(M; Z_2)$.

Theorem 11.9. Let M^m be a k-connected closed manifold, $k \leq m-4$. Let $f_o: M \to E^{2m-k}$ be a P. L. embedding. Then $g \to d(f_o, g)$ defines a map of isotopy classes of embeddings onto $\tilde{H}_{k+1}(M; Z_2)$.

We first prove this theorem in a special case. Then we use this special case to prove the general result.

Let S^j and B^k denote a P. L. sphere and a P. L. ball of dimension j and k respectively.

<u>Lemma 11.10.</u> Let $f: S^0 \times B^s \longrightarrow B^{2s+1}$ be a proper P. L. embedding with $s \geq 3$. Then there exists a level preserving P. L. map $F: S^0 \times B^s \times 1 \longrightarrow B^{2s+1}$ in general position such that

(1) $F_o = f$

(2) F_1 is a P. L. embedding

(3) $F_t | S^0 \times \partial B^s = F_o | S^0 \times \partial B^s$, for all $t \in I$

and

(4) $\alpha(F) \in \tilde{H}_0(S^0 \times B^s; Z_2)$ is non-zero

<u>Proof.</u> Write $S^0 \times B^s = B_1 \cup B_2$. By general position, any map $g: B_1 \longrightarrow B^{2s+1} - fB_2$ with $g|\partial B_1 = f|\partial B_1$ is homotopic to a P.L. embedding keeping the boundary fixed. Homotopy classes of such maps are determined by elements of $\pi_s(B^{2s+1} - fB_2) = Z$. Choose g so that $gB_1 \cup fB_1$ determine a generator of $\pi_s(B^{2s+1} - fB_2)$. Define $F: (B_1 \cup B_2) \times 1 \longrightarrow B^{2s+1} \times 1$ by

(a) $F_o = f$

(b) $F_1 | B_1 = g$, $F_1 | B_2 = f$

(c) $F_t | (\partial B_1 \cup \partial B_2) = f | \partial B_1 \cup \partial B_2$, for all $t \in I$.

Now extend conically on each ball.

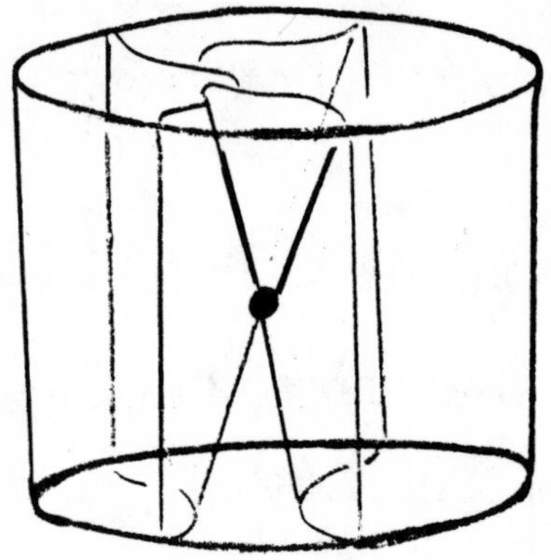

Then $\overline{\alpha}(F)$ = linking number of $F\,\partial(B_1 \times 1)$ and $F\,\partial(B_2 \times I)$ in $\partial(B^{2s+1} \times I)$ reduced mod 2, which is one by construction.

Let M be a regular neighborhood of an r-sphere, $\dim M = r+s$. Let $f: M \longrightarrow B^{r+2s+1}$ be a P. L. embedding with $s \geq 3$. Then there is a level preserving P. L. map $F: M \times I \longrightarrow B^{r+2s+1} \times I$ such that

(1) $F_o = f$

(2) F_1 is an embedding

(3) $F_t | \partial M = f | \partial M$ for all $t \in I$

(4) $\overline{\alpha}(F) \neq 0$ in $H_r(M; Z_2) = Z_2$.

Proof. The proof is by induction on r, keeping s fixed. When $r = 0$ this is simply Lemma 11.10.

The inductive step: Let $K \subset L$ triangulate $S^r \subset M$ with K full in L. Let N be the derived neighborhood of K in L. Then $M \cong N$.

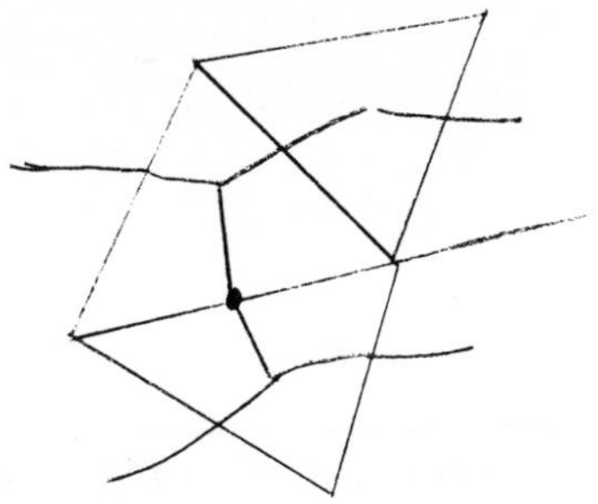

Let σ be an r-simplex of K. Let σ^* be the dual cell of σ in K'.

Notice that

(1) σ^* is an s-ball properly embedded in N;

(2) $N \cap \overline{\text{star}(\sigma, K)}$ is a regular neighborhood of σ^* in N meeting ∂N regularly;

(3) $N \cap \overline{\text{star}(\sigma, K)} \cap \overline{N - \text{star}(\sigma, K)}$ is a derived neighborhood of $\dot{\sigma}$ in $\dot{\sigma} \cdot \text{link}(\sigma, K)$, and so is P. L. homeomorphic to $S^{r-1} \times B^s$.

(1) and (3) are clear enough. To show (2): Let $\tau_1 \ldots \tau_N$ be the simplexes of $\dot{\sigma}$ in order of decreasing dimension. Then $N \cap \hat{\sigma}\dot{\tau}_i \text{link}(\sigma, K) \searrow N \cap \hat{\sigma}\dot{\tau}_i \text{link}(\sigma, K)$ by an elementary polyhedral collapse. Similarly, $\dot{N} \cap \hat{\sigma}\tau_i \text{link}(\sigma, K) \searrow \dot{N} \cap \hat{\sigma}\dot{\tau}_i \text{link}(\sigma, K)$ by an elementary (simplicial) collapse.

Let $h: N \longrightarrow M$ be a P. L. homeomorphism. Let $D = h\sigma^*$. $fD \cap \partial B^{r+2s+1} = f\partial D$. Now (B^{r+2s+1}, fD) is an unknotted ball pair, so there is an $\overline{s+1}$ ball E in B^{r+2s+1} with $\partial E = fD \cup (E \cap \partial B^{r+2s+1})$.

By general position we may assume that $\dim(E \cap f(M)) \leq (r+s) + (s+1) - (r+2s+1) = 0$. So $f^{-1}E = D \cup X$. X = a finite number of points. M is connected, so there is a polyhedron D' with $D \cup X \subset D' \searrow D$, $\dim(D'-D) \leq 1$.

We can assume $D' - D \subset \text{Int } M$. Now choose E' in B^{r+2s+1} with $E \cup fD' \subset E' \searrow E$, $\dim(E' - E) \leq 2$, $E' - E \subset \text{Int } B^{r+2s+1}$. By general position we may assume $E' \cap fM = fD'$. Now triangulate with D', E' as subcomplexes and f simplicial. Let N_1 = 2nd derived neighborhood of D' in M and N_2 = 2nd derived neighborhood of E' in B^{r+2s+1}. Then put $U_1 = N_1 \cap \partial M$, $U_2 = N_2 \cap \partial B^{r+2s+1}$, $V_1 = \text{Fr}_M N_1$, $V_2 = \text{Fr } N_2$, $W_1 = \text{cl}[\partial M - U_1]$, and $W_2 = \partial B^{r+2s+1} - \text{Int } U_2$. Then U_2, V_2, W_2 are P. L. $(r+2s)$-balls, $N_2, \text{cl}[B^{r+2s+1} - N_2]$ are $\overline{r+2s+1}$ balls. N_1, being a regular neighborhood of D in M is an $(r+s)$-ball and, from the above remarks on σ^* etc., $V_1 \cong S^{r-1} \times B^s$. N_1 and $\text{cl}(M-N)$ are $(r+s)$-balls.

By induction, there is a level preserving P. L. map $F' : V_1 \times I \longrightarrow V_2 \times I$ with

1) $F'_o = f | V_1 \times I$,
2) F'_1 = a P. L. embedding ,
3) $F'_t | \partial V_1 \times I = f | \partial V_1 \times I$, for all $t \in I$,
4) $\overline{\alpha}(F') \neq 0$ in $H_{r-1}(V_1 \times I; Z_2) = Z_2$.

Define $F : M \times I \longrightarrow B^{r+2s+1} \times I$ as follows: put

$$F_o = f,$$

$$F_t | \partial M = f | \partial M \quad \text{for all } t \in I,$$

$$F_1 | V_1 \times I = F'_1 .$$

Extend F_1 over

$$N_1 \times 1 \longrightarrow N_2 \times 1$$

$$\overline{M - N_1} \times 1 \longrightarrow \text{cl}[B^{r+2s+1} - N_2] \times 1$$

by conical extension. Then $S_2(F) \cong$ suspension of $S_2(F')$. Moreover, the linking numbers correspond and $\overline{\alpha}(F)$ = suspension of $\overline{\alpha}(F')$

$$\neq 0 \text{ in } H_r(M; Z_2).$$

Proof of Theorem 11.9. M is a compact k-connected closed manifold. $k \leq m-4$, $f_o: M \longrightarrow E^{2m-k}$ is a P. L. embedding. Let $\xi \in H_{k+1}(M; Z_2)$. Let $\eta \in \pi_{k+1}(M)$ be an element representing ξ. Let $i: S^{k+1} \longrightarrow M$ be a P. L. embedding representing μ [which exists by embedding Theorem 8.1]. Now $f_o iS^{k+1}$ is unknotted in E^{2m-k}, so bounds a $\overline{k+2}$ disc, D say, in E^{2m-k}. By general position assume $E \cap f_o(M)$ has dimension $\leq$ $(k+2)+m - (2m-k) = 2k-m+2 \leq k-2$. By the familiar argument used for example in proving the embedding theorems, we define inductively sets $C_i \subset M$, $D_i \subset E^{2m-k}$, $X_i \subset M$ with $C_i \searrow iS^{k+1}$, $D_i \searrow 0$, $f_o^{-1}D_i = C_i \cup X_i$, $\dim X_i < \dim X_{i-1}$. Eventually, for $i = R$ say, X_R is empty.

Now triangulate with f_o simplicial, C_k and D_k as subcomplexes, and let N_2 = 2nd derived neighborhood of D_k in E^{2m-k}. Let $N_1 = f_o^{-1}N_2$, a 2nd derived neighborhood of C_k in M. Now let $F: M \times I \longrightarrow E^{2m-k} \times I$ be such that $F = f_o \times 1$ outside N_1, F is in general position, F_1 is an embedding, $f_o = f$, $F(N_1 \times I) \subseteq N_2 \times I$, and $\overline{\alpha}(F|N_1 \times I)$ is the non-zero element of $H_{k+1}(N_1 \times I; Z_2)$. (in the notation of Lemma 11.1, $r = k+1$, $s = m-(k+1) \geq 3$, $r + 2s+1 = 2m-1$.) But clearly, $\overline{\alpha}(F) = J_* \overline{\alpha}(F|N_1 \times I)$, where $J: N_1 \times I \longrightarrow M \times I$ is inclusion; in fact, both elements are represented by the same chain. But $j_*: H_{k+1}(N_1 \times I; Z_2) \longrightarrow H_{k+1}(M \times I)$ maps the non-zero element onto ξ. So $d(F_1, f_o) = \xi$. Thus we have found a new embedding having the required "difference class" from f_o.

4. <u>Other Results</u>.

In this section we outline some more results that can be proven about obstruction to isotopy of embeddings.

I) Suppose M^m is a k-connected compact closed P. L. manifold, $k \leq m-4$, and suppose m-k is <u>even</u>. Suppose $f_o: M^m \longrightarrow E^{2m-k}$ is an embedding. Then the correspondence between isotopy classes of embeddings of M in E^{2m-k} and $H_{k+1}(M; Z_2)$ given in section 3 is also one-to-one.

II) Consider maps of an orientable closed manifold M^m in a manifold Q^q. Then one can develop an obstruction theory analogous to the above, but with coefficients in Z, provided q-m is odd. Then if M is orientable, k-connected and closed and $f_o: M \longrightarrow E^{2m-k}$ is an embedding, one gets a map from isotopy classes of embeddings of M in E^{2m-k} to $H_{k+1}(M; Z)$. For $k \leq m-4$, this map is one-to-one and onto.

III) Suppose $f: M \longrightarrow Q$ is in general position. Let $\mathbb{C}_f$ = mapping cylinder of $f = \dfrac{(M \times I) \cup Q}{\{(x,0) \sim f(x)\}}$. If σ is a (2m-q)-simplex of $S_2 f$, let σ' be such that $f\sigma = f\sigma'$, $\sigma' \neq \sigma$, and let $\phi_f(\sigma)$ = linking number (mod 2) of $f(\text{link}(\sigma; M))$ and $f(\text{link}(\sigma'; M))$ in $\text{link}(f\sigma; Q)$. Then let

$C(f) = \sum_{\sigma} \phi_f(\sigma)[\sigma \times I] \in C_*(\mathbb{C}_f) \times Z_2$, where $[\sigma \times I]$ denotes the chain one obtains from the usual triangulation of $\sigma \times I$ (or denotes a chain in <u>prismatic</u> homology theory). Then $\partial C(f) = C(f) \in C_*(M \times 0)$. So $C(f)$ represents $A(f) \in H_{2m-q+1}(C_f; M; Z_2)$, and $\partial A(f) = \alpha(f) \in H_{2m-g}(M)$.

Suppose $F: M \times I \longrightarrow Q \times I$ is a homotopy of f and g. Then the inclusions $(\mathbb{C}_f; M) \longrightarrow (\mathbb{C}_F; M \times I)$ and $(\mathbb{C}_g; M) \longrightarrow (\mathbb{C}_F; M \times I)$ are homotopy equivalences. So F induces an isomorphism $F_*: H_{2m-q+1}(C_f; M; Z_2) \longrightarrow H_{2m-q+1}(C_g; M; Z_2)$. $F_* A(f) = A(g)$. So A(f) depends on the homotopy class of f. In particular, if f is homotopic to an embedding, $A(f) = 0$.

If $\partial M = \partial Q = \emptyset$, $q-m \geq 3$, $2m-q \geq 1$, $\pi_i(\mathbb{C}_f; M) = 0$ for $i \leq 2m-q$, $\pi_i(M) = 0$ for $i \leq 3m-2q+2$, and $q-m$ is even, then $A(f) = 0$ implies f is homotopic to an embedding. If $q-m$ is odd, then there is an analogous theory over Z, and the analogous result is true.

If F is a homotopy of f and g, fixed on the boundary, say, we can use A(F) to measure the obstruction to getting an isotopy. In general, however, A(F) depends not only upon f and g but also upon the choice of F.

Chapter XII: Embedding Up to Homotopy Type

1. Introduction.

Theorem (Browder, Sullivan, Cassen): If $f: M^m \longrightarrow Q^q$ is a homotopy equivalence (M compact), $q-m \geq 3$, $\partial M = \emptyset$, and if $i_*: \pi_1(\partial Q) \longrightarrow \pi_1(Q)$ is an isomorphism, then f is homotopic to an embedding.

Corollary. Let K^k be a finite simplicial complex, M^m a closed P. L. manifold, Q^q a P. L. manifold without boundary. Suppose $q-m \geq 3$, $q-k \geq 3$, $\emptyset: M \longrightarrow K$ is a homotopy equivalence, and the following diagram (of continuous maps) is homotopy commutative:

$$\begin{array}{ccc} M^m & \xrightarrow{\quad f \quad} & Q^q \\ & {\scriptstyle \emptyset} \searrow & \cup\!\! \mid \\ & & K^k \end{array}$$

Then f is homotopic to an embedding.

Proof. Let N be a regular neighborhood of K in Q. By general position, $\pi_i(N; N-K) = 0$ for $i \leq 2$. The generalized annulus theorem implies that $N-K \cong \partial N \times [0, \infty]$, and so $N-K$ has ∂N as a deformation retract. Therefore $\pi_1(\partial N) \longrightarrow \pi_1(N)$ is an isomorphism. $\emptyset: M \longrightarrow N$ is a homotopy equivalence, as $N \searrow K$. Hence the theorem applies to $\emptyset$.

In this chapter we are going to find a condition on $f: M \longrightarrow Q$ which implies the existence of a homotopy commutative diagram as in the corollary.

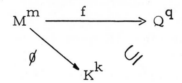

Definition. Let $f: X \longrightarrow Y$ be a continuous map of topological spaces. Let $\mathbb{C}_f$ = mapping cylinder of $f = \dfrac{(X \times I) \cup Y}{\{(x,0) \sim f(x)\}}$. Identify $X \subsetneq \mathbb{C}_f$ by identifying $x \in X$ with $(x, 1)$. Then define $\pi_i(f) = \pi_i(C_f; X)$.

Theorem 12.1: Let $f: K^k \longrightarrow Q^q$ be continuous, K a finite simplicial complex, $\partial Q = \emptyset$, $k \leq q-3$. Suppose $\pi_i(f) = 0$ for $i \leq 2k-q+1$. Then there is a homotopy commutative diagram in which K' is a finite simplicial complex, $\emptyset$ a (simple) homotopy equivalence, and $\dim K' \leq k$:

$$\begin{array}{ccc} K & \xrightarrow{\ f\ } & Q \\ & {\scriptstyle \emptyset}\searrow & \quad \subsetneq \\ & & K' \end{array}$$

2. Lemma on Homotopy Groups of a Triad.

Lemma 12.3. Let $K^k \subsetneq U \subsetneq M^m$, K a simplicial complex, U open, M a manifold, $\partial M = \emptyset$. Then if $\pi_i(M\text{-}K; U\text{-}K) = 0$ for $i \leq r$, then $\pi_i(M; M\text{-}K; U) = 0$ for $i \leq r+m-k-1$.

(Compare Blakers & Massey, Homotopy Groups of a Triad, Annals of Math, 55, (1953). Note that $\pi_i(U; U\text{-}K) = 0$ for $i \leq m-k-1$, by general position.)

Proof. Let $\alpha \in \pi_i(M; M\text{-}K; U)$, $i \leq r+m-k-1$. Let $f: (B, F_1; F_2) \longrightarrow (M, M\text{-}K, U)$ represent α, where B = i-ball, F_1 and F_2 are (i-1)-balls, $F_1 \cup F_2 = \partial B$, $F_1 \cap F_2 = \partial F_1 = \partial F_2$. Since $M\text{-}K$ and U are open, we may assume, after a small homotopy if necessary, that f is P. L. non-degenerate and $f(B)$ is in general position with respect to K.

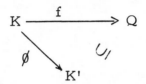

Let $X = f^{-1}(K)$. Then $X \cap F_1 = \emptyset$ and $\dim X \leq i+k-m$. For engulfing in a ball, codimension hypotheses are not necessary; so there a polyhedron $C \subseteq B$ with $X \subseteq C \searrow C \cap F_2$, $\dim C \leq i+k-m+1 \leq r$. Let P be a polyhedron in C with $P \cap f^{-1}K = \emptyset$ and $C - f^{-1}U \subset \mathrm{Int}_C P$. Let $P_0 = \mathrm{Fr}_C P$. So $fP_0 \subset U$. Now $(M-K, U-K)$ is r-connected and $\dim P \leq r$, so there is a homotopy of P, in M-K, fixed on P_0 carrying P into U-K. This extends to a homotopy of $B, F_1, F_2 \longrightarrow M, M-K, U$ carrying f onto f' where

(1) $(f')^{-1}K = f^{-1}K$,

(2) $f'(C) \subset U$.

Let R be a second derived neighborhood of $F_2 \cup C$ in B with $f'(R) \subset U$. $F_2 \cup C \searrow F_2$. So R is an i-ball in B, $R \cap \partial B$ is a face. So there is a strong deformation retraction $\beta : B \longrightarrow \overline{B-R}$. $f' \cong f'\beta : B, F_1, F_2 \longrightarrow M, M-K, U$ and $f'\beta(B) \subseteq M-K$. So $f'\beta$ represents zero in $\pi_i(M; M-K; U-K)$.

<u>Lemma 12.4.</u> Say $K^k \subseteq M^m$, $k \leq m-3$, K a finite complex, M a manifold. Let N be a regular neighborhood of K in M. Say $\pi_i(M, K) = 0$, $i \leq r$. Then $\pi_i(M, N, N-K) = 0$ if $i \leq r+m-k-1$.

<u>Proof.</u> The following sequence is exact:

$$\pi_i(M-K; N-K) \longrightarrow \pi_i(M, N) \longrightarrow \pi_i(M; M-K; N) \xrightarrow{\partial} \pi_{i-1}(M-K; N-K)$$

$$\pi_i(M,N) \cong \pi_i(M, K)$$

So $(M; M-K; N)$ i-connected, $i \leq r+1 \implies (M-K, N-K)$ $(i-1)$-connected $\implies$ $(N, M-K, N)$ is $(i-1)+m-k-1 \geq i+1$ connected. So by induction, the result follows. (Observe that in applying 12.3 we can replace N by N because $N \longrightarrow N$ is a homotopy equivalence.)

3. <u>Proof of Theorem 12.1.</u>

Let $f: X^k \longrightarrow Q^q$, $q \geq k+3$, $\partial Q = 0$, $\pi_i(f) = 0$ for $i \leq 2k-q+1$, X a finite complex. Then we want to find $X' \subseteq Q$, a subpolyhedron, $\dim X' \leq \dim X$, and a homotopy equivalence $\phi: X \longrightarrow X'$ such that $\phi: X \longrightarrow Q$ and $f: X \longrightarrow Q$ are homotopic.

We proceed by induction. Let $\{A_i\}$ = simplices of K, $|K| = X$, in order of increasing dimension. Let $K_i = \{A_j \mid j \leq i\}$, a subcomplex. Then we use the following inductive statement: f is homotopic to $f_i: K \longrightarrow Q$, where $f_i(K_i) \subseteq L_i \subseteq Q$, L_i a subpolyhedron, $\dim L_i \leq k$, and $f_i | K_i : K_i \longrightarrow L_i$ is a homotopy equivalence.

When $i = 0$, K_o = a point, and there is nothing to prove. So assume f_i has been constructed, and let $A = A_{i+1}$. Let N be a regular neighborhood of L_i in Q. Let $r = \dim A_i$. Then K_i contains the $(r-1)$-skeleton of K. Therefore $\pi_j(K; K_i) = 0$ for $j \leq r-1$, by the cellular approximation theorem (cf Spanier, Alg. Topology, p. 404).

Let C = mapping cylinder of f_i. Then

$$\longrightarrow \pi_j(K, K_i) \longrightarrow \pi_j(C, K_i) \longrightarrow \pi_j(C, K) \xrightarrow{\partial} \pi_{j-1}(K, K_i) \text{ is exact.}$$

$$\pi_j(C, K_i) = \pi_j(Q, L_i), \qquad \pi_j(C, K) = \pi_j(f_i).$$

So $\pi_j(Q, L_i) = 0$ for $i \leq \min(2k-q+1, r-1)$. If N is a regular neighborhood of L_i in Q, we have $\pi_j(Q, N, N-L_i) = 0$ for $j \leq \min[r+q-k-2, k]$. So $\pi_r(Q-L_i, N-L_i) \longrightarrow \pi_r(Q, N)$ is onto. ∂N is a strong deformation retract of $N-L_i$, so $\pi_r(\overline{Q-N}, \partial N) \longrightarrow \pi_r(Q, N)$ is onto. Furthermore, from the exact sequence of the triad,

$$\longrightarrow \pi_j(Q-L_i, N-L_i) \longrightarrow \pi_j(Q, N) \longrightarrow \pi_j(Q, N, N-L_i) \xrightarrow{\partial} \cdots ,$$

$\pi_j(Q-L_i, N-L_i) = 0$ whenever $j \leq \min(2k-q+1, r-1)$ <u>and</u> $j+1 \leq \min(r+q-k-2, k)$. So, in particular, whenever $j \leq 2r-2+1$. Let $A = A_{i+1}$ and choose $\phi: A, \partial A \longrightarrow \overline{Q-N}, \partial N$ such that $\phi \cong f_i | A: A, \partial A \longrightarrow Q, N$. By the embedding theorem 8.2, we may assume f to be an embedding. By the homotopy extension property $f_i \cong \psi: K \longrightarrow Q$ where $\psi | A = \phi A$, $\psi | K_i \cong f_i | K_i: K_i \longrightarrow N$. Then $\psi | K_i \cup A: K_i \cup A \longrightarrow N \cup \phi A$ is a homotopy equivalence. Now $N \searrow L_i$, so $N \searrow L_i \cup T$ where $\phi A \cap N \subset T$, $\dim T \leqslant k$. So $N \cup \phi A \searrow L_i \cup T \cup \phi A = L_{i+1}$ say. If $\alpha: N \cup \phi A \longrightarrow L_{i+1}$ is a corresponding deformation retraction define $f_{i+1} | K_{i+1} = \alpha\phi$ and using the homotopy extension property extend f_{i+1} over the whole of K with $f_{i+1} \cong f$.

This completes the inductive step.

Handle-Body Theory and the s-Cobordism Theorem

Introduction.

A cobordism is a manifold W with boundary the disjoint union $\partial W = \partial_+ W \cup \partial_- W$. An h-cobordism W satisfies the further requirements $\partial_+ W \subset W$ and $\partial_- W \subset W$ are homotopy equivalences.

The method of Smale consists of representing a cobordism as the union of handles and sliding these handles around to obtain a product structure on certain h-cobordisms of dimension ≥ 6. That is, for such an h-cobordism W, there is a P. L. homeomorphism of W onto $\partial_- W \times I$, written $W \cong \partial_- W \times I$.

In this process an obstruction called torsion occurs naturally. An h-cobordism with no torsion is called an s-cobordism. Alternatively, an s-cobordism is defined as a cobordism satisfying the requirements: $\partial_+ W \subset W$ and $\partial_- W \subset W$ are simple homotopy equivalences.

A simple definition of simple homotopy equivalence is given as the equivalence relation on compact polyhedra generated by collapsing $(K \searrow L)$ and by P. L. equivalence $(K \cong L)$. For example, the finite sequence $K_1 \searrow K_2 \nearrow K_3 \cong K_4$ defines a simple homotopy equivalence of K_1 and K_4. With any such sequence we can associate a sequence of maps of one term into the next, the composition map is well-defined up to homotopy and is called a simple homotopy equivalence.

The object of these lectures is to obtain the following

Theorem: If W is an s-cobordism, $\dim W \geq 6$, then $W \cong \partial_- W \times I$.

1. Suppose W^n is given and suppose $i: \partial B^r \times B^{n-r} \longrightarrow \partial_+ W$ is a PL embedding. Let $W' = W \cup_i B^r \times B^{n-r}$, then we say W' is got by attaching an r-handle to W. W' is still regarded as a cobordism with $\partial_- W' = \partial_- W$, $\partial_+ W' = \partial W' - \partial_- W'$. We will frequently be attaching several handles simultaneously. Suppose $i_1, i_2, \ldots, i_k : B^r \times B^{n-r} \longrightarrow \partial_+ W$ are PL embeddings with disjoint images. Then we can stick all the handles corresponding to $i_1, i_2, \ldots, i_k$ on at once, say

$$W' = W \cup_{i_1} B_1^r \times B_1^{n-r} \cup_{i_2} B_2^r \times B_2^{n-r} \cup \ldots \cup_{i_k} B_k^r \times B_k^{n-r} ,$$

and we say W' is obtained from W by attaching r-handles.

A standard handle body decomposition of W is a sequence $W_0 \subset W_1 \subset \ldots \subset W_{n+1}$ where $W_0 \cong \partial_- W \times I$, we insist that W_{i+1} is obtained from W_i by attaching i-handles and $W_{n+1} \cong W$. The main question of the theory may be stated: what handle body decompositions give the same manifold?

<u>Lemma 1</u>. Every cobordism W has a standard decomposition.

<u>Proof</u>. Let K be a simplicial complex triangulating W with K_0 a subcomplex triangulating $\partial_- W$. Let $L_0 = K_0$, $L_i = K_0 \cup$ ((i-1)-skeleton of K) and write $W_i = N(L_i'', K'')$, the simplicial neighborhood of the 2nd derived L_i'' of L_i in the 2nd derived K'' of K.

Now W_0 is a regular neighborhood of $\partial_- W$ in W (Chapter II) but by the collar neighborhood theorem (Chapter I) there is a regular neighborhood of ∂W in W, PL homeomorphic to $\partial_- W \times I$ and so by the uniqueness of regular neighbourhoods. $W_0 \cong \partial_- W \times I$. The proof will be completed after establishing the following assertions.

<u>Assertion:</u> $W_i = \bigcup_{\sigma \in L_i} \overline{St}(\hat{\sigma}, K'')$ where $\hat{\sigma}$ = barycentre of σ. (1)

Let A be an i-simplex of K, then

$$\overline{St}(\hat{A}, K'') \cap W_i = \overline{St}(A, K'') \cap N(\dot{A}_i, K'') . \qquad (2)$$

Let L = { simplexes of K' whose vertices are barycentres of simplexes having A as a face } = $\{\hat{B}_1 \hat{B}_2 \ldots \hat{B}_r \mid A < B_1 < B_2 < \ldots < B_r\}$. Alternatively, we can write $B_i = AC_i$ with $C_i \in$ link(A, K), then the map $\hat{B}_i \longrightarrow \hat{C}_i$ induces a PL homeomorphism $L \longrightarrow$ link(A, K) called pseudo-radial projection.

We can make the same construction again; let p: link$(\hat{A}, K'') \longrightarrow \dot{A} L$ be the pseudo-radial projection defined by $\widehat{AC} \longrightarrow \hat{C}$ for $C \in$ link$(\hat{A}, K')$ (2)

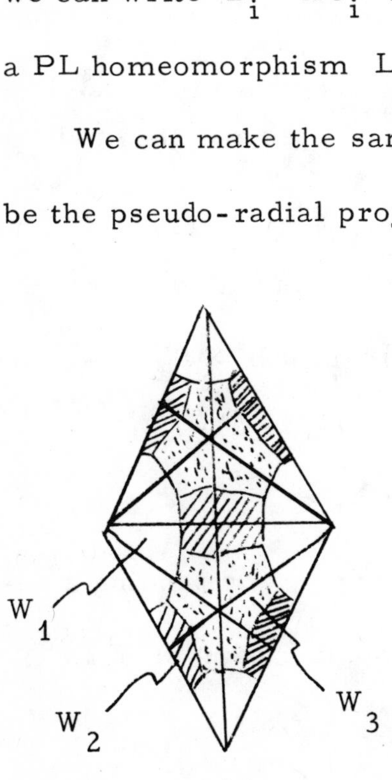

(1)

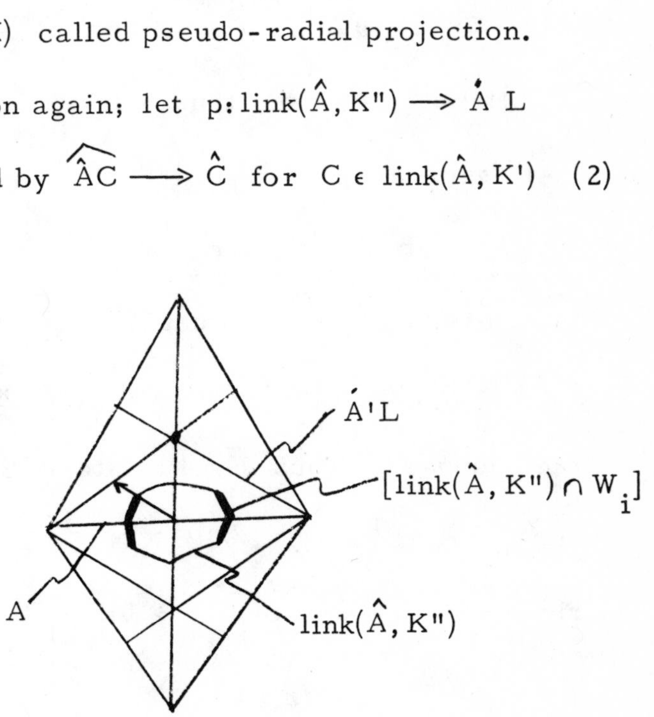

(2)

The fact that p sends $\text{link}(\hat{A}, K'') \cap W_i \longrightarrow$ derived neighborhood of A' in $\dot{A}'L$ follows from standard considerations (cf Chapter II). Since $\dot{A}'$ is full in $\dot{A}'L$, $p[\text{link}(\hat{A}, K'') \cap W_i]$ is a regular neighborhood if $\dot{A}'$ in $\dot{A}'L$ (see Chapter II).

The remainder of the proof divides into two cases.

Case 1. $A \not\subset \partial_+ W$.

In this case, $L = \text{link}(A, K')$ is a PL sphere so $\dot{A}$ is an unknotted $(i-1)$-sphere in the $(n-1)$-sphere $\dot{A}L$. Thus by uniqueness of regular neighborhoods there is a PL homeomorphism $\alpha : \dot{A}L \longrightarrow \partial(B^i \times B^{n-i})$, sending $\dot{A} \longrightarrow \partial(B^i \times 0)$ and sending $p[\text{link}(\hat{A}, K'') \cap W_i] \longrightarrow \partial B_i \times B^{n-i}$. Now extend α conically to give a PL homeomorphism from $\overline{\text{Star}}(\hat{A}, K'') \longrightarrow B^i \times B^{n-i}$. Thus attaching $\overline{\text{star}}(\hat{A}, K'')$ to W_i is attaching an i-handle.

Case 2. $A \in \partial_+ W$.

Here L is a ball, thus $\dot{A}L$ is a ball and $\dot{A} \subset \partial(\dot{A}L)$ as an unknotted $(i-1)$-sphere.

Let $\partial B^{n-i} = F_1 \cup F_2$ where F_1, F_2 are $(n-i-1)$-balls with disjoint interiors, and observe that $(B^i \times F_1) \cup (\partial B^i \times B^{n-i}) = \text{cl}[\partial(B^i \times B^{n-i}) - (B^i \times F_2)]$ is an $(n-1)$-ball with $\partial B^i \times *$ as an unknotted $(i-1)$-sphere in the boundary. Thus there exists a PL homeomorphism $\alpha: \dot{A}L \longrightarrow (B^i \times F_1) \cup (\partial B^i \times B^{n-i})$ sending $\dot{A} \longrightarrow \partial B^i \times *$, and sending a derived neighborhood of $\dot{A} \longrightarrow \partial B^i \times B^{n-i}$. ($*$ is an interior point of F_1.)

Then $\alpha p: \text{link}(\hat{A}, K'') \longrightarrow (B^i \times F) \cup (\partial B^i \times B^{n-i})$ extends conically to a PL homeomorphism

$$h: \overline{\text{star}}(\hat{A}, K'') \longrightarrow \nu \cdot [(B^i \times F) \cup (\partial B^i \times B^{n-i})] \cong B^i \times B^{n-i} ,$$

where the last PL homeomorphism extends the identity on the base of the cone. Thus we have again attached an L-handle.

2. We now consider methods of altering the standard handlebody decomposition so as to eliminate handles. The first crucial way of modifying a handlebody decomposition uses the boundary collar to slide handles around as in the following lemma.

Lemma 2.1. If $f, g: \partial B^i \times B^{n-i} \longrightarrow \partial_+ W$ are PL ambient isotopic imbeddings, then $W \cup_f (B^i \times B^{n-i}) \cong W \cup_g (B^i \times B^{n-i})$.

Proof. Let c be a boundary collar of W (restricted to $\partial_+ W$). That is, $c: \partial_+ W \times I \longrightarrow W$ with $c(x, 0) = x$ for all $x \in \partial_+ W$. Let $H: \partial_+ W \times I \longrightarrow \partial_+ W \times I$ be a PL ambient isotopy with $H_1 f = g$. Define $\alpha : W \longrightarrow W$ by $\alpha c(x, t) = c(H_{1-t} x, t)$ and by $\alpha = \text{id.}$ outside $\text{Im}\, c$. Then α extends to a PL homeomorphism

$$W \cup_f (B^i \times B^{n-i}) \longrightarrow W \cup_g (B^i \times B^{n-i}). \qquad]$$

We will now look at homotopy classes. If $f: \partial B^i \times B^{n-i} \longrightarrow \partial_+ W$ is an imbedding, then $f(\partial B^i \times 0) \subset \partial_+ W$ is called the a-sphere of this handle and is said to represent the element $\xi \in \pi_{i-1}(\partial_+ W)$ if by homotoping a point on the a-sphere to the base point in $\partial_+ W$ we obtain a map representing ξ.

ξ is determined to within the action of $\pi_1(\partial_+ W)$ on $\pi_{i-1}(\partial_+ W)$. If $i = 2$, this action of π_1 on π_1 is an inner automorphism.

We introduce the following notation. If $\xi \in \pi_{i-1}(\partial_+ W)$ and $\omega \in \pi_1(\partial_+ W)$ then ξ^ω is the element of $\pi_{i-1}(\partial_+ W)$ induced by carrying the base point around the path ω. If $i = 2$, $\xi^\omega = \omega^{-1}\xi\,\omega$.

3. We will now look at the following main construction. If we have two handles attached to a cobordism, both attached to the same level, then we can slide one handle over the other.

Theorem 3.1 (Handle addition theorem): Let $\partial_+ W$ be connected and let $W' = W \cup_f h_1^r \cup_g h_2^r$ where $h_i^r \cong B^r \times B^{n-r}$, $i = 1, 2$ and f, g disjoint embeddings $\partial B^r \times B^{n-r} \longrightarrow \partial_+ W$. Suppose f represents ξ, g represents η in $\pi_{i-1}(\partial_+ W)$ and $2 \leq r \leq n-3$. Let $\omega \in \pi_1(\partial_+ W)$.

Then $W' \cong W \cup_f h_1^r \cup_{g'} h_2^r$ with f, g' disjoint imbeddings of $\partial B^r \times B^{n-r}$ in $\partial_+ W$ and g' representing $\eta \pm \xi^\omega$ with prescribed sign. [If $i = 2$ we can choose g' to represent either $\omega^{-1}\xi\omega$ or $\omega^{-1}\xi^{-1}\omega$.]

Proof. Choose $x \in \partial B^{n-r}$ and let $D = B^r \times x \subset h_1$. Let c be a boundary collar of $\partial_+ W - f(\partial B^r \times B^{n-r})$. c is an imbedding of $f(\partial B^r \times \partial B^s) \times I \longrightarrow \partial_+ W$. Let c be chosen so that $\mathrm{Im}(c) \cap h_2 = \emptyset$ and let $D' = D \cup c[(\partial B^i \times x) \times I] = D \cup c[\partial D \times I]$.

For convenience in notation write $S_2^a = g(\partial B^r \times 0)$. Since $f(\partial B^r \times B^{n-r}) \searrow f(\partial B^r \times 0)$ of codimension 3 in $\partial_+ W$, $\partial_+ W - h_1^r \cap W$ is still connected. Let P be a path in $\partial_+ W$ from $\partial D'$ to S_2^a with $P \cap h_1^r = \emptyset$. By general position, P can be chosen as an embedded path with $\mathring{P} \cap D = \mathring{P} \cap S_2^a = \emptyset$.

Let N be a 2nd-derived neighborhood of P in $\partial_+ W$, so that N is an (n-1)-ball and $N \cap \partial D'$, $N \cap S_2^a$ are both properly embedded (r-1)-balls (3). We now apply Irwin's embedding theorem (Chapter 8) to embed a cylinder $S^{r-2} \times I$ in N joining the boundaries of the two (r-1)-discs. Since we are embedding $S^{r-2} \times I$ in an (n-1)-ball, Irwin's connectivity conditions reduce to the condition that $S^{r-2} \times I$ be 2(r-1)-(n-1) connected, that is, $r-2 > 2r-n-1$ or $n-1 > r$. The condition is satisfied, so let $i: S^{r-2} \times I \longrightarrow N$ be an embedding mapping the boundary onto $\partial N \cap \partial D'$ and $\partial N \cap S_2^a$,

(3)

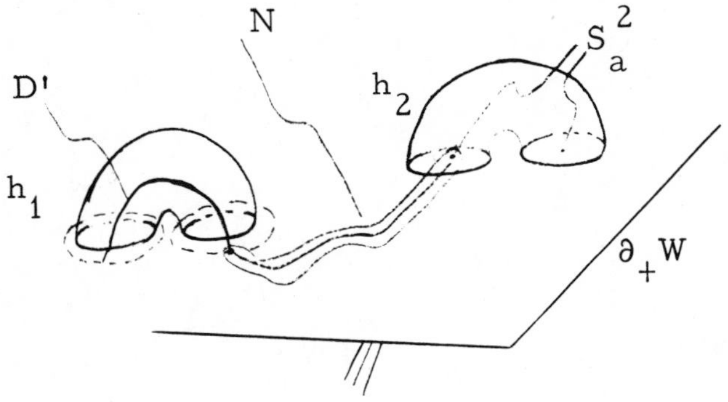

Let $g': \partial B^r \times 0 \longrightarrow \partial_+ W$ send $\partial B^r \times 0$ onto $S_2^a - (S_2^a \cap N) \cup i(S^{n-2} \times I) \cup (\partial D' - N)$ (4). Let $W_1 = W \cup_f h_1^r$. Claim $g', g | \partial B^r \times 0$ are ambient isotopic in $\partial_+ W_1$.

(4)

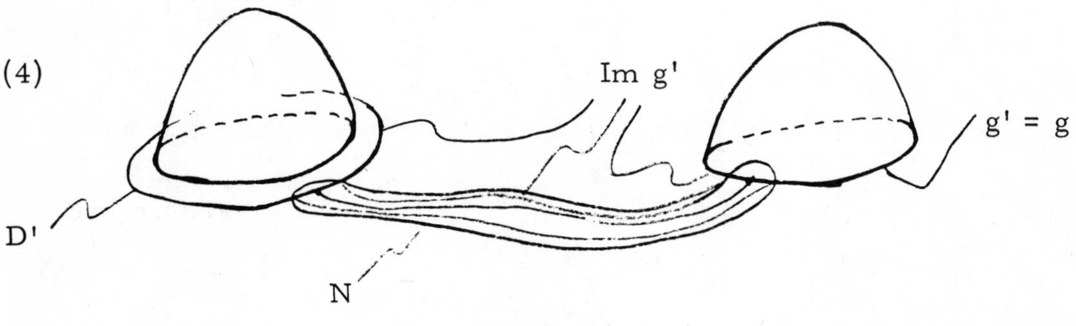

First subdivide further with N a subcomplex. Let N' = 2nd derived neighborhood of D' - D' $\cap$ Int N in $\partial_+ W_1$ - Int N. N' is an (n - 1) ball meeting ∂N in an (n - 2) ball, therefore N $\cup$ N' is an (n - 1) ball. g' and g$|\partial B^r \times 0$ agree outside N $\cup$ N'. In (N $\cup$ N') we have two properly embedded balls which agree on the boundary. By Zeeman's "Unknotting balls" (Chapter 5), g' is isotopic to g in (N $\cup$ N'), keeping the boundary fixed.

Any ambient isotopy of $\partial_+ W_1$ throwing g$|\partial B^r \times 0$ onto g' $(\partial B^r \times 0)$ gives an extension g" : $\partial B^r \times B^{n-r} \to \partial_+ W_1$ of g', ambient isotopic to g in $\partial_+ W_1$. By uniqueness of regular neighborhoods there exists an ambient isotopy of $\partial_+ W_1$, fixed on g' $(\partial B^r \times 0)$ and throwing

$g'(\partial B^r \times B^{n-r})$ onto a 2nd derived neighborhood of $g'(\partial B^r \times 0)$. Thus we can arrange for $g'(\partial B^r \times B^{n-r})$ to be disjoint from h_1^r.

We have two important choices

(1) The path P

(2) The orientations of the homeomorphisms

$$S^{r-2} \times 0 \longrightarrow \partial N \cap \partial D'$$

$$S^{r-2} \times 1 \longrightarrow \partial N \cap S_2^a .$$

Then g' represents an element of the form $\gamma \pm \xi^{\omega}$ where P determines ω and the orientations determine the sign.

4. We now consider the problem of cancelling handles. We first prove a simplifying lemma.

Lemma 4.1. Suppose $M_1^n \subset M_2^n$ are compact PL manifolds, $M_2 \searrow M_1$. Then $M_2 \cong M_1$.

Proof. (Using regular neighborhood theory): If c is a boundary collar of M_1, then $M_2 \searrow M_1 \searrow M_o = cl[M_1 - Im\, c]$ and hence M_1, M_2 are both regular neighborhoods of M_o in M_2. Thus $M_1 \cong M_2$.

Definition. Let $M^m, N^n \subset Q^{m+n}$ be PL manifolds. We say M and N are transverse at x if there exists a closed neighborhood U of x in Q and a PL homeomorphism $U, U \cap M; U \cap N \longrightarrow B^m \times B^n, B^m \times 0, 0 \times B^n$. M and N are transverse if they are transverse at each point of $M \cap N$.

Note: If M, N are transverse at x, then

$$\overline{\text{star}}(x, Q), \overline{\text{star}}(x, M), \overline{\text{star}}(x, N) \cong B^m \times B^n,\ B^m \times 0, 0 \times B^n .$$

(Recall that the star of a point is well-defined up to PL homeomorphism.)

Now suppose $W' = W \cup_f h_1^r \cup_g h_2^{r+1}$. We introduce the following notation:

$$S_2^a = g(\partial B^{r+1} \times 0) \subset \partial_+(W \cup h_1^r),$$

$$S_1^b = 0 \times \partial B^{n-r} \subset \partial_+(W \cup h_1^r) ,$$

$$D = 0 \times B^{n-r} \subset h_1^r .$$

Theorem 4.2. If S^a, S^b intersect transversally in a single point then $W' \cong W$.

(5)

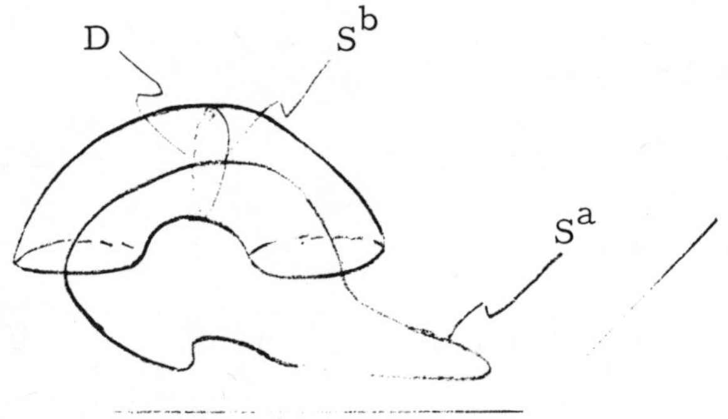

Proof. We shall prove $W' \searrow W$ and apply Lemma 4.1.

First note that $B^{r+1} \times B^{n-r-1} \searrow (\partial B^{r+1} \times B^{n-r-1}) \cup (B^{r+1} \times 0)$ by the collapse $B^{r+1} \times B^{n-r-1} \searrow \partial B^{r+1} \times B^{n-r-1} \cup B^{r+1} \times B^{n-r-2} \searrow \ldots$ $\searrow \partial B^{r+1} \times B^{n-r-1} \cup B^{r+1} \times B^i \searrow \ldots \searrow \partial B^{r+1} \times B^{n-r-1} \cup B^{r+1} \times 0$. (6).

(6)

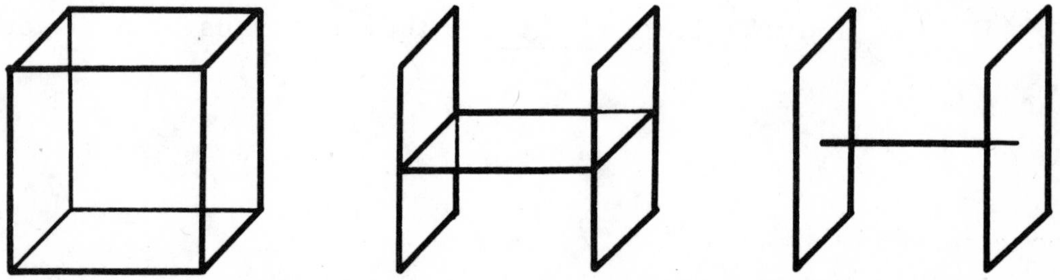

So $W' \searrow (W \cup_f h_1^r) \cup_g \partial B^{r+1} \times B^{n-r-1} \cup_g (B^{r+1} \times 0) = (W \cup_f h_1^r) \cup_g (B^{r+1} \times 0)$.

Let $W_1 = W \cup_f h_1^r$ and triangulate with S^a, D as subcomplexes. Let $U_1 = \overline{\text{star}}(x, W_1)$ and let N_1 = the 2nd barycentric derived of $\overline{D - U_1}$ in $\overline{W_1 - U_1}$. Note $N_1 \cap \overline{\partial W_1 - U}$ = the 2nd barycentric derived neighborhood of $S^b - U$ in $\overline{\partial_+ W_1 - U}$ = an (n-1)ball in ∂N_1. Now collapse N_1 away from $N_1 \cap \overline{\partial W - U}$; $N_1 \searrow \partial N_1 - (\overline{N_1 \cap \partial W_1 - U}) = \text{Fr}_{\overline{N_1 - U_1}} N_1 \cup (N_1 \cap U_1)$.

Notice that $U_1 \cap D = \overline{\text{star}}(x, D)$, so $U_1 \cap D \cap \overline{D - U_1} = \text{link}(x, D)$ an (n-r-1) ball. Hence $U_1 \cap N_1$ = 2nd derived neighborhood of $U_1 \cap \overline{D - U_1}$ = 2nd derived neighborhood of a ball = an (n-1) ball. This ball is a face of U_1, so $U_1 \searrow U \cup \text{Fr}_{\overline{W_1 - N_1}} U_1$.

From the above remarks, $W_1 \searrow \overline{W_1 - N_1} \searrow \overline{W_1 - N_1 - U_1} \cup U$.

By transversality there exists a PL homeomorphism $U, U \cap S^a, U \cap S^b \longrightarrow B^r \times B^{n-r-1}, B^r \times 0, 0 \times B^{n-r-1}$ (U is the star of x).

Now $\partial U \cap N_1$ = 2nd derived neighborhood of $\partial U \cap S^b$ and $b(\partial U \cap N_1)$ is a regular neighborhood of $0 \times \partial B^{n-r-1}$ in $\partial(B^r \times B^{n-r-1})$, so we can assume $b(\partial U \cap N_1) = B^r \times \partial B^{n-r-1}$. Also $B^r \times B^{n-r-1} \searrow (B^r \times 0) \cup (\partial B^r \times B^{n-r-1})$ so $U \searrow (U \cap S^a) \cup (\text{Fr}_{\overline{\partial W - N_1}} U)$.

We have now shown that by a sequence of collapses $W_1 \searrow \overline{W_1 - N_1 - U_1} \cup S^a$, $W_1 \cup_g (B^{r+1} \times 0) \searrow \overline{W_1 - N_1 - U_1} \cup_g (B^{r+1} \times 0)$ and $B^{r+1} \times 0$ has been undisturbed during the sequence of collapses. Since $S^a \cap U$ is a face of $B^{r+1} \times 0$ we can collapse $B^{r+1} \times 0 \searrow \overline{S^a - S^a \cap U}$ so $W_1 \cup_g (B^{r+1} \times 0) \searrow \overline{W_1 - N_1 - U_1}$.

$N_1 \cap U_1$ is a regular neighborhood of D in W_1 and h_1^r is a regular neighborhood of D in W_1 so $\overline{W_1 - N_1 - U_1} \cong \overline{W_1 - h_1^r} = W$.

The first application of Theorem 4. 2 will be in

(7)

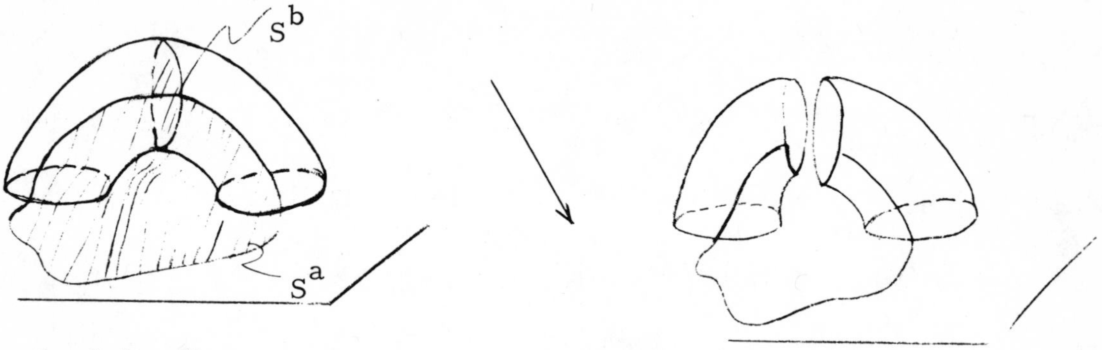

removing the 0-handles.

<u>Lemma 4. 3.</u> Let $W_1 = W \cup h_1^0 \cup h_2^0 \cup \ldots \cup h_p^0$ and $W_2 = W_1 \cup k_1^1 \cup k_2^1 \cup \ldots \cup k_q^1$. If (W_2, W) is 0-connected, then $W_2 \cong W \cup$(a number of 1-handles).

<u>Proof</u>. By induction on the number of 0-handles. The exact sequence of the triple (W_2, W_1, W_0) shows that $H_1(W_2, W_1) \xrightarrow{\partial} H_0(W_1 W_0)$ is onto. Thus for each pair of points x, y in two different components of W_1 we can find an explicit 1-chain having x-y as boundary. Thus there exists a 1-handle, k_j say, with one endpoint in h_p.

Note that a 0-handle has the form $B^0 \times B^n$ so the b-sphere of a 0-handle is the whole of its boundary $S^b = 0 \times \partial B^n$. Similarly, for a 1-hanlde $B^1 \times B^{n-1}$, the a-sphere is a pain of points $S^a = \partial B^1 \times 0$, so an a-sphere of h^1 always meets the b-sphere of h^0 transversely.

By Theorem 4. 2, $W_2 \cong W \cup (p-1)$ 0-handles $\cup$ 1-handles. This completes the inductive step.

§5. We now want to deliberately add on an extra pair of handles for cancellation.

Theorem 5.1. Suppose W is given with $r \leq \dim W-1$ and U open in $\partial_+ W$. Then $W \cong W' = W \cup h_1^r \cup h_2^{r+1}$, where

(1) $(h_1 \cup h_2) \cap W \subset U$

(2) S_2^a and S_1^b meet transversely in one point.

Proof. In $v.B^r$, let $C_1 = \{\lambda v + (1-\lambda)x : x \in B^r, x \leq \frac{1}{2}\}$

$$C_2 = \{\lambda v + (1-\lambda)x : x \in B^r, x \geq \frac{1}{2}\}$$

Observe that $vB^r \times B^{n-r-1}$ is an n- ball and $v(\partial B^r) \times B^{n-r-1}$ is a face, say F. Let $i : F \longrightarrow U$ be an embedding, then $W \cong W \cup_i (vB^r \times B^{n-r-1})$. Now $C_1 \cong B^r \times I$, so put $h_1 = C_1 \times B^{n-r-1}$. Then

$h_1, h_1 \cap W \cong B^r \times I \times B^{n-r-1}$, $\partial B^r \times I \times B^{n-r-1}$. Thus h_1 is an r-handle,

$C_2 \cong vB^r \cong B^{r+1}$, and if $h_2 = C_2 \times B^{n-r-1}$

$h_2 \cap (W \cup h_1) = \partial C_2 \times B^{n-r-1}$, so h_2 is an (r+1) handle attached to $W \cup h_1$.

(8)

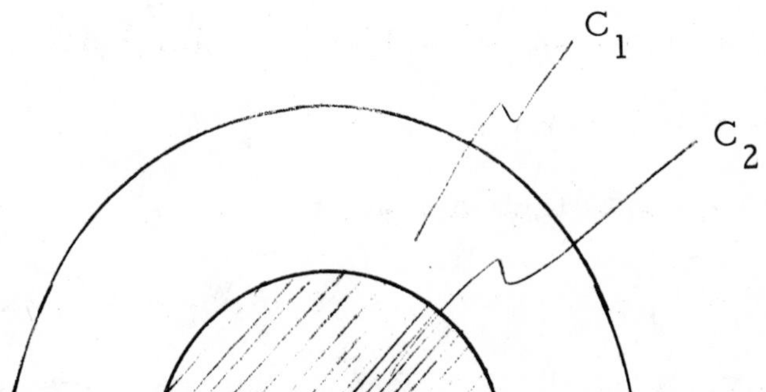

§6. Transversality and intersections

<u>Lemma 6.1.</u> Suppose K^k, L^ℓ are compact combinatorial manifolds in $E^{k+\ell}$ and suppose given $\sigma \in K$, $\tau \in L$, $\dim(\mathring{\sigma} \cap \mathring{\tau}) \leq \dim \sigma + \dim \tau = k+\ell$ (i. e., simplexes meet at most in isolated points in their interior). Then, K, L meet transversely in a finite number of points.

<u>Proof.</u> This is clear from general position considerations .

<u>Corollary 1.</u> If $B^m, B^n \subset B^{m+n}$ are properly embedded balls with $B^m \cap B^n \cap \partial B^{m+n} = \emptyset$, then there exists an arbitrarily small PL homeomorphism $h: B^{m+n} \longrightarrow B^{m+n}$ fixed on the boundary with B^m, hB^n transverse.

<u>Proof.</u> Suppose $B^{m+n} \cong I^{m+n}$ and triangulate B^m, B^n so they are linearly embedded in I^{m+n}. Now shift the vertices by a small amount into general position (Chapter 4).

<u>Corollary 2.</u> If $M^n, N^n \subset Q^{m+n}$ are manifolds without boundary and M compact, then there is an arbitrarily small PL homeomorphism $h: Q \longrightarrow Q$ with M, hN transverse.

<u>Proof.</u> By general position assume $M \cap N$ is a finite set of points. Now apply Corollary 1 in disjoint neighborhoods of these points.

§7. Geometric and algebraic intersections.

Let $W_1 = W \cup h_1^r \cup \ldots \cup h_p^r$, $W_2 = W_1 \cup k_1^{r+1} \cup \ldots \cup k_q^{r+1}$ and suppose $\pi_1(W) = \pi_1(W_2)$. Let $\widetilde{W} \subset \widetilde{W}_2$ be the universal covers of W, W_2 and let $\widetilde{W}_1 = p^{-1} W_1$ where $p: \widetilde{W}_2 \longrightarrow W_2$ is the natural projection map of the covering space.

Now for each handle h_i choose a lift $\tilde{h}_i$ of h_i and for each j a lift $\tilde{k}_j$ of k_j. Given $x \in \pi_1(W)$ we regard x as a transformation of the covering space and write $x\tilde{h}_i$ as the handle obtained by applying the transformation to $\tilde{h}_i$ chosen above.

Let ξ_i generate $H_r(h_i, h_i \cap W)$, $\tilde{\xi}$ be the corresponding generator of $H_r(\tilde{h}_i, \tilde{h}_i \cap \tilde{W})$. Similarly, define η_j as a generator of $H_{r+1}(k_j, k_j \cap W)$ and write $\tilde{\eta}_j$ as the corresponding generator of $H_{r+1}(\tilde{k}_j, \tilde{k}_j \cap \tilde{W})$. Let Λ be the group ring of $\pi_1(W_2)$. Now $\tilde{\xi}_1 \ldots \tilde{\xi}_p$ generate $H_r(\tilde{W}_1, \tilde{W})$ as a free Λ module since every handle in the covering is got by a translation of one of the $\tilde{\xi}_i$'s. Similarly $\tilde{\eta}_1 \ldots \tilde{\eta}_q$ generate $H_{r+1}(\tilde{W}_2, \tilde{W})$ as a free Λ module and we obtain a matrix relating these generators from the boundary operator ∂, writing

$$\partial(\tilde{\eta}_j) = \sum_i \lambda_{ji} \tilde{\xi}_i \qquad \text{with } \lambda_{ji} \in \Lambda .$$

We will now see how these elements of the group ring are tied up with the intersections of the a-spheres and the b-spheres. Let

S_j^a = a-sphere of $k_j \subset \partial_+ W_1$

S_i^b = b-sphere of $h_i \subset \partial_+ W$

D_i = usual disc spanning S_i^b $(0 \times B^{n-r} \subset h_i)$.

Notice S^a, S^b bound discs in W_2 so we have also chosen lifts $\tilde{S}_j^a, \tilde{S}_i^b$ in $\tilde{W}_2$ and $\tilde{D}_i$ spanning S_i^b.

The first thing to observe is that S_j^a, S_i^b transverse in $\partial_+ W$ implies xS_j^a, yS_i^b are transverse in $\partial_+ \tilde{W}_1$ for all $x, y \in \pi_1(W_2)$. This is true since the condition of transversality is local and p is a local homeomorphism.

Further, $\widetilde{W}_2$ is orientable, so to each transverse intersection we may give a sign.

(9)

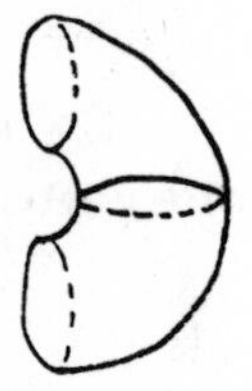

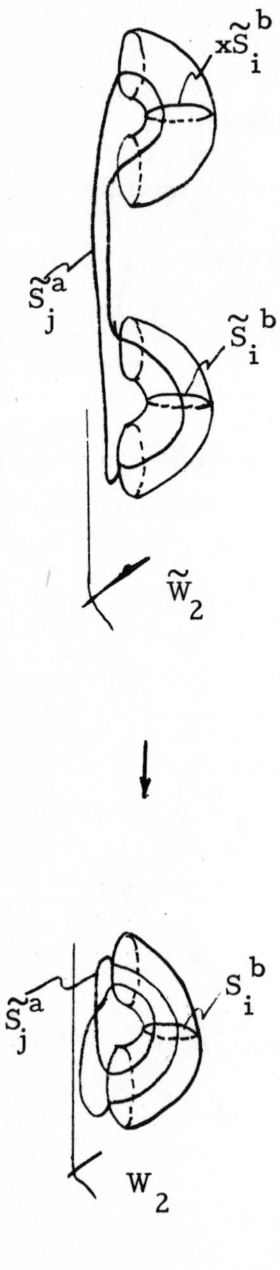

In general if M^m and N^n are submanifolds of an orientable manifold Q^{m+n} which meet transversely at a point x, there is a homeomorphism $h: U, U \cap M, U \cap N \longrightarrow B^m \times B^n, B^m \times 0, 0 \times B^n$, where U is a neighborhood of x in Q. Geometrically, we can choose h so $U \cap M$, $U \cap N$ are mapped with the natural orientation and give intersection sign ± 1 according as whether U is mapped with correct orientation.

More precisely, in the diagram

$$\begin{array}{ccc} H_m(M) & \longrightarrow & H_m(Q, Q-N) \\ \downarrow & & \uparrow \\ H_m(M, M-\bigcup_{i=1}^{k}[U_i \cap M]) & & \\ \wr\wr & & \\ \sum_{i=1}^{k} H_m(U_i \cap M, \partial U_i \cap M) & \longrightarrow & \end{array},$$

for each i the generator of $H_m(U_i \cap M, \partial U_i \cap M)$ maps onto $\pm$ the generator of $H_m(Q, Q-N)$ by the local product structure, the sign $\pm$ is precisely the sign of the intersection.

We define the algebraic intersection of $\widetilde{S}_j^a$ with $x\widetilde{S}_i^b$ by taking the signed intersections and adding. Then the algebraic intersection is the coefficient of x in λ_{ji}.

Lemma 7.1. If $B^p, B^q \subset B^{p+q}$ are properly embedded balls, $p, q \geq 1$ and (B^{p+q}, B^q) unknotted with B^p, B^q meeting transversely at two points with opposite sign, then ∂B^r is inessential in $B^{p+q} - B^q$.

Proof. ∂B^p is homologous to zero in $B^{p+q} - B^q$ [because ∂B^p is cobordant to two spheres each linking B^q once in opposite directions] and is therefore inessential since

$$\pi_{p-1}(B^{p+q} - B^q) \approx H_{p-1}(B^{p+q} - B^q) \approx H_{p-1}(S^{p-1}) = \mathbb{Z}.$$

Corollary. If $p \leq p+q-3$ and the above hypotheses hold, ∂B^q spans a p-disc B^p properly PL embedded in $B^{p+q} - B^q$.

Proof. This is a direct application of Irwin's embedding theorem. Note that $2p - (p+q) + 1 \leq p-2$, thus the connectivity condition on the image space is satisfied.

Theorem 7.3. Let $W_1 = W \cup h^r$, $W_2 = W_1 \cup k^{r+1}$ with $2 \leq r \leq n-4$ and $\pi_1(\partial_+ W) \cong \pi_1(W)$. Let S^a, S^b represent the a-sphere of k and the b-sphere of h respectively, in $\partial_+ W_1$. Assume S^a, S^b meet transversely. Now lift to the universal cover and assume $\tilde{S}^a$, $x\tilde{S}^b$ meet in two points P_1, P_2 with opposite sign (plus some more, possibly).

Then we can alter the attaching map of k by an isotopy to an attaching map k' so that $S^{a'}$ (corresponding to k') is transverse to S^b and meets it in two fewer points than S^a and so that $W_2 \cong W_1 \cup k'^{r+1}$.

Proof. Let Γ_1, Γ_2 be paths in S^a, S^b from P_1 to P_2. By general position $(r \geq 3,\ n-r-1 \geq 3)$ we can assume that Γ_1, Γ_2 are embedded and do not meet $S^a \cap S^b$ except in their end points.

We now have to notice that Γ_1, Γ_2 lift to paths in the universal cover $\partial_+\widetilde{W}_1$ having the same endpoints. In fact, by the choice of P_1, P_2 we can lift Γ_1 in $\widetilde{S}^a$, Γ_2 in $\widetilde{S}^b$. So, $\Gamma_1 \cup \Gamma_2$ is inessential in ∂_+W_1.

We will split the proof into two cases:

Case 1. $r \geq 3$. Let D be a disc in ∂_+W_1 spanning $\Gamma_1 \cup \Gamma_2$. By general position, assume D is embedded ($\dim \partial_+W \geq 5$), $D \cap S^a = \Gamma_1$ ($\dim \partial_+W_1 - \dim S^a = n-1-r \geq 3$), and similarly $D \cap S^b = \Gamma_2$ ($\dim \partial_+W_1 - \dim S^b = r \geq 3$).

Let N be the 2nd derived neighborhood of D in ∂_+W, then N is a ball with Γ_1, Γ_2 properly embedded, meeting in two points with opposite sign. By Corollary 7.2, we can shift $N \cap S^a$ off $N \cap S^b$ keeping $\partial_+W_1 - N$ fixed.

Case 2. $r = 2$. Here, the spanning disc used in the previous argument might hit S^b in a number of points.

Notice that $\partial_+W_1 - S^b \simeq \partial_+W_1 - (h_1 \cap \partial_+W_1)$ (10)

But now, if $(S')^a$ is the a-sphere of h, $\partial_+W_w - (S')^a \simeq \partial_+W - (h \cap \partial_+W)$. So, $\pi_1(\partial_+W_1 - S^b) = \pi_1(\partial_+W - (S')^a) = \pi_1(\partial_+W) = \pi_1(\partial_+W_1)$ where the isomorphism is induced by inclusion.

Let Γ_1, Γ_2 be as before, N_1 = 2nd derived neighborhood of Γ_2 in ∂_+W_1 with Γ_1, Γ_2, S^a, and S^b as subcomplexes. Let $\Gamma_1' = \Gamma_1 - (\Gamma_1 \cap N_1)$, P_1', P_2' endpoints of Γ_1'. $\partial N_1 - (\partial N_1 \cap S^b) =$ (n-2) sphere - (n-4) sphere and is therefore connected. So let Γ_2' be a path in $\partial N_1 - (\partial N_1 \cap S^b)$ from P_1' to P_2'. (11).

(10)

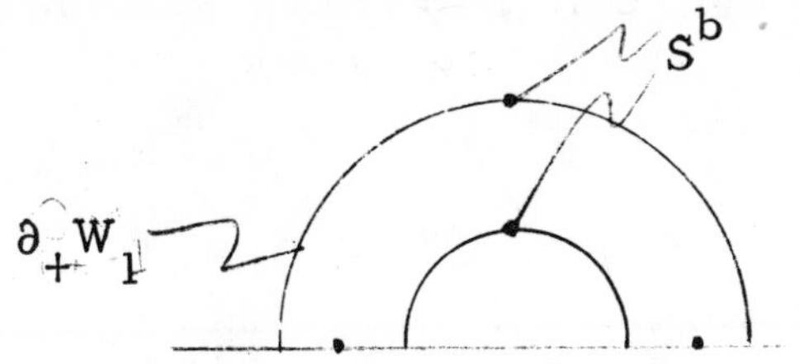

From the diagram (11) it is clear that $\Gamma_1' \cup \Gamma_2'$ is homotopic in $\partial_+ W_1$ to $\Gamma_1 \cup \Gamma_2$ and is therefore inessential in $\partial_+ W_1$, hence in $\partial_+ W_1 - S^b$ by the previous isomorphism. Thus there is a disc D in $\partial_+ W_1 - \text{Int } N_1 - S^b$ spanning $\Gamma_1' \cup \Gamma_2'$. By general position we can assume D is embedded, $D \cap S^a = \Gamma_1'$ and $D \cap \partial N_1 = \Gamma_2'$.

Now let N_2 be a 2nd derived neighborhood of D in $\partial_+ W_1 - \text{Int } N_1$. Since N_1 meets N_2 in a common face, $N = N_1 \cap N_2$ is an (n-1) ball (12). Notice that $N \cap S^a$ is a regular neighborhood of Γ_1 in S^a and $N \cap S^b = N_1 \cap S^b$ is a regular neighborhood of Γ_2 in S^b. For, $N_1 \cap S^a$ = 2nd derived neighborhood of Γ_1 in S^a, $N_2 \cap S^a$ = 2nd derived neighborhood of Γ_1' in $\overline{S^a - N_1}$, so $N \cap S^a$ is an r-ball. Similarly, for $N \cap S^b$.

(11)

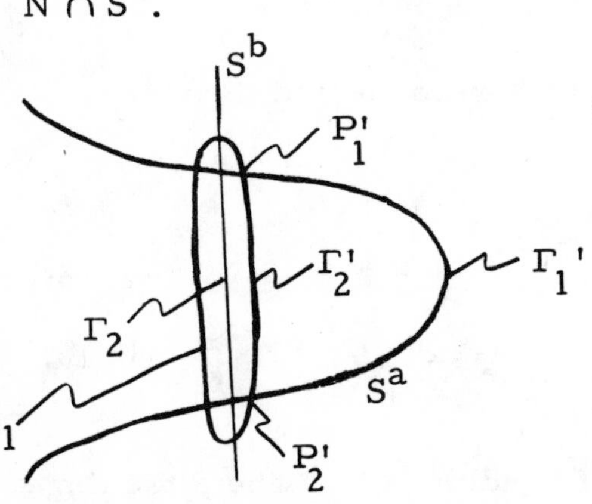

(12)

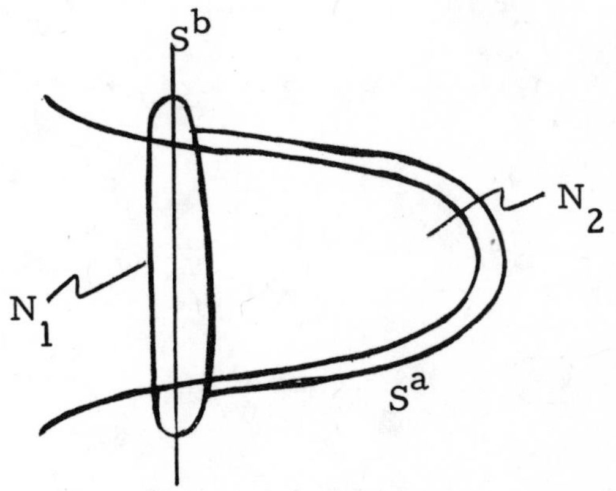

Using this construction we may manipulate S^a and S^b to get them to intersect transversely in a single point, provided we know something about their algebraic intersection.

Corollary 7.4. Let $W_1 = W \cup h^r$, $W_2 = W_1 \cup k^{r+1}$, $\pi_1(\partial_+ W) = \pi_1(W)$ and $2 \le r \le n-4$. Suppose ξ generates $H_r(W_1, W)$, η generates $H_{r+1}(W_2, W)$ and $\tilde{\xi}, \tilde{\eta}$ are lifts generating $H_r(\tilde{h}, \tilde{h} \cap \tilde{W})$ and $H_{r+1}(\tilde{k}, \tilde{k} \cap \tilde{W}_1)$ respectively.

If $\partial \tilde{\eta} = \tilde{\xi}$, then $W_2 \cong W$.

Proof. We have to look at how this algebraic condition ties up with intersection numbers. We know $\partial \tilde{\eta} = \sum_{x \in \pi_1} a_x x \tilde{\xi}$ where the integer a_x is the intersection number of $\tilde{S}^a$ with $x\tilde{S}^b$. So if $\partial \tilde{\eta} = \tilde{\xi}$, $a_x = 0$ if $x \neq 1$ and $a_1 = 1$. So by repeated application of Lemma 7.3, observing, for example, that $\tilde{S}^a$ meets $x\tilde{S}^b$ in pairs of points with opposite intersection sign and cancelling these pairs, it follows that $W_2 \cong W_1 \cup (k')$ where $S^{a\prime}$ cuts $S^{b\prime}$ transversely in a single point and cancelling the handle, $W_2 \cong W$.

We now show how to cancel r handles by adding $(r+1)$ and $(r+2)$ handles.

Lemma 7.5. Suppose $W_1 = W \cup h^r$, $W_2 = W_1 \cup k_1^{r+1} \cup \dots \cup k_q^{r+1}$, $\pi_1(\partial_+ W) = \pi_1(W)$, $2 \le r \le n-4$. If (W_2, W) is r-connected then $W_2 \cong W \cup (r+1)$ handles $\cup$ an $(r+2)$ handle.

Proof. $\partial: H_{r+1}(\tilde{W}_2, \tilde{W}_1) \longrightarrow H_r(\tilde{W}_1, \tilde{W})$ is onto and so we can write $\tilde{\xi} = \sum_{i=1}^{q} \lambda_i \partial \tilde{\eta}_i$ where $\lambda_i \in \Lambda$ and $\tilde{\eta}_i$ generate $H_{r+1}(\tilde{k}_i^{r+1}, \tilde{k}_i^{r+1} \cap W_1)$.

We will introduce a complementary pair of handles (14). The attaching spheres of $k_1 \ldots k_q$ do not cover $\partial_+ W_1$, therefore the attaching maps do not cover $\partial_1 W_1$. So choose $U \subset \partial_+ W_1$ with U disjoint from $k_1 \ldots k_q$. We may attach a pair of trivially cancelling handles in U. Let

(14)

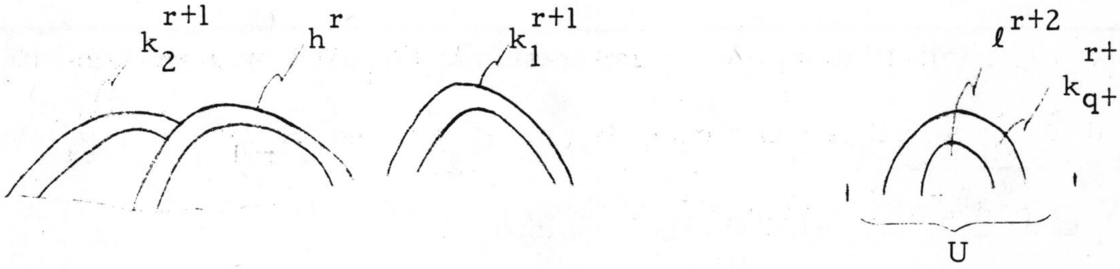

k_{q+1}^{r+1}, ℓ^{r+2} be the pair of complementary handles attached in U. So, $W_2 \cong W_1 \cup (k_1 \cup \ldots \cup k_{q+1}) \cup \ell$. Let $W_2' = W_1 \cup k_1 \cup \ldots \cup k_{q+1}$. K_{q+2} is null homotopic in W_2'. Thus under the boundary map $\partial: H_{r+1}(\widetilde{W}_2', \widetilde{W}_1) \longrightarrow H_r(\widetilde{W}_1, \widetilde{W})$, $\widetilde{\eta}_{q+1} \longrightarrow 0$.

We will now apply the handle addition Theorem 3.1. Since the theorem is stated in terms of homotopy classes, we must pass from the spherical homology class $\widetilde{\eta}$ to the corresponding homotopy class. Let $h: \pi_r(\partial_+ \widetilde{W}\ ) \longrightarrow H_r(\partial_+ \widetilde{W}_1)$ be the Hurewicz map. If the a-sphere of k_i represents $\alpha_i \in \pi_r(\partial_+ W_1) = \pi_r(\partial_+ \widetilde{W}_1)$ (up to the indeterminate $\alpha_i - \alpha_i^{\omega}$) we obtain from the following diagram

$$\pi_r(\partial_+ \widetilde{W}_1) \xrightarrow{\ h\ } H_r(\partial_+ \widetilde{W}_1) \begin{array}{l} \xrightarrow{\ j\ } H_r(\widetilde{W}_1, W) \\ \qquad\qquad\quad \uparrow \\ \longrightarrow H_r(\widetilde{W}_1) \end{array}$$

the relation $jh\alpha_i = \partial \widetilde{\eta}_i$. By the handle addition theorem we can choose k'_{q+1} so that its a-sphere represents $\alpha'_{q+1} = \alpha_{q+1} + \sum_{i=1}^{q} \lambda_i \alpha_i$. So

$jh(\alpha'_{q+1}) = \partial \tilde{\eta}'_{q+1} = \partial[\tilde{\eta}_{q+1} + \sum_{i=1}^{q} \lambda_i \tilde{\eta}_i] = \tilde{\xi}$ We can now use 7.4 to cancel the r-handle in $W_2'' = W_1 \cup k_1 \cup \ldots \cup k'_{q+1}$ and hence $W_2 \cong W_2'' \cup \ell \cong W \cup (r+1)$ handles $\cup$ an $(r+2)$ handle.

The following handle rearrangement lemma is sometimes useful.

Lemma 7.6. If $W_1 = W \cup h^r$, $W_2 = W_1 \cup k^s$, $s \leq r$, then $W_2 \cong W_1 \cup k'^s$ where k'^s is disjoint from h^r.

Proof. First of all, if S^a = a-sphere of k and S^b = b-sphere of h, $\dim S^a + \dim S^b = (s-1) + (n-r-1) \leq n-2 < n-1$. By general position S^a can be moved off S^b by an ambient isotopy. Let N_1 be a 2nd derived neighborhood of S^b in $\partial_+ W_1$ not meeting S^a (15). There exists an ambient isotopy of $\partial_+ W_1$ throwing N_1 onto $\partial_+ W_1 \cap h$ which is also a regular neighborhood of S^b in $\partial_+ W_1$. So S^a is now disjoint from h.

If $f: \partial B^s \times B^{n-s} \to \partial_+ W_1$ is the attaching map of k with $S^a \cap h = \emptyset$, let N_2 be a 2nd derived neighborhood of S^a in $\partial_+ W_1$ not meeting h. There exists an ambient isotopy carrying $f(\partial B^s \times B^{n-s})$ onto N_2, and now the two handles are disjoint.

(15)

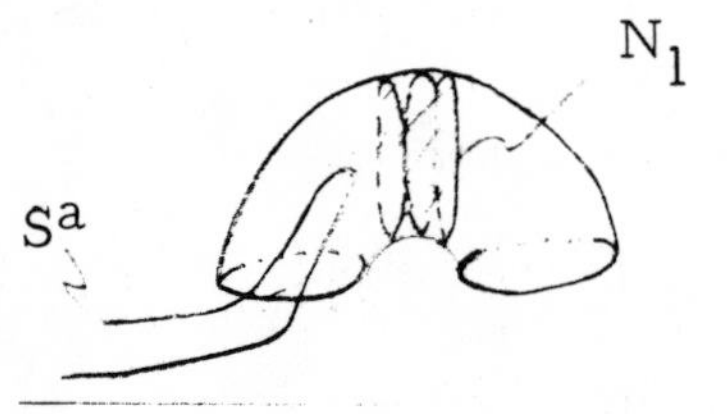

Collecting all our results, we have

Lemma 7.7. If $W_1 = W \cup h_1^r \cup \ldots \cup h_p^r$, $W_2 = W_1 \cup k_1^{r+1} \cup \ldots \cup k_q^{r+1}$, $\pi_1(\partial_+ W) = \pi_1(W)$, $2 \leq r \leq n-4$ and (W_2, W) is r-connected, then $W_2 \cong W \cup (r+1)$ handles $\cup$ $(r+2)$ handles.

Proof. By induction on p. Let $W_1' = W \cup h_1^r \cup \ldots \cup h_{p-1}^r$. Now we look at the exact sequence $\pi_r(W_1', W) \longrightarrow \pi_r(W_2, W) \longrightarrow \pi_r(W_2, W_1') \longrightarrow 0$ and conclude that $\pi_r(W_2, W_1') = 0$. By 7.5, $W_2 \cong W_1' \cup (r+1)$ handles $\cup$ $(r+2)$ handles. By induction, $W_1' \cup (r+1)$ handles $\cong W \cup (r+1)$ handles $\cup (r+2)$ handles.

§8. We have now done all the geometry necessary to cancel r-handles, $r \geq 2$. In this section we show how to cancel 1-handles.

Lemma 8.1. Let $W_1 = W \cup h^1$, $W_2 = W_1 \cup k_1^2 \cup \ldots \cup k_q^2$, $n \geq 5$, $\pi_1(\partial_+ W) = \pi_1(W)$ and (W_2, W) 1-connected. Under these conditions $W_2 \cong W \cup$ 2-handles $\cup$ 3-handle.

The proof will be very much like the case $r \geq 2$. Let $P = B^1 \times x \subset h'$, $x \in \partial B^{n-1}$. We can assume that P is disjoint from all 2-handles, since we can move the attaching spheres off P by general position and use regular neighborhood theory to move the 2-handles off P.

Since (W_2, W) 1-connected, P is homotopic in W_2 keeping endpoints fixed to a path in $\partial_+ W$. So there is a new path P' in $\partial_+ W - h'$ with $\partial P' = \partial P$ and $P \cup P'$ inessential in W_2 (16). By general position we may assume that $P \cup P'$ is an embedded 1-sphere in $\partial_+ W_1$, which cuts the b-sphere of h' transversely in a single point.

(16)

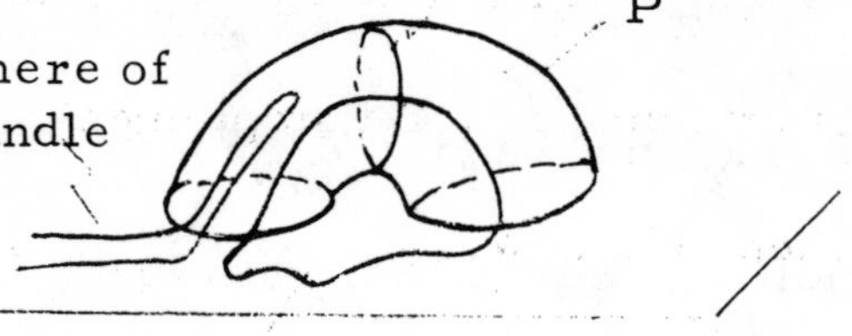

We will now introduce k_{q+1}^2, ℓ^3, a pair of complementary handles and slide the attaching map of the 2-handle around to throw it onto $P \cup P'$. Let S^a = attaching sphere of k_{q+1}, by construction (§ 5) S^a is inessential in $\partial_+ W_2$. So by Zeeman's unknotting theorem, $P \cup P'$, S^a are ambient isotopic in $\partial_+ W_2$.

Thus $W_2 \cong W_1 \cup k_1^2 \cup \ldots \cup k_q^2 \cup k'^2_{q+1} \cup \ell'^3$ where the attaching sphere of k'_{q+1} is $P \cup P'$. So we can cancel h and k'^2_{q+1}, by 4. 2. We can cancel a whole lot of 1-handles by using this technique repeatedly. Collecting the various preceding theorems we obtain

<u>Theorem 8. 2.</u> Let W be a connected cobordism, with $(W, \partial_- W)$ r-connected, $r \leq n-3$. Then $W \cong (\partial_- W \times I)$ handles of index $\geq r$.

<u>Proof.</u> Choose a standard handle decomposition and apply various lemmas above.

One of the important things about cobordism is that we can turn them upside down. By this process, an r-handle becomes an (n-r) handle.

If $W_0 \cup W_1 \cup \ldots . \cup W_{n+1}$ is a standard handle body decomposition, let $W' = W \cup (\partial_+ W \times I)$ and identifying $\partial_+ W \times 0$ with $\partial_+ W$, let $\partial_+ W' = \partial_- W$,

$\partial_- W' = \partial_+ W \times 1$. Notice that attaching an i-handle to W_i removes an (n-i) handle from $W' - W_i$. That is, $B^i \times B^{n-i}$ is attached to W_i by $\partial B^i \times B^{n-i}$ and so is attached to the complement by $B^i \times \partial B^{n-i}$. If $W_i' = W' - W_{n-i+1}$, then $W_0' \cup W_1' \cup \dots \cup W_{n+1}'$ is a standard handle body decomposition. This enables us to state a stronger form of Theorem 8. 2.

Theorem 8. 2'. If W is as in 8. 2, $2 \leq r \leq n-3$ and $(W, \partial_+ W)$ is (n-r-2) connected, then

$$W \cong \partial_- W \times I \cup \text{r-handles} \cup (r+1) \text{ handles}.$$

Proof. Turning upside down we must cancel the handles of index $\leq n-r-2$. This is possible by our lemmas provided $n-r-2 \leq n-4$, i. e., $r \geq 2$.

Now suppose $W_1 = W \cup h_1^r \cup \dots \cup h_p^r$, $W_2 = W_1 \cup k_1^{r+1} \cup \dots \cup k_q^{r+1}$, $\pi_1(\partial_+ W) = \pi_1(W)$ and $2 \leq r \leq n-4$. Let $\tilde{\xi}_i \in H_r(\tilde{W}_1, \tilde{W})$, $\tilde{\eta}_i \in H_{r+1}(\tilde{W}_2, \tilde{W}_1)$ be generators chosen as before.

Then the boundary $\partial: H_{r+1}(\tilde{W}_2, \tilde{W}_1) \longrightarrow H_r(\tilde{W}_1, \tilde{W})$ is represented by a matrix $M = (m_{ij})$ where

$$\partial \tilde{\eta}_i = \sum_j m_{ij} \tilde{\xi}_j \quad \text{with } m_{ij} \in \Lambda.$$

First of all we know that:

(1) If $\pi_i(W_2, W) = 0$ for all i, then $H_*(\tilde{W}_2, \tilde{W}) = 0$. Thus M has an inverse as it represents an isomorphism between two free Λ-modules. In particular, M is square, p = q.

(2) M is not completely determined by the handle body decomposition; there is an element of choice in the orientations of the ξ_i and in the choice of lift $\xi_i \to \tilde{\xi}_i$. M is determined by the handle body decomposition up to left multiplication of a row or right multiplication of a column by elements $\pm x$ where $x \in \pi_1$.

(3) If $M = \begin{bmatrix} 1 & & & 0 \\ & 1 & & \\ & & \ddots & \\ 0 & & & 1 \end{bmatrix}$ $2 \leq r \leq n-4$, then by Corollary 7.4, $W_2 \cong W$.

We are going to look at ways of altering a handle body decomposition by adding complementary handles and sliding handles around to get M in this form.

§9. Whitehead torsion of a handle body decomposition

Let R be a ring with identity. Let $GL_n(R) = n \times n$ invertible matrices over R and note $GL_n(R) \subset GL_{n+1}(R)$ under the natural identification $M \in GL_n(R) \sim \begin{bmatrix} M & 0 \\ 0 & 1 \end{bmatrix} \in GL_{n+1}(R)$. Let $GL(R) = \lim GL_n(R)$.

A matrix $M \in GL(R)$ is called elementary if it agrees with $I = \begin{bmatrix} 1 & & & 0 \\ & 1 & & \\ & & \ddots & \\ 0 & & & 1 \end{bmatrix}$ except for at most one off diagonal element. Let $E(R) \subset GL(R)$ be the subgroup generated by elementary matrices.

<u>Theorem of Whitehead:</u> $E(R)$ = commutator subgroup of $GL(R)$.

Thus $K_1(R) = GL(R)/E(R)$ is an abelian group, usually written additively.

Consider $(-1) \in GL_1(R) \subset GL(R)$. Let $[-1]$ be the image of (-1) in $K_1(R)$ and let $\overline{K}_1(R) = K_1(R)/[-1]$.

If Π is a group, write $\mathbb{Z}\Pi$ = group ring of Π. We have a natural map $\Pi \longrightarrow GL_1(\mathbb{Z}\Pi)$, since every element of Π has an inverse in Π and is hence a unit in $\mathbb{Z}\Pi$ and therefore a non singular 1×1 matrix. We have $h: \Pi \longrightarrow GL_1(\mathbb{Z}\Pi) \longrightarrow GL(\mathbb{Z}\Pi) \longrightarrow K_1(\mathbb{Z}\Pi) \longrightarrow \overline{K}_1(\mathbb{Z}\Pi)$. Then $Wh(\Pi)$ = the Whitehead group of $\Pi = \overline{K}_1(\mathbb{Z}\Pi)/h\Pi$.

If M is the matrix associated with a handle body decomposition as in §8 with $W_1 = W \cup$ r-handles and $W_2 = W_1 \cup (r+1)$ handles, let $\tau = [M] \in Wh(\Pi)$. τ is called the Whitehead torsion associated with the handle body decomposition. The main theorem of this section enables us to cancel the handles of this particular decomposition in case $\tau = 0$. Note that τ is well determined by the handle body decomposition. In fact, first note that if we permute the rows of M we do not change $[M]$. Write $E_{ij} = [a_{k\ell}]$ with $a_{ij} = 1$ and $a_{k\ell} = 0$ otherwise, for $i \neq j$, and observe $I + aE_{ij}$ is elementary given $a \in \mathbb{Z}\Pi$. Let $M' = M(1 + E_{1j})(1 - E_{j1})(1 + E_{1j})$. The effect of this posmultiplication is to add the first column to the jth, subtract the jth from the first and add the new first column to the jth. Write

$$M'' = M' \begin{bmatrix} -1 & & & \\ & 1 & & \\ & & 1 & \\ & & & \ddots \end{bmatrix}$$

All these extra factors go to zero in $\overline{K}_1$ and we have $M'' = M$ with the first and j^{th} columns interchanged. A similar argument using premultiplication shows that we can interchange the rows of M.

Now if we multiply a row or column by an element $\pm \Pi$ we don't alter τ. For, we may permute columns, postmultiply by $\begin{bmatrix} \pm x & & & 0 \\ & 1 & & \\ & & 1 & \\ 0 & & & \ddots \end{bmatrix}$ and then permute again. The matrix $\begin{bmatrix} \pm x & & & 0 \\ & 1 & & \\ & & 1 & \\ 0 & & & \ddots \end{bmatrix} \longrightarrow 0$ in $Wh(\Pi)$.

<u>Theorem 9.1.</u> Let $W_1 = W \cup h_1^r \cup \ldots \cup h_p^r$, $W_2 = W_1 \cup k_1^{r+1} \cup \ldots \cup k_p^{r+1}$ $\pi_1(\partial_+ W) = \pi_1(W)$, $2 \leq r \leq n-4$ and (W_2, W) $(r+1)$ connected. Let τ be defined as above. Then $\tau = 0$ implies $W_2 \cong W$.

<u>Proof.</u> $\tau = 0$ means that $M \longrightarrow 0$ under the map $GL_n(\mathbb{Z}\Pi) \longrightarrow GL(\mathbb{Z}\Pi) \xrightarrow{\alpha} Wh(\Pi)$ where $\ker \alpha$ is the subgroup of $GL(\mathbb{Z}\Pi)$ generated by elementary matrices, $\begin{bmatrix} -1 & & & 0 \\ & 1 & & \\ & & 1 & \\ 0 & & & \ddots \end{bmatrix}$ and $\begin{bmatrix} x & & & 0 \\ & 1 & & \\ & & 1 & \\ 0 & & & \ddots \end{bmatrix}$.

Then for some N, $\begin{bmatrix} M & 0 \\ 0 & I_N \end{bmatrix} = EU$ where E = finite product of elementary matrices and $U = \begin{bmatrix} \pm x & & & 0 \\ & 1 & & \\ & & 1 & \\ 0 & & & \ddots \end{bmatrix}$ with $x \in \Pi$.

First of all we can choose a new lift $\tilde{\xi}_1$ to eliminate U. Introduce N pairs of complementary r and $(r+1)$ handles, all disjoint from $h_1^r \cup \ldots \cup h_p^r \cup k_1^{r+1} \cup \ldots \cup k_p^{r+1}$. This gives a new handle body decomposition represented by the matrix $E = \prod_{i-1}^{k} e_i$ with e_i elementary. Let $e_1 = (I + aE_{ij})$.

If we now have $W_1' = W \cup h_1^r \cup \dots \cup h_{p+N}^r$, $W_2' = W_1' \cup k_1^{r+1} \cup \dots \cup k_{p+N}^{r+1}$ and $\tilde{\xi}_i, \tilde{\eta}_i$ chosen to give E, we apply the handle addition theorem to slide one of the handles k_j^{r+1} over the others to get

$$W_2' \cong W_1' \cup k_1^{r+1} \cup \dots \cup k_{j-1}^{r+1} \cup k_j'^{r+1} \cup k_{j+1}^{r+1} \cup \dots \cup k_{p+N}^{r+1}$$

where $\partial \tilde{\eta}_j' = \partial(\tilde{\eta}_j - a\tilde{\eta}_i)$ (see 7.5).

The matrix of the new handle body decomposition is E with a times the ith row subtracted from the jth row, i.e., is $(I - aE_{ij})E$. So the new matrix is $\prod_{i=2}^{k} e_i$. We repeat this process unitl we get a new handle body decomposition with matrix $\begin{bmatrix} 1 & & & 0 \\ & 1 & & \\ & & 1 & \\ & & & \ddots \\ 0 & & & \end{bmatrix}$. This enables us to cancell all the handles.

§10. Whitehead torsion.

Let R be a ring with identity. We also make the following assumption: If F_n = free module over R with n generators, $m \neq n$ implies $F_m \neq F_n$. This assumption is certainly true for group rings $R = \mathbb{Z}\Pi$. For, we can make Π operate trivially on the rationals Q and regard Q as a right R module. Then $Q \otimes_R F_n$ = vector space of dimension n over Q and so $m \neq n$ implies $F_m \neq F_n$.

Definition. Let A be an R module, A is s-free if $A \oplus F_n$ is free for some n.

Lemma 10.1. If $0 \to A \to B \to C \to 0$ is exact and B, C are s-free, then A is s-free.

Proof. $0 \to A \to B \oplus F_n \to C \oplus F_n \to 0$ is exact. For large enough n, $B \oplus F_n$ and $C \oplus F_n$ are free, so the sequence splits and $B \oplus F_n \cong A \oplus (C \oplus F_n)$, therefore A is s-free.

Definition. If A is s-free, an s-basis for A is a basis for $A \oplus F_n$ for some n. We will use a single letter underlined for a basis. If A is free, and $\underline{b} = (b_1 \dots b_r)$, $\underline{c} = (c_1 \dots c_r)$ are bases for A, write $b_i = \sum \lambda_{ij} c_j$ where the λ_{ij} form an invertible matrix. Write $[\underline{b}/\underline{c}] = [\lambda_{ij}] \in \overline{K}_1(R)$.

We can do the same thing for s-free bases. In general, if $\underline{b}$ is a basis for $A \oplus F_m$, $\underline{c}$ is a basis for $A \oplus F_n$, and $\underline{b} + \underline{f}_{k-m}$, $\underline{c} + \underline{f}_{k-n}$ are free bases for $A \oplus F_n$ where $\underline{f}_{k-m}, \underline{f}_{k-n}$ are standard bases for F_{k-m}, F_{k-n}, define $[\underline{b}/\underline{c}] = [\underline{b} + \underline{f}_{k-m} / \underline{c} + f_{k-n}] \in \overline{K}_1(R)$.

This element does not depend on the choice of k, and we write $\underline{b} \sim \underline{c}$ if $[\underline{b}/\underline{c}] = 0$. In particular, if $\underline{b}$ is obtained from $\underline{c}$ by permutation or adding multiples of one element to another, then $\underline{b} \sim \underline{c}$. Note that $[\underline{a}/\underline{b}] + [\underline{b}/\underline{c}] = [\underline{a}/\underline{c}]$.

Let $0 \to A \to B \to C \to 0$ be exact, A, B, C s-free. Then the following sequence is also exact:

$$0 \longrightarrow A \oplus F_m \xrightarrow{\lambda} B \oplus F_m \oplus F_n \xrightarrow{\mu} C \oplus F_n \to 0.$$

Let $\underline{a}$, $\underline{c}$ be chosen as bases for $A \oplus F_m$, $C \oplus F_n$ respectively, $\underline{a} = (a_1 \dots a_r)$, $\underline{c} = (c_1 \dots c_s)$. Given $i \leq s$, suppose $\mu c_i' = c_i$. Then $(\lambda a_1 \dots \lambda a_r, c_1' \dots c_s')$ is a basis for $B \oplus F_m \oplus F_n$. Call this s-basis for B $\underline{ac}$. Then $\underline{ac}$ is defined up to a choice of the c_i'. If c_i'' is another choice with

$\mu c''_i = c_i$, then $c''_i - c_i \in \operatorname{Im} \lambda$ and we can write down a matrix comparing these as follows:

$$\begin{bmatrix} \lambda a_1 \\ \vdots \\ \lambda a_r \\ c''_1 \\ \vdots \\ c''_s \end{bmatrix} = M \begin{bmatrix} \lambda a_1 \\ \vdots \\ \lambda a_r \\ c'_1 \\ \vdots \\ c'_s \end{bmatrix},$$

where M is of the form $\begin{bmatrix} I_r & M_1 \\ 0 & I_s \end{bmatrix}$, so $[M] = 0$ in $\overline{K}_1(R)$. Thus the equivalence class of $\underline{ac}$ is well determined.

Suppose now $\underline{a}$, $\underline{a}'$ are s-bases for A, $\underline{c}, \underline{c}'$ are s-bases for C and choose related s-bases $\underline{ac}$, $\underline{a'c'}$ for B. We would now like to compare these s-bases.

<u>Lemma 9.2.</u> $[\underline{ac}/\underline{a'c'}] = [\underline{a}/\underline{a}'] + [\underline{c}/\underline{c}']$.

<u>Proof.</u> Assume A, B, C free; $\underline{a}, \underline{c}, \underline{a}', \underline{c}'$ are actual bases. We have $0 \to A \xrightarrow{\lambda} B \xrightarrow{\mu} C \to 0$, choose $\alpha: C \to B$ with $\mu\alpha = 1$, then $B = \lambda A \oplus \alpha C$.

We can suppose $\underline{ac} = (\lambda \underline{a}, \alpha \underline{c})$, $\underline{a'c'} = (\lambda \underline{a}', \alpha \underline{c}')$. Then $\underline{ac} = M \underline{a'c'}$, where M of of the form $\begin{bmatrix} M_1 & 0 \\ 0 & M_2 \end{bmatrix} = \begin{bmatrix} M_1 & 0 \\ 0 & I \end{bmatrix} \begin{bmatrix} I & 0 \\ 0 & M_2 \end{bmatrix}$ with $\underline{a} = M_1 \underline{a}'$, $\underline{b} = M_2 \underline{b}'$. So in $\overline{K}_1(R)$, $[M] = [M_1] + [M_2]$.

We will now define torsion for a general chain complex over R. Suppose $0 \to C_n \to C_{n-1} \to \cdots \to C_0 \to 0$ is a chain complex of free R modules.

Given i, let $\underline{c}_i$ be a basis for C_i. If either

(1) $H_*(C) = 0$

(2) $H_i(C)$ is s-free for each i with given basis $\underline{h}_i$,

let $0 \to B_i \to Z_i \to H_i \to 0$ and $0 \to Z_i \to C_i \to B_{i-1} \to 0$ be the short exact sequences associated with C. Now by induction on i and 10.1, B_i and Z_i are s-free.

Choose s-bases $\underline{b}_i$ for B_i and choose in the usual manner s-bases $\underline{b_i h_i}$ for Z_i, $\underline{(b_i h_i) b_{i-1}}$ for C_i. Define $\tau = \sum (-1)^i [\underline{(b_i h_i) b_{i-1}}/\underline{c}_i]$. If $\underline{b}'_i$ is another basis for B_i, $[\underline{(b'_i h_i) b'_{i-1}}/\underline{c}_i] = [\underline{(b'_i h_i) b'_{i-1}}/\underline{(b_i h_i) b_{i-1}}] + [\underline{(b_i h_i) b_{i-1}}/\underline{c}_i] = [\underline{b'_i/b_i}] + [\underline{b}'_{i-1}/\underline{b}_{i-1}] + [\underline{(b_i h_i) b_{i-1}}/\underline{c}_i]$ and in the alternating sum the terms $[\underline{b'_i/b_i}]$ cancel. τ is thus independent of the choice of $\underline{b}_i$ and is called the Whitehead torsion of the based chain complex $(C, \underline{c}_i)$.

Let us now consider the actual geometric situation. Let $K_o \subset K$ be a pair of finite simplicial complexes with $\pi_1(K_o) \cong \pi_1(K)$ by inclusion.

If $K_o \subset K$ is a homotopy equivalence, let $\tilde{K}_o \subset \tilde{K}$ be the universal cover, this has a standard simplicial structure given by that on $K_o \subset K$. Consider

$$\cdots \longrightarrow C_i(\tilde{K}, \tilde{K}_o) \longrightarrow C_{i-1}(\tilde{K}, \tilde{K}_o) \longrightarrow \cdots .$$

Given $\sigma \in K - K_o$, let $\tilde{\sigma}$ be a lift of σ to $\tilde{K}$, $\tilde{\sigma}$ is determined to whithin an action of π_1. $C_i(\tilde{K}, \tilde{K}_o)$ is a finitely generated free $\mathbb{Z}\Pi$ module with generators of the form $\tilde{\sigma}$, $\dim \sigma = i$, $\sigma \in K - K_o$.

Since $K_o \subset K$ is a homotopy equivalence, the chain complex above has no homology and $\tau(C)$ is defined in $\overline{K}_1(\mathbb{Z}\Pi)$ and depends on the choices of the lifts $\{\tilde{\sigma}\}$. A different $\tilde{\sigma}$ differs by an element of $\mathbb{Z}\Pi$. Let $\tau(K, K_o) = [\tau] \in Wh(\Pi)$, then is well determined . We will show that this $\tau(K, K_o)$ element of $Wh(\Pi)$ does not depend on the triangulation, i. e., is invariant under subdivision.

More generally, if $H_i(\tilde{K}, \tilde{K}_o)$ is s-free with s-bases $\underline{b}_i$ we can still define $\tau(K, K_o)$, now depending on the choice of s-bases $\underline{b}_i$. If b_i' is another s-base of $H_i(\tilde{K}, \tilde{K}_o)$ and $[\underline{b}_i'/\underline{b}_i] \to 0$ under $\bar{K}_i(\mathbb{Z}\Pi) \to Wh(\Pi)$, then $\tau(K, K_o)$ is not changed by replacing $\underline{b}_i$ by $\underline{b}_i'$

Suppose we have a sequence of inclusions of R modules $G_o \to G_1 \to G_2 \to G_3 \to \cdots$ we attach symbols a, b, c ... to the arrows $G_o \xrightarrow{a} G_1 \xrightarrow{b} G_2 \xrightarrow{c} G_3 \to \cdots$ where a is an s-basis for G_1/G_o, etc.

In the short exact sequence $0 \to G_1/G_o \to G_2/G_o \to G_2/G_1 \to 0$

the s-bases a and b of G_1/G_o and G_2/G_1 give rise to an s-base ab for G_2/G_o . We write $G_o \xrightarrow{a} G_1 \xrightarrow{b} G_2 \to$ (with $G_o \xrightarrow{ab} G_2$) . By exactly the same process, we define $\underrightarrow{bc}$ and finally $\underrightarrow{a(bc)}$ and $\underrightarrow{(ab)c}$. Then $\underrightarrow{a(bc)} \sim \underrightarrow{(ab)c}$, i. e., $[\underrightarrow{a(bc)} / \underrightarrow{(ab)c}] = 0$.

Proof. We can assume all quotients free and all s-bases are actual bases. Let $(x_1 \ldots x_r)$ be a basis for G_1/G_o which extends to a basis $(x_1 \ldots x_s)$ for G_2/G_o such that $(x_{r+1} \ldots x_s) \to b$, the given basis for G_2/G_1. Let $(x_{s+1} \ldots x_n) \to c$ in G_3/G_2. Now $(x_1 \ldots x_n)$ is equivalent to both a(bc) and (ab)c.

This process is therefore associative. It is also commutative in a reasonable sense. Suppose we have a diagram of inclusions

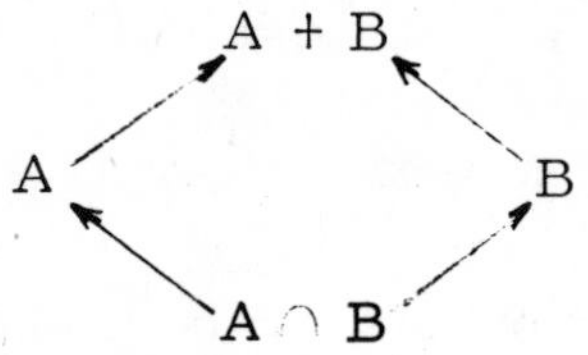

with $A, B, \subset C$ say, $A + B = \{a + b \mid a \in A, b \in B\}$. We have the natural isomorphism

$$\frac{A}{A \cap B} \longrightarrow \frac{A+B}{B} .$$

Thus $A \cap B \xrightarrow{a} A$ gives $B \xrightarrow{b} A + B$. Similarly for b.

<u>Lemma 10. 2.</u> $ba \sim ab$ in the diagram

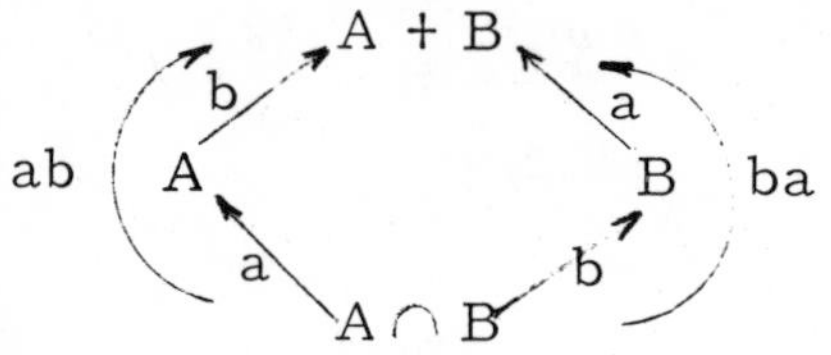

<u>Proof</u>. Recall that this equivalence is defined in $\overline{K}_1(R)$, hence even and odd permutations of the basis elements are allowed. We have got $\frac{A+B}{A \cap B} \cong \frac{A}{A \cap B} \oplus \frac{B}{A \cap B}$, and going one way we get the basis (a, b), the other way (b,a). We can thus choose ab, ba to be the same basis permuted.

Now suppose we have a short exact sequence of chain groups (finitely generated free R-modules)

$$0 \longrightarrow C' \longrightarrow C \longrightarrow C'' \longrightarrow 0 .$$

Let c_i, c_i' and c_i'' be generators for C_i, C_i' and C_i'' respectively. We also want to suppose that the homology groups $H_i = H_i(C)$, $H_i' = H_i(C')$

$H_i'' = H_i(C'')$ are all stably free with given s-bases b_i, b_i' and b_i''. Here we regard $H_i' \to H_i \to H_i'' \to H_{i-1}' \to \cdots$ as a chain complex $\mathcal{H}$ of length $\leq 3n$.

Theorem 10.3. If $c_i \sim c_i' c_i''$ for each i, then

$$\tau(C) = \tau(C') + \tau(C'') + \tau(\mathcal{H}).$$

This is the main lemma used to prove combinatorial invariance of torsion. The first thing we will prove is that the torsion doesn't change if the basis for H_i is changed. We have the short exact sequences

$$0 \longrightarrow X_i' \longrightarrow H_i' \longrightarrow X_i \longrightarrow 0$$

$$0 \longrightarrow X_i \longrightarrow H_i \longrightarrow X_i'' \longrightarrow 0$$

$$0 \longrightarrow X_i'' \longrightarrow H_i'' \longrightarrow X_{i-1}' \longrightarrow 0$$

where $X_i' = \ker(H_i' \to H_i)$, etc. To form the torsion we choose arbitrary s-bases x_i, h_i, etc., and b_i, b_i', b_i'' for B_i, B_i' and B_i'' respectively with $B_i \subset C_i$ the boundaries in C_i, etc. Then the general formula for torsion $\tau = \sum (-1)^i [b_i h_i b_{i-1}/c_i]$ becomes

$$\tau(\mathcal{H}) = \sum (-1)^{3i} \{[x_i'' x_{i-1}'/h''_i] - [x_i x_i''/h_i] + [x_i' x_i/h_i']\},$$

$$\tau(C) - \tau(C') - \tau(C'') = \sum (-1)^i \{[b_i h_i b_{i-1}/c_i] - [b_i' h_i' b_{i-1}'/c_i'] - [b_i'' h_i'' b_{i-1}''/c''_i]\}.$$

(1) Notice that changing bases c_i' or c_i'' does not alter $\tau(C) - \tau(C') - \tau(C'')$ so long as $c_i \sim c_i' c_i''$, and c_i, c_i', c_i'' do not appear in the expression for $\tau(\mathcal{H})$.

(2) Choosing a different basis for the H_i's, that is, replacing h_i by $\bar{h}_i$, adds to $\tau(\mathcal{H})$ a factor $(-1)^{i+1}[h_i/\bar{h}_i] = (-1)^i[\bar{h}_i/h_i]$ since $[x_i x_i''/\bar{h}_i] = [x_i x_i''/h_i] + [h_i/\bar{h}_i]$, and adds $(-1)^i\ [b_i \bar{h}_i b_{i-1}/c_i[- [b_i h_i b_{i-1}/c_i]$ $= (-1)^i\ [b_i \bar{h}_i b_{i-1}/b_i h_i b_{i-1}] = (-1)^i[\bar{h}_i/h_i]$ to $\tau(C) - \tau(C') - \tau(C'')$.

Thus changing bases h_i, h_i', h_i'' adds equal quantities to $\tau(\mathcal{H})$, $\tau(C) - \tau(C') - \tau(C'')$.

So long as we can prove $\tau(C) = \tau(C') + \tau(C'') + \tau(\mathcal{H})$ for one basis, we will have shown the equality for all bases. Choose

$$h_i = x_i x_i'' \qquad c_i = b_i' h_i' h_{i-1}'$$

$$h_i' = x_i' x_i \qquad c_i'' = b_i'' h_i'' b_{i-1}'' \quad .$$

$$h_i'' = x_i'' x_i'$$

(This choice will make $\tau(C') = \tau(C'') = \tau(\mathcal{H}) = 0$.) We are now going to draw an enormous diagram of subgroups and quotient groups of the H_i's and C_i's.

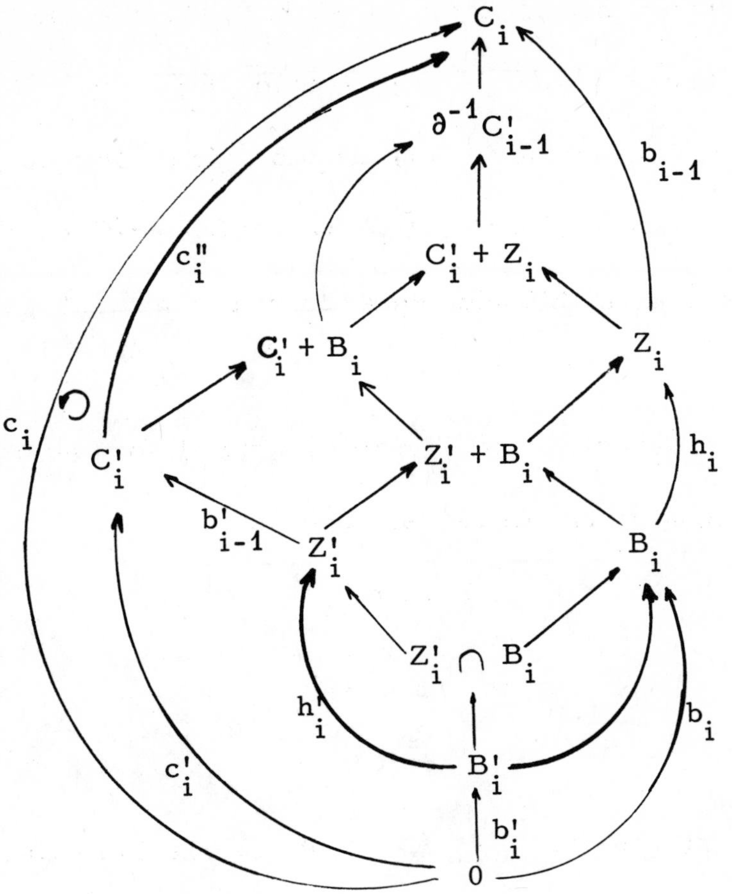

Here 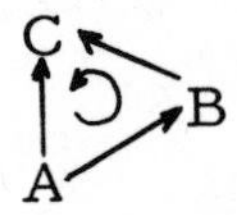 means the basis represented by 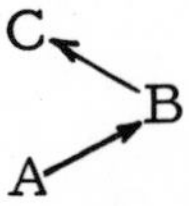 is equivalent to the basis represented by . All the arrows in the diagram represent inclusions; note that $C'_{i-1} \subset C_{i-1} \xleftarrow{\ \partial\ } C_i$. We also have the diagram

$$\begin{array}{ccccccccc} 0 & \longrightarrow & C' & \xrightarrow{\ \lambda\ } & C & \xrightarrow{\ \mu\ } & C'' & \longrightarrow & 0 \\ & & \downarrow{\scriptstyle\partial} & & \downarrow{\scriptstyle\partial} & & \downarrow{\scriptstyle\partial} & & \\ 0 & \longrightarrow & C' & \xrightarrow{\ \lambda\ } & C & \xrightarrow{\ \mu\ } & C'' & \longrightarrow & 0 \end{array}$$

Note that $x \in \mu^{-1}B''_i$ if and only if there is a $y \in C_{i+1}$ with $\mu\partial y = \mu x$, i.e., if and only if $x - \partial y \in C'_i$, so $\mu^{-1}B''_i = B_i + C'_i$. We thus get

(1) $$X_i = \ker(H_i \longrightarrow H''_i) = \frac{Z_i \cap \mu^{-1}B''_i}{B_i} = \frac{Z_i \cap (B_i + C'_i)}{B_i} = \frac{B_i + Z'_i}{B_i} = \frac{Z'_i}{B_i \cap Z'_i},$$

(2) $$X'_i = \ker(H'_i \longrightarrow H_i) = \frac{Z'_i \cap B_i}{B'_i} = \frac{B_i \cap C'_i}{B'_i} \cong \frac{\partial^{-1}C'_i}{C'_{i+1} + Z_{i+1}},$$

($Z'_i \cap B_i = C'_i \cap B_i$ since everything in B_i is a cycle)

(3) $$X''_i = \operatorname{Im}(H_i \longrightarrow H''_i) = \frac{Z_i}{Z_i \cap \mu^{-1}B''_i} = \frac{Z_i}{B_i + C'_i},$$

(4) $$B''_i = \frac{B_i}{B_i \cap C'_i} = \frac{B_i}{B_i \cap Z'_i} = \frac{C_{i+1}}{\partial^{-1}C'_i}$$ (since $C_{i+1} \longrightarrow B_i \longrightarrow 0$).

From (1),(2),(4) and Lemma 10.2 we have

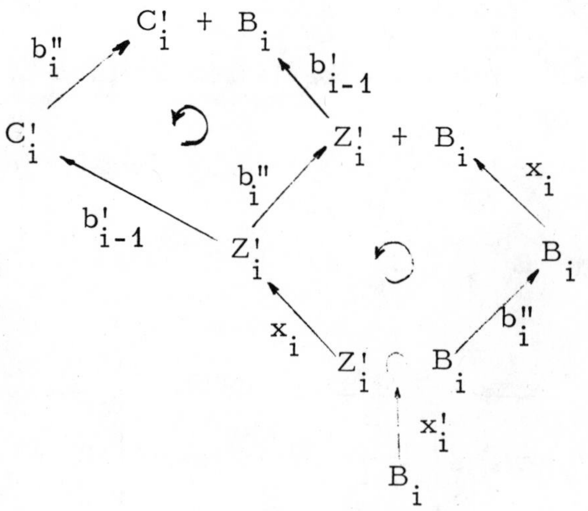

Using (2), (3) and Lemma 10.2, we get

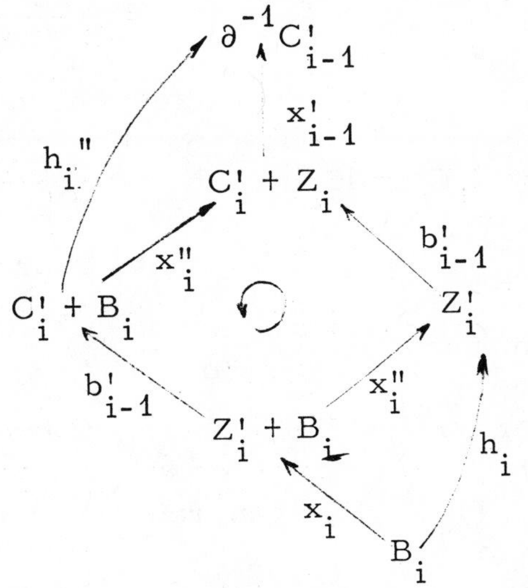

We can choose $b_i = b'_i x'_i b''_i$ so that all the remaining squares and triangles commute. So $c_i \sim b_i h_i b_{i-1}$ and therefore $\tau(C) = 0$. We have now proved

$$\tau(C) = \tau(C') + \tau(C'') + \tau(\mathcal{H}).$$

Now suppose we have a cobordism and add on a whole lot of handles. We will compare the torsion of the resulting cobordism with that of the original one.

<u>Lemma 10.4</u>. Suppose W is a cobordism, $W_1 = W \cup h_1^r \cup \dots \cup h_p^r$. Let $K_0 \subset K$ be a simplicial pair triangulating $W \subset W_1$, $\pi_1(K_0) \cong \pi_1(K)$ and let $\widetilde{K}_0 \subset \widetilde{K}$ be the corresponding universal covers. Now $H_*(\widetilde{K}, \widetilde{K}_0)$ is a free $\mathbb{Z}\Pi$ module with given generators in each dimension. If

(1) Each component of $|K| - |K_0|$ is simply connected, and

(2) Each given generator of $H_*(\widetilde{K}, \widetilde{K}_0)$ is representable by a chain in

one component of $\widetilde{K} - \widetilde{K}_o$, i.e., a chain which is a combination of closed simplexes whose interiors are in one component of K_o,

Then $\tau(K, K_o) = 0$.

Proof. Let $\Gamma_1 \ldots \Gamma_r$ be the connected components of $K - K_o$, let $\widetilde{\Gamma}_1 \ldots \widetilde{\Gamma}_r$ be lifts of $\Gamma_1 \ldots \Gamma_r$. If $b_1 \ldots b_s \in H_*(\widetilde{K}, \widetilde{K}_o)$ are the given generators. let $\xi_1 \ldots \xi_s \in C(\widetilde{K}, \widetilde{K}_o)$ be cycles representing them, each ξ_i is contained in one component of $\widetilde{K} - \widetilde{K}_o$.

Choose $x \in \pi_1$, regarded as a covering transformation so that $x\xi_i$ is contained in one of the $\{\widetilde{\Gamma}_j\}$. The generators $\{x_i b_i\} \in H_*(\widetilde{K}, \widetilde{K}_o)$ are also a free $\mathbb{Z}\Pi$ basis. Moreover, this basis gives rise to the same τ since multiplication by x_i does not alter an element in $Wh(\Pi)$. Choose free $\mathbb{Z}\Pi$ generators of $C_i(\widetilde{K}, \widetilde{K}_o)$ and stably free generators of $B_i(\widetilde{K}, \widetilde{K}_o)$, all lying in one of the $\{\widetilde{\Gamma}_j\}$.

Now all operations done in calculating τ are done with integer coefficients. In fact, $C_i(\widetilde{K}, \widetilde{K}_o) \cong C_i(K, K_o) \otimes_{\mathbb{Z}} \mathbb{Z}\Pi$ where the isomorphism sends generators onto generators. So

$$\tau(K, K_o) \in \mathrm{Im}\{\overline{K}_1(\mathbb{Z}) \longrightarrow \underline{K}_1(\mathbb{Z}\Pi) \longrightarrow Wh(\Pi)\}.$$

But $\overline{K}_1(\mathbb{Z}) = 0$, i.e., every invertible matrix with integer coefficients is equivalent under elementary operations to the identity matrix I. In fact, let M be an $m \times m$ matrix with integer coefficients. First add rows until the smallest non zero element of the first column divides all the elements in the first column (this uses the division algorithm inductively). Cancel out the other elements in the first column. Repeat with the other columns.

So $M = TE$ with T upper triangular and E a product of elementary matrices. Now M invertible implies $\det M = \pm 1$, thus the diagonal elements of T are ± 1. Therefore, we can cancel the upper right hand corner of T by elementary row operations. In $\overline{K}_1$, $\overline{M}$ is then equivalent to I.

<u>Corollary 10.5.</u> Suppose $W_1 = W \cup h_1^r \cup \dots \cup h_p^r$, $W_2 = W_1 \cup k_1^{r+1} \cup \dots \cup k_q^{r+1}$, $r \geq 2$ and $\pi_i(W_2, W) = 0$, all i. Choose generators $\tilde{\xi}_i, \tilde{\eta}_j$ of $H_r(\tilde{h}_i, \tilde{h}_i \cap \tilde{W}) \subset H_r(\tilde{W}_1, \tilde{W})$, $H_{r+1}(k_j, k_j \cap \tilde{W}_1) \subset H_{r+1}(\tilde{W}_2, \tilde{W}_1)$, respectively. Now then, we know that we have a matrix expressing ∂, $\partial \tilde{\eta}_j = \sum_i m_{ji} \tilde{\xi}_i$.

Suppose that W_2 is triangulated with W_1, W as subcomplexes. Then $\tau(W_2, W) = (-1)^r [m_{ji}] \in Wh(\pi_1 W)$.

<u>Proof.</u> We look at the exact sequence of chain complexes

$$0 \to C(\tilde{W}_1, \tilde{W}) \to C(\tilde{W}_2, \tilde{W}) \to C(\tilde{W}_2, \tilde{W}_1) \to 0$$

$$0 \to C' \longrightarrow C \longrightarrow C'' \longrightarrow 0 .$$

By 10.3 and 10.4,

$$\tau(C) = \tau(C') + \tau(C'') + \tau(\mathcal{H}) = 0 + 0 + \tau(\mathcal{H}).$$

For $\mathcal{H}$ we have $0 \to \cdots \to 0 \to H_{r+1}(\tilde{W}_2, \tilde{W}_1) \xrightarrow{\partial} H_r(\tilde{W}_1, \tilde{W}) \to 0 \to \cdots \to 0$ with bases $\{\tilde{\eta}_j\}$ and $\{\tilde{\xi}_i\}$ for the two non zero terms. We write this as

$$\begin{array}{ccccccccc} 0 \longrightarrow & C_{r+1} & \longrightarrow & C_r & \longrightarrow 0 \longrightarrow \cdots \longrightarrow 0 \\ & \tilde{\eta}_j & & \tilde{\xi}_i & \end{array}$$

and split up the sequence, obtaining exact sequences

$$0 \to B_r \to Z_r \to 0 \to 0 \qquad 0 \to Z_r \to C_r \longrightarrow 0 \longrightarrow 0$$

$$0 \to 0 \longrightarrow Z_{r+1} \longrightarrow 0 \longrightarrow 0$$

and so $0 \to Z_{r+1} \to C_{r+1} \to B_r \to 0$ becomes $0 \to 0 \xrightarrow{\partial} \underset{\tilde{\eta}_j}{C_{r+1}} \xrightarrow{\partial} \underset{\tilde{\xi}_i}{B_r} \to 0.$

We compare the new bases with the original one to get

$$(-1)^r [\partial \tilde{\eta} / \tilde{\xi}] = (-1)^r [m_{ji}].$$

To complete the proof that τ is invariant under subdivision we have

Theorem 10. . Let $K_o \subset K$ be simplicial complexes, $\pi_i(K, K_o) = 0$ all i and αK a subdivision of K. Then $\tau(\alpha K, \alpha K_o) = \tau(K, K_o)$.

Proof. Let $L_i = K_o \cup$ i-skeleton of K. Let $\tilde{K}$ be the universal cover of K with the standard triangulation, and let $\tilde{L}_i$ be the cover of L_i in $\tilde{K}$. We consider chain complexes defined as follows:

Let $\overline{C}$ be the chain complex

$$\longrightarrow H_i(\alpha\tilde{L}_i, \alpha\tilde{L}_{i-1}) \xrightarrow{\partial} H_{i-1}(\alpha\tilde{L}_{i-1}, \alpha\tilde{L}_{i-2}) \xrightarrow{\partial} \cdots \to H_o(\alpha\tilde{L}_o, \alpha\tilde{K}_o) \to 0$$

with each term a finitely generated free $Z\Pi$ module. By standard arguments $H(\overline{C}) \approx H(\alpha\tilde{K}, \alpha\tilde{K}_o)$.

Let $\overline{C}_r$ be the chain complex

$$0 \to H_r(\alpha\tilde{L}_r, \alpha\tilde{L}_{r-1}) \xrightarrow{\partial} H_{r-1}(\alpha L_{r-1}, \alpha L_{r-2}) \to \cdots \to H_o(\alpha\tilde{L}_o, \alpha\tilde{K}_o) \to 0$$

with $H(\overline{C}_r) = H(\alpha\tilde{L}_r, \alpha\tilde{K}_o)$.

We shall prove inductively that $\tau(\overline{C}_r) = \tau(\alpha L_r, \alpha K_o)$ in $Wh(\pi)$ with the generators for $\overline{C}_r$ chosen as follows: Given $\sigma^i \in K - L_{i-1}$ let $\tilde{\sigma}^i$ be a lift of σ^i in $\tilde{K}$ and let $\tilde{\xi}_i$ be a generator of $H_i(\alpha\tilde{\sigma}^i, \partial(\alpha\tilde{\sigma}^i)) \subset H_i(\alpha\tilde{L}_i, \alpha\tilde{L}_{i-1})$. This gives a set of free generators for $H_i(\alpha\tilde{L}_i, \alpha\tilde{L}_{i-1})$.

We now pass from L_r to L_{r+1} and look at the exact sequence

$$0 \longrightarrow C(\alpha L_r, \alpha K_o) \longrightarrow C(\alpha L_{r+1}, \alpha K_o) \longrightarrow C(\alpha L_{r+1}, \alpha L_r) \longrightarrow 0 .$$
$$c' \qquad\qquad c \qquad\qquad c''$$

The bases c, c', c'' satisfy the condition $c \sim c'c''$ by the usual definition. So $\tau(\alpha\tilde{L}_{r+1}, \alpha\tilde{K}_o) = \tau(\alpha\tilde{L}_r, \alpha\tilde{K}_o) + \tau(\alpha\tilde{L}_{r+1}, \alpha\tilde{L}_r) + \tau(\mathcal{H})$. The homology exact sequence $\mathcal{H}$ is

$$0 \longrightarrow H_{r+1}(\alpha\tilde{L}_{r+1}, \alpha\tilde{K}_o) \longrightarrow H_{r+1}(\alpha\tilde{L}_{r+1}, \alpha\tilde{L}_r) \longrightarrow H_r(\alpha\tilde{L}_r, \alpha\tilde{K}_o) \longrightarrow 0 .$$

For the sequence $\overline{C}$, we have

$$0 \longrightarrow \overline{C}_r \longrightarrow \overline{C}_{r+1} \longrightarrow \overline{C}_{r+1}/\overline{C}_r \longrightarrow 0 ,$$

but $\overline{C}_{r+1}/\overline{C}_r$ is zero except for a group in dimension $(r+1)$ and we have $\tau(\overline{C}_{r+1}) = \tau(\overline{C}_r) + \tau(\overline{C}_{r+1}/\overline{C}_r) + \tau(\overline{\mathcal{H}})$ where $\overline{\mathcal{H}}$ is the exact sequence

$$0 \longrightarrow H_{r+1}(\overline{C}_{r+1}) \longrightarrow H_{r+1}(\overline{C}_{r+1}/\overline{C}_r) \xrightarrow{\partial} H_r(\overline{C}_r) \longrightarrow 0$$

By the inductive hypothesis $\tau(\alpha\tilde{L}_r, \alpha\tilde{K}_o) = \tau(\overline{C}_r)$. Recall that $H_*(\overline{C}_r) = H_*(\alpha\tilde{L}_r, \alpha\tilde{K}_o)$ where the generators are chosen to corresponds under the natural isomorphism. Further, $H_{r+1}(\overline{C}_{r+1}/\overline{C}_r)$ can be calculated from the chain complex $0 \longrightarrow H_{r+1}(\alpha\tilde{L}_{r+1}, \alpha\tilde{L}_r) \longrightarrow 0$. So $\mathcal{H}$, $\overline{\mathcal{H}}$ are isomorphic by an isomorphism sending generators to generators.

Now since the chain complex $0 \longrightarrow H_{r+1}(\alpha\tilde{L}_{r+1}, \alpha\tilde{L}_r) \longrightarrow 0$ is trivial, $\tau(\overline{C}_{r+1}/\overline{C}_r) = 0$. All we need to prove to show the inductive step is that $\tau(\alpha\tilde{L}_{r+1}, \alpha\tilde{L}_r) = 0$ using the generators already chosen for $C(\alpha\tilde{L}_{r+1}, \alpha\tilde{L}_r)$, $H\ (\alpha\tilde{L}_{r+1}, \alpha\tilde{L}_r)$. This follows from Lemma 10.4 since $|\alpha L_{r+1}| - |\alpha L_r|$ is the disjoint union of simply connected sets.

Starting the induction with $L_{-1} = K_o$, we have proved $\tau(\alpha K, \alpha K_o) = \tau(\overline{C})$. Now

$$\begin{array}{llll} \overline{C}: & \to H_{r+1}(\alpha\tilde{L}_{r+1}, \alpha\tilde{L}_r) & \xrightarrow{\partial} & H_r(\alpha\tilde{L}_r, \alpha\tilde{L}_{r-1}) \to \cdots \\ & \quad \wr\!\| \alpha & & \quad \wr\!\| \alpha \\ & \to C_{r+1}(K, K_o) & \longrightarrow & C_r(K, K_o) \longrightarrow \end{array}$$

where $\alpha\tilde{\sigma}$ ($\tilde{\sigma}$ a lift of an $(r+1)$ simplex of $K - K_o$), is a generator of $H_{r+1}(\alpha\tilde{\sigma}, \partial(\alpha\tilde{\sigma}))$.

So $\overline{C} = C(K, K_o)$ by an isomorphism sending the generator suitably. Therefore $\tau(\overline{C}) = \tau(K, K_o)$.

We introduce the notation $\tau(W) = \tau(W, \partial_- W)$.

Lemma 10.7. Let W_1, W_2 be h-cobordisms with $\partial_+ W_1 \overset{h}{\cong} \partial_- W_2$, h a simplicial homeomorphism. Let $W = W_1 \cup_h W_2$.

Then $\tau(W) = \tau(W_1) + \tau(W_2)$.

Proof. We have the exact sequence of chain groups

$$0 \to C(\tilde{W}_1, \partial_- \tilde{W}_1) \to C(\tilde{W}, \partial_- \tilde{W}_1) \longrightarrow C(\tilde{W}, \tilde{W}_1) \longrightarrow 0$$
$$C(\tilde{W}, \tilde{W}_1) \cong C(\tilde{W}_2, \partial_- \tilde{W}_2) .$$

Now the homology exact sequence is zero, so

$$\tau(W, \partial_- W) = \tau(W_1, \partial_- W_1) + \tau(W_2, \partial_- W_2).$$

Lemma 10.8. $\tau(M \times I, M \times 0) = 0$.

Proof. Put $W_1 = W_2 = M \times I$ in 10.7. Then

$$\tau(M \times I) = \tau(M \times I) + \tau(M \times I).$$

Lemma 10.9. If $K_o \subset K_1 \subset K_2$ are complexes, $\pi_i(K_1, K_o) = 0$, all i and $K_2 \searrow K_1$, then $\tau(K_2, K_o) = \tau(K_1, K_o)$.

Proof. Suppose $K_2 \searrow K_1$ by one elementary polyhedral collapse, so $\overline{K_2 - K_1}$ is a PL ball B^r say, with $B^r \cap K_1$ a face F of B, and $(\overline{K_2 - K_1}, \overline{K_2 - K_1} \cap K_1) \cong (F \times I, F \times 0)$.

We have the exact sequence

$$0 \longrightarrow C(\tilde{K}_1, \tilde{K}_o) \longrightarrow C(\tilde{K}_2, \tilde{K}_o) \longrightarrow C(\tilde{K}_2, \tilde{K}_1) \longrightarrow 0.$$

These complexes have zero homology, so

$$\tau(K_2, K_o) = \tau(K_1, K_o) + \tau(K_2, K_1).$$

Now $K_2 - K_1$ is simply connected so by Lemma 10.4, $\tau(K_2, K_1) = 0$.

Lemma 10.10. If $n \geq 6$, W^n is an h-cobordism, then

$$W \cong \partial_- W \times I \quad \text{if and only if} \quad \tau(W) = 0.$$

Proof. Certainly by 10.8, $W \cong \partial_- W \times I$ implies $\tau(W) = 0$. By §§7, 8 if $n \geq 6$ and W is an h-cobordism, $W \cong (\partial_- W \times I) \cup$ r-handles $\cup$ (r+1) handles with $2 \leq r \leq n-4$. In §9, we showed how to cancel these handles if the matrix representing the boundary map $H_{r+1}(\tilde{W}_2, \tilde{W}_1) \longrightarrow H_r(\tilde{W}_1, \tilde{W})$ from the homology of the (r+1) handles to the homology of the r-handles was equivalent to zero in $Wh(\pi)$. We have now shown (10.5, 10.6) that the equivalence class of this matrix is $\tau(W, \partial_- W)$.

Lemma 10.11. If $n \geq 6$, W^n is an h-cobordism, then $W \cong \partial_- W \times I$ if and only if there is a PL space X with $W \subset X$, $X \searrow W$ and $X \searrow \partial_- W$.

Proof. $W \cong \partial_- W \times I$ implies $W \searrow \partial_- W$. If $W \subset X \searrow W$, $X \searrow \partial_- W$, then $\tau(W, \partial_- W) = \tau(X, \partial_- W) = \tau(\partial_- W, \partial_- W) = 0$ by 10.9, and so $W \cong \partial_- W \times I$ by 10.10.

§11. How many handles do we need in the case of an h-cobordism with non zero torsion?

Theorem 11.1. Let W^n be an h-cobordism, $n \geq 6$. Given r, $2 \leq r \leq n-4$, let $j_p : GL_p(\mathbb{Z}\pi_1(W)) \longrightarrow Wh(\pi_1(W))$. Then $W \cong \partial_- W \times I \cup p$ r-handles $\cup$ p (r+1)-handles if and only if $\tau(W) \in \operatorname{Im} j_p$.

Proof. We know $W \cong (\partial_- W \times I) \cup h_1^r \cup \ldots \cup h_q^r \cup k_1^{r+1} \cup \ldots \cup k_q^{r+1}$. Let $\tilde{h}_i, \tilde{k}_j$ be lifts of h_i, k_j; let $\tilde{\xi}_i, \tilde{\eta}_j$ genrate $H_r(\tilde{h}_i, \tilde{h}_i \cap \partial_- W \times I)$, $H_{r+1}(\tilde{k}_j, \tilde{k}_j \cap \tilde{W}_i)$ respectively.

With $W_1 = (\partial_- W \times I) \cup h_1^r \cup \ldots \cup h_q^r$, $\partial : H_{r+1}(\tilde{W}, \tilde{W}_1) \longrightarrow H_r(\tilde{W}_1, \partial_- W \times I)$ given by $\partial \tilde{\eta}_j = \sum \lambda_{ij} \tilde{\xi}$, we know $[\lambda_{ij}] = \tau(W) \in Wh(\pi)$. Thus $q \leq p$ implies $\tau(W) \in \operatorname{Im} j_p$.

Now if $\tau \in \operatorname{Im} j_p$ there is an $M \in GL_p$ such that for some N,

$$\begin{bmatrix} [\lambda_{ij}] & 0 \\ 0 & I_{N-q} \end{bmatrix} = \begin{bmatrix} M & 0 \\ 0 & I_{N-p} \end{bmatrix} EU$$

where E is a product of elementary matrices and

$$U = \begin{bmatrix} \pm x_1 & & 0 \\ & \pm x_2 & \\ 0 & & \ddots \end{bmatrix}$$

with $x_i \in \Pi$.

We first add $N-q$ complementary pairs of r, $(r+1)$ handles. By altering the choice of the generators $\tilde{\xi}_i, \tilde{\eta}_j$ we can get the matrix representing the new handlebody decomposition equal to $\begin{bmatrix} M & 0 \\ 0 & I_{n-p} \end{bmatrix}$ E. Sliding the $(r+1)$ handles over each other according to the handle addition theorem we can find a new handlebody decomposition of W with matrix $\begin{bmatrix} M & 0 \\ 0 & I_{N-p} \end{bmatrix}$.

So $W \cong (\partial_- W \times I) \cup N$ r-handles $\cup N$ $(r+1)$ handles and the a-spheres of the last $N-q$ $(r+1)$ handles cut the b-spheres of the last $N-q$ r-handles algebraically once. Thus we can arrange that they intersect transversely in one point. So we can cancel the last $N-p$ $(r+1)$- and r-handles.

Note that $\operatorname{Im} j_1 = 0$ and $\bigcup_p \operatorname{Im} j_p = Wh(\Pi)$.

Suppose now that W is a cobordism, $\pi_1(W) = \pi_1(\partial_- W) = \pi_1(\partial_+ W)$ by the natural inclusions, $3 \leq r \leq n-3$, and $H_i(\tilde{W}, \partial_- \tilde{W}) = 0$ for $i \neq r$ and free of rank p as a $\mathbb{Z}\Pi$ module if $i = r$.

Given a free basis for $H_r(\tilde{W}, \partial_- \tilde{W})$ we can define $\tau(W)$. Altering this free basis of $H_r(\tilde{W}, \partial_- \tilde{W})$ adds an element of $\operatorname{Im} j_p$ to $\tau(W)$. So we can define $\tau(W) \in Wh(\Pi)/\operatorname{Im} j_p$.

<u>Theorem 11.2</u>. $W \cong (\partial_- W \times I) \cup p$ r-handles if and only if $\tau = 0$. Thus τ is an obstruction whose vanishing implies we can eliminate all but the r-handles.

<u>Proof</u>. We know $W \cong (\partial_- W \times I) \cup (r-1)$ handles $\cup$ r-handles. Let $W_o = \partial_- W \times I$, $W_1 = W_o \cup h_1^{r+1} \cup \dots \cup h_s^{r-1}$ and

$W_2 = W_1 \cup k_1^r \cup \ldots \cup k_t^r \quad (W_2 \cong W)$.

Choose generators for $H_r(\widetilde{W}, \partial_- \widetilde{W}) \cong H_r(W_2, W_0)$, so τ is defined in $Wh(\Pi)$. Then $\tau(W_2, W_0) = \tau(W_1, W_0) + \tau(W_2, W_1) + \tau(\mathcal{H})$ where $\mathcal{H}$ is the homology exact sequence

$$0 \longrightarrow H_r(\widetilde{W}_2, \widetilde{W}_0) \xrightarrow{i} H_r(\widetilde{W}_2, \widetilde{W}_1) \xrightarrow{\partial} H_{r-1}(W_1, W_0) \longrightarrow 0.$$

Let $\widetilde{\xi}, \widetilde{\eta}$ be bases for $H_{r-1}(\widetilde{W}_1, \widetilde{W}_0)$, $H_r(\widetilde{W}_2, \widetilde{W}_1)$ respectively, chosen by lifting the handles in the usual way. Then $\tau(W_1, W_0) = \tau(W_2, W_1) = 0$, by Lemma 10.4.

Let h be chosen a basis for $H_r(\widetilde{W}_2, \widetilde{W}_0)$, $\widetilde{\xi}'$ a lift of the basis $\widetilde{\xi}$ back into $H_r(W_2, W_1)$. If $h' = ih$, $(h', \widetilde{\xi}')$ form a basis for $H_r(W_2, W_1)$.

Write $\widetilde{\eta} = M(h', \widetilde{\xi}')$ where M is an invertible $t \times t$ matrix over Π and $[M] = \pm\tau$ in $Wh(\Pi)$. Now write $\partial\widetilde{\eta}_j = \sum_i \lambda_{ji} \widetilde{\xi}_i$, i.e., $\partial\widetilde{\eta} = B\widetilde{\xi}$ where B is a $t \times s$ matrix over $\mathbb{Z}\Pi$. Since $t > s$, $M = (A, B)$ with A a $t \times p$ matrix.

Now $\tau(W_2, W_0) \in \operatorname{Im} j_p$ if and only if for some N,

$$\begin{bmatrix} M & 0 \\ 0 & I_{N-t} \end{bmatrix} = EU \begin{bmatrix} M' & 0 \\ 0 & I_{N-p} \end{bmatrix}$$

where M' is $p \times p$, E is the product of elementary matrices and $U = \begin{bmatrix} \pm x_1 & & 0 \\ & \pm x_2 & \\ 0 & & \ddots \end{bmatrix}$, $x_i \in \pi_1$. So

$$\begin{bmatrix} M & 0 \\ 0 & I_{n-t} \end{bmatrix} \text{ can be converted to } \begin{bmatrix} M' & 0 \\ 0 & I_{N-p} \end{bmatrix}$$ by the elementary row

operations:

(1) permuting rows ,

(2) multiplying a row by $\pm x$ with $x \in \pi_1$,

(3) adding one row to another .

Notice that B is given by the last columns of M, and row operations do not confuse the columns. Thus, by elementary row operations

$$\begin{bmatrix} M & 0 \\ 0 & I_{n-t} \end{bmatrix} = \begin{bmatrix} A & B & 0 \\ 0 & 0 & I_{n-t} \end{bmatrix} \longrightarrow \begin{bmatrix} M' & 0 \\ 0 & I_{n-p} \end{bmatrix}$$

p columns

and so $\begin{bmatrix} B & 0 \\ 0 & I_{N-t} \end{bmatrix}$ can be converted to $\begin{bmatrix} 0 \\ I_{n-p} \end{bmatrix}$.

Recall $\partial \tilde{\eta} = B\tilde{\xi}$. Add in N-t pairs of complementary (r-1)- and r-handles, so B will be replaced by $\begin{bmatrix} B & 0 \\ 0 & I_{N-t} \end{bmatrix}$. Now each row operation of type (1) or (2) on $\begin{bmatrix} B & 0 \\ 0 & I_{N-t} \end{bmatrix}$ can be effected by altering the choice of generators $\tilde{\eta}$, either by permuting , altering sign or translating by a covering transformation. Type (3) row operations are effected by altering the handle body decomposition by handle addition.

So we get $\mathbf{W} \cong W_2'$ with $W_1' = W_o \cup h_1^{r-1}{}' \cup \ldots \cup h_{N-p}^{r-1}{}'$ and $W_2' = W_1' \cup k_1^r{}' \cup \ldots \cup k_N^r{}'$ where $\partial: (\tilde{W}_2', \tilde{W}_1') \longrightarrow H_{r-1}(\tilde{W}_1', \tilde{W}_o)$ is represented by $\begin{bmatrix} 0 \\ I_{N-p} \end{bmatrix}$. Then we may cancel the last (N-p) r-handles with the (r-1) handles.

This proves the first part of the theorem. The converse follows from a previous argument.

We now look at duality. If we have a cobordism and turn it over, what effect is there on the torsion?

Suppose $W_o = \partial_- W \times I$, $W_1 = W_o \cup h_1^r \cup \ldots \cup h_p^r$ and $W_2 = W_1 \cup k_1^{r+1} \cup \ldots \cup k_p^{r+1}$ is an h-cobordism W. Suppose to start that W is <u>orientable</u>.

To get the torsion we choose generators $\tilde{\xi}_i, \tilde{\eta}_j$ of $H_r(\tilde{W}_1, \tilde{W}_o)$, $H_{r+1}(\tilde{W}_2, \tilde{W}_1)$ respectively and look at the boundary map $\partial \tilde{\eta}_j = \sum_i a_x x$, where a_x = algebraic intersection of $\tilde{S}_j^a$ with $x\tilde{S}_i^b$. $\tilde{S}_j^a$ = a-sphere of $\tilde{k}_j$, $x\tilde{S}_i^b$ = b-sphere of $x\tilde{h}_i$ (17).

(FIGURE 17 WITH ACCOMPANYING TEXT IS ON NEXT PAGE)

(17)

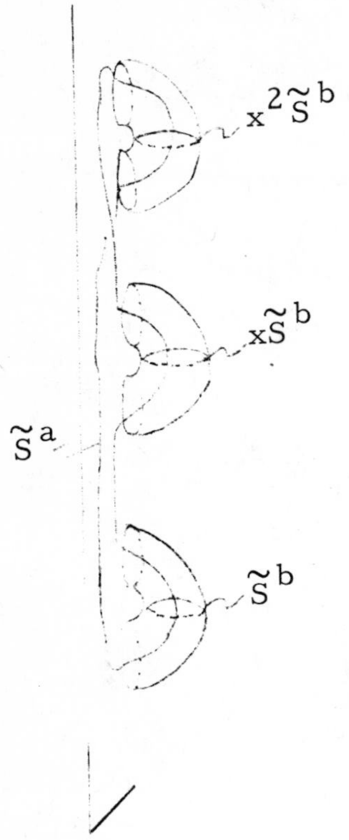

$(\lambda = 1 + x - x^2)$

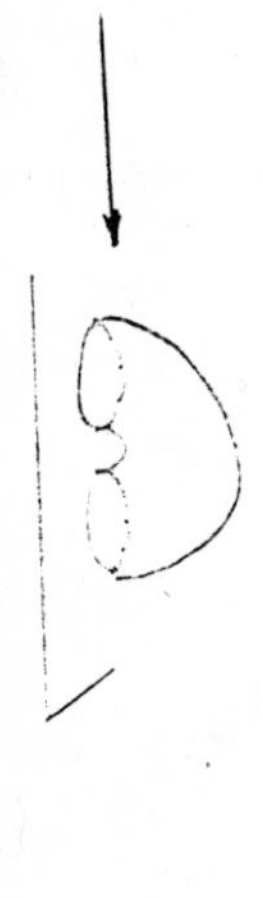

If we turn the whole picture around, the a-spheres become b-spheres and the b-spheres become a-spheres. So the torsion is given by a matrix λ'_{ij}, $\lambda'_{ij} = \sum_{x \in \pi_1} a'_x x$, where a'_x = algebriac intersection of $\tilde{S}^b_i$ with $x\tilde{S}^a_j$ = algebraic intersection of $x^{-1}\tilde{S}^b_i$ with $\tilde{S}^a_j$.

So $\tau(W, \partial_+ W) = (-1)^{n-1} \phi\, \tau(W, \partial_- W)$, where ϕ: $Wh(\Pi) \longrightarrow Wh(\Pi)$ sends M into its transpose conjugate, with conjugation in $\mathbb{Z}\Pi$ induced by sending $x \longrightarrow x^{-1}$. ϕ induces an anti homomorphism $GL_n(\mathbb{Z}\Pi) \longrightarrow GL_n(\mathbb{Z}\Pi)$ and so induces a homomorphism $Wh(\Pi) \longrightarrow Wh(\Pi)$, since $Wh(\Pi)$ is abelian.

In the non orientable case we define $\alpha: \mathbb{Z}\Pi \longrightarrow \mathbb{Z}\Pi$ by $x \longrightarrow x^{-1}$ if x is orientation preserving and $x \longrightarrow -x^{-1}$ if x is orientation reversing. This induces a map ϕ': $Wh(\Pi) \longrightarrow Wh(\Pi)$ and we get $\tau(W, \partial_+ W) = (-1)^{n-1} \phi'\, \tau(W, \partial_- W)$.

§12. h-cobordisms with given torsion.

Theorem 12.1. If M is a compact connected PL manifold of dimension ≥ 5, given any element $\tau \in Wh(\pi_1(M))$, there is an h-cobordism W with $\partial_- W \cong M$ and $\tau(W) = \tau$.

Theorem 12.2. If W_1, W_2 are h-cobordisms of dimension ≥ 6, $\partial_- W_1 \cong \partial_- W_2$ and $\tau(W_1) = \tau(W_2)$ then $W_1 \cong W_2$.

Proof that 12.1 implies 12.2. Choose W with $\partial_- W = \partial_+ W$ and $\tau(W) = -\tau(W_1)$. Then by 10.7, $\tau(W \cup W_1) = 0$. So $W \cup W_1 \cong \partial_- W_1 \times I$ and $\partial_+ W \cong \partial_- W_1 \cong \partial_- W_2$. So form $W_3 = W_1 \cup W \cup W_2$

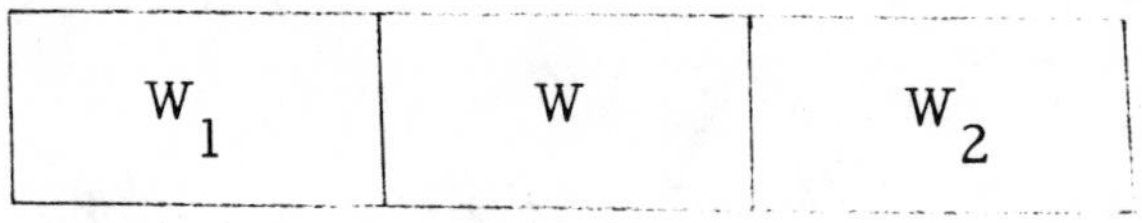

$\tau(W \cup W_2) = 0$. So $W \cup W_2 \cong \partial_- W \times I$. So $W_1 \cong W_1 \cup (\partial_+ W_1 \times I) \cong W_3 \cong (\partial_- W_2 \times I) \cup W_2 \cong W_2$.

In order to prove Theorem 12.1 we first need a lemma:

Lemma 12.3. If M^m is a PL man ifold, let $i, j: S^2 \times B^{m-2} \longrightarrow M$ be disjoint PL embeddings representing elements $\xi, \eta \in \pi_2 M$. If $\omega \in \pi_1(M)$, there is a PL embedding $k: S^2 \times B^{m-2} \longrightarrow M$ representing the element $\xi + \eta^\omega \in \pi_2 M$.

Proof. Let $x \in S^2$, $y \in \partial B^{m-2}$, let P be a PL path in M from $i(x, y)$ to $j(x, y)$ not meeting $\text{Im}(i)$ or $\text{Im}(j)$ again. Let N be a second derived neighborhood of P in $cl[M - \text{Im}\, i - \text{Im}\, j]$.

The choice of the path P will determine the element ω. By the uniqueness of regular neighborhoods we may assume that $i^{-1}N = j^{-1}N = U \times V$, where U is a regular neighborhood of x in S^2 and V is a regular neighborhood of y in ∂B^{m-2}. Now the embeddings $i|U \times V: U \times V \longrightarrow \partial N$, $j|U \times V: U \times V \longrightarrow \partial N$ are ambient isotopic to "standard" ones, since any two orientation preserving embeddings of a PL ball in a connected manifold of the same dimension are isotopic. So there is a PL homeomorphism $h: N \longrightarrow U \times V \times I$ with $hi|U \times V: U \times V \longrightarrow U \times V \times 0$, $hj|U \times V: U \times V \longrightarrow U \times V \times 1$ equal to the natural identifications. Now consider B^{m-2} as $B^1 \times B^{m-3}$, with the point y lying in $\partial B^1 \times 0$, and take $V = V_1 \times V_2$, where V_1 is a regular neighborhood of y in ∂B^1, and V_2 is a regular neighborhood of 0 in B^{m-3}. Then there is a PL embedding $\alpha: \mathrm{Im}\, i \cup \mathrm{Im}\, j \cup N \longrightarrow R^m$ such that $\alpha[i(S^2 \times B^1) \cup j(S^2 \times B^1) \cup h^{-1}(U \times V_1 \times I)]$ lies in R^3.

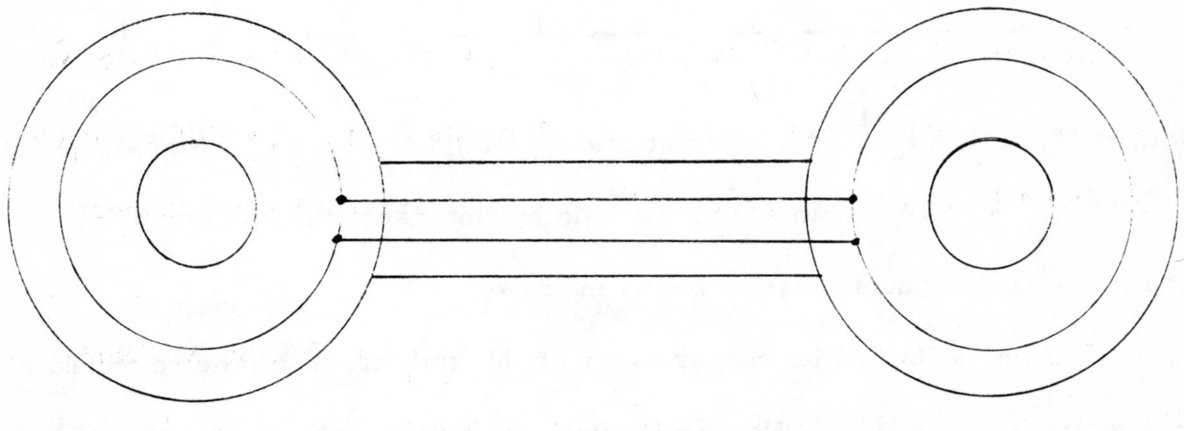

If V_1' is a regular neighborhood of y inside V_1, let

$$\Sigma = i(\overline{S^2 \times 0) - V_1'} \cup i(\dot{V}_1' \times 0y) \cup h^{-1}(\dot{V}_1' \times I) \cup j(\dot{V}_1' \times 0y) \cup j\ \overline{S^2 \times 0 - V_1'}$$

where 0y denotes the segment of B' from 0 to y. Then $\alpha\Sigma$ has a product neighborhood R^3 and so in R^m, so Σ has a product neighborhood in M. Σ will represent $\xi + \eta^\omega$ provided we choose a suitable path P.

Proof of Theorem 12.1. Given M and $\tau \in Wh(\pi_1(M))$. Represent τ by a matrix $A \in GL_p(\mathbb{Z}\pi_1)$ for some p. Let $T_i \cong S^2 \times B^{m-1}$ for $i = 1, 2, \dots, p$. Let W_1 be formed by taking $(M \times I) \cup \bigcup_1^p T_i$ and attaching p 1-handles, $h_1, \dots, h_p$, where h_i connects T_i to $(M \times I)$.

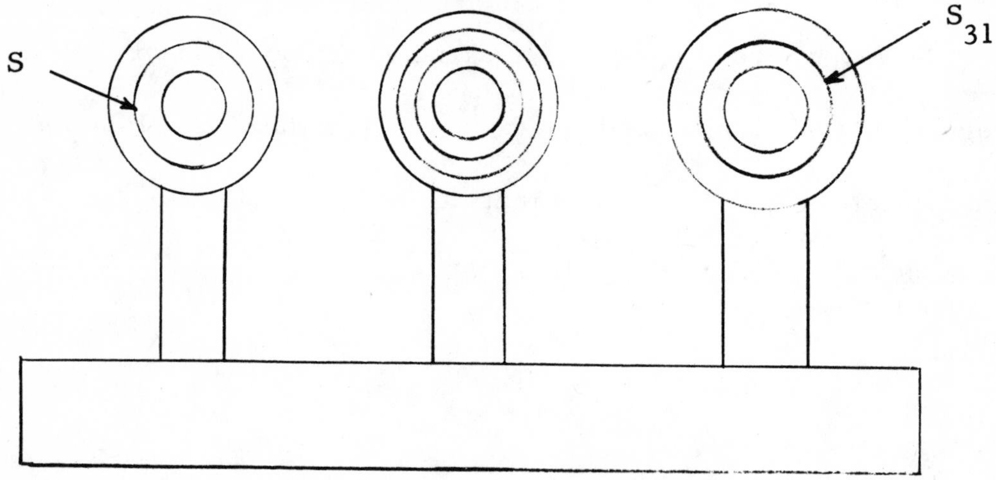

Now in $T_i \cong S^2 \times B^{m-1}$, choose a set of disjoint spheres $S_{ij} = S^2 \times x_{ij}$, $x_{ij} \in \partial B^m$. We may assume that these do not intersect the handles $h_1, \dots, h_p$. These all have product neighborhoods in $\partial_+ W_1$.

Now let $\widetilde{M}$ be the universal cover of M and let $\widetilde{W}$ be the corresponding covering space of W. Now every element of $H_2(\widetilde{W}, \widetilde{M} \times 0)$ can be represented by a 2-sphere in $\partial_+ W$ formed by piping together a finite number of the spheres S_{ij} in accordance with Lemma 12.3. Let ξ_i generate $H_2(T_i)$, $\tilde{\xi}_i$ generate $H_2(\tilde{T}_i)$, where $\tilde{T}_i$ is a lift of T_i in $\tilde{W}$.

If the matrix $A = (a_{ij})$, we can find, as above, disjoint PL embeddings $\alpha_i : S^2 \times B^{m-2} \longrightarrow \partial_+ W_1$ $i = 1, 2, \ldots, p$, representing the homology classes $\sum_{j=1}^{p} a_{ij} \tilde{\xi}_j$. Attaching 2-handles by these maps gives rise to the required h-cobordism W with torsion τ.

BIBLIOGRAPHY

Alexander, J. W. On the deformation of the n-cell. **Proc. nat. Acad. Sci., Wash., 9** (1923), 406-407.

— On the subdivision of space by a polyhedron. **Proc. nat. Acad. Sci., Wash., 10** (1924), 6-8.

— The combinatorial theory of complexes. **Ann. Math., 30** (1930), 292-320.

Armstrong, M. A. Transversality for polyhedra. **Ann. Math., 86** (1967), 172-191.

— Extending triangulations. **Proc. Amer. math. Soc., 18** (1967), 701-704.

— and Zeeman, E. C. Piecewise linear transversality. **Bull. Amer. math. Soc., 73** (1967), 184-188.

— — Transversality for piecewise linear manifolds. **Topology, 6** (1967), 433-466.

Barden, D. The structure of manifolds. Doctoral thesis, Cambridge University (1963).

Brown, M. A proof of the generalised Schoenflies theorem. **Bull. Amer. math. Soc., 66** (1960), 74-76.

— The monotone union of open n-cells. **Proc. Amer. math. Soc., 12** (1961), 812-814.

— Locally flat embeddings of topological manifolds. **Ann. Math., 75** (1962), 334-341.

Cohen, M. M. A proof of Newman's theorem. **Proc. Camb. phil. Soc.** (to appear).

Curtis, M. L. and Zeeman, E. C. On the polyhedral Schoenflies theorem. **Proc. Amer. math. Soc., 11** (1960), 888-889.

Gugenheim, V. K. A. M. Piecewise linear isotopies and embeddings of elements and spheres. **Proc. Lond. math. Soc.**, 3, 3 (1953), 29-53.

Haefliger, A. Plongements différentiables de variétés dans variétés. **Comment. math. Helv.**, **36** (1961), 47-82.

— Differentiable embeddings. **Bull. Amer. math. Soc.**, **67** (1961), 109-112.

— Knotted (4k-1)-spheres in 6k-space. **Ann. Math.**, **73**, (1963), 501-526.

— and Hirsch, M. W. Existence and classification of differentiable embeddings. **Topology**, 2 (1963), 129-135.

— and Poenaru, V. La classification des immersions combinatoires. **Pub. I. H. E. S., Paris**, **23** (1964), 651-667.

— and Wall, C. T. C. Piecewise linear bundles in the stable range. **Topology**, **4** (1965), 209-214.

Hilton, P. T. and Wylie, S. **Homology Theory**. Cambridge University Press (1960).

Hirsch, M. W. On embedding differentiable manifolds in euclidean space. **Ann. Math.**, **73** (1961), 566-571.

— On combinatorial submanifolds of differentiable manifolds. **Comment. math. Helv.**, **36** (1962), 103-111.

— Smooth regular neighbourhoods. **Ann. Math.**, **76** (1962), 524-530.

— On embedding 4-manifolds in $\mathbb{R}^7$. **Proc. Camb. phil. Soc.**, **61** (1965), 657-658.

— and Zeeman, E. C. Engulfing. **Bull. Amer. math. Soc.**, **72** (1966), 113-115.

Hudson, J. F. P. Piecewise linear embeddings and isotopies. **Bull. Amer. math. Soc.**, **72** (1963), 536-537.

— Knotted Tori. **Topology**, **2** (1963), 11-22.

— A non-embedding theorem. **Topology**, **2** (1963), 123-128.

Hudson, J. F. P. Concordance and isotopy of PL manifolds. **Bull. Amer. math. Soc., 72** (1966), 534-535.

— Extending piecewise linear isotopies. **Proc. Lond. math. Soc.**, 3, 16 (1966), 651-668.

— Piecewise linear embeddings. **Ann. Math., 85** (1967), 1-31.

— and Zeeman, E. C. On regular neighbourhoods. [And correction.] **Proc. Lond. math. Soc.**, 3, 43 (1964), 719-745. [Correction to appear.]

— — On combinatorial isotopy. **Pub. I. H. E. S., 19** (1964), 69-94.

Irwin, M. C. Embeddings of polyhedral manifolds. **Ann. Math., 82** (1965), 1-14.

Kervaire, M. A. A manifold which does not admit any differentiable structure. **Comment. math. Helv., 34** (1960), 257-270.

— Le théorème de Barden-Mazur-Stallings. **Comment. math. Helv., 40** (1965), 31-42.

Levine, J. Unknotting homology spheres in codimension 2. **Topology, 4** (1965), 9-16.

Lickorish, W. B. R. A representation of orientable combinatorial 3-manifolds. **Ann. Math., 76** (1962), 531-540.

— The piecewise linear unknotting of cones. **Topology, 4** (1965), 67-91.

Mazur, B. Relative neighbourhoods and the theorems of Smale. **Ann. Math., 77** (1963), 232-249.

Milnor, J. On manifolds homeomorphic to S^7. **Ann. Math., 64** (1956), 399-405.

— A procedure for killing the homotopy groups of differentiable manifolds. **A. M. S. Symposium in Pure Mathematics, 3** (1961), 39-55.

— Two complexes which are homeomorphic but combinatorially distinct. **Ann. Math., 74** (1961), 575-590.

Milnor, J. Whitehead torsion. **Bull. Amer. math. Soc.**, 72 (1966), 358-426.

Newman, M. H. A. On the foundations of combinatorial analysis situs. **Akad. Wer., Amsterdam, 29** (1926), 611-641.

— On the superposition of n-dimensional manifolds. **J. Lond. math. Soc. 2** (1926), 56-64.

— On the division of Euclidean n-space by topological n-1 spheres. **Proc. Roy. Soc.**, **257** (1960), 1-12.

Penrose, R., Whitehead, J. H. C. and Zeeman, E. C. Imbedding of manifolds in euclidean space. **Ann. Math.**, **73** (1961), 613-623.

Rourke, C. P. and Sanderson, B. J. An embedding without a normal micro-bundle. **Invent. Math.**, **3** (1967), 293-299.

— — Blockbundles: I, II & III. **Ann. Math.**, **87** (1968), 1-28, 255-277, 431-483.

Scott, A. Infinite regular neighbourhoods. **J. Lond. math. Soc.**, **42** (1963), 245-253.

Shapiro, A. Obstructions to the embedding of a complex in euclidean space. **Ann. Math.**, **66** (1957), 256-269.

Smale, S. Generalised Poincaré conjecture in dimensions greater than four. **Ann. Math.**, **74** (1961), 391-406.

— Differentiable and combinatorial structures on manifolds. **Ann. Math.**, **74** (1961), 498-502.

— On the structure of manifolds. **Amer. J. Math.**, **84** (1962), 387-399.

Stallings, T. Polyhedral homotopy spheres. **Bull. Amer. math. Soc.**, **66** (1960), 485-488.

— The piecewise linear structure of euclidean space. **Proc. Camb. phil. Soc.**, **58** (1962), 481-488.

— On topologically unknotted spheres. **Ann. Math.**, **77** (1963), 490-503.

Tindall, R. A counter-example on relative regular neighbourhoods. **Bull. Amer. math. Soc.**, **72** (1966), 894-897.

Wall, C. T. C. Classification problems of differential topology: IV. **Topology**, **5** (1966), 73-94.

— On PL submanifolds of codimension 2. **Proc. Camb. phil. Soc.**, **63** (1967), 5-8.

Weber, C. Plongements de polyhèdres dans le domaine metastable. Doctoral Thesis, Geneva (1967).

Whitehead, J. H. C. On subdivisions of complexes. **Proc. Camb. phil. Soc.**, **31** (1935), 69-75.

— Simplicial spaces, nuclei and m-groups. **Proc. Lond. math. Soc.**, **45** (1939), 243-327.

— On C^1 complexes. **Ann. Math.**, **41** (1940), 809-824.

— Simple homotopy types. **Amer. J. Math.**, **72** (1940), 1-57.

Williamson, R. E. Cobordism and combinatorial manifolds. **Ann. Math.**, **83** (1966), 1-33.

Zeeman, E. C. The generalised Poincaré conjecture. **Bull. Amer. math. Soc.**, **67** (1961), 270.

— Isotopies of manifolds;
Polyhedral manifolds;
The Poincaré conjecture for $n \geq 5$;
Topology of 3-manifolds (Ed.; M. K. Fort), Prentice Hall (1962).

— Seminar on combinatorial topology. (Mimeographed notes.) **I. H. E. S., Paris** (1963).

— Unknotting combinatorial balls. **Ann. Math.**, **78** (1963), 501-526.

— On the dunce hat. **Topology**, **2** (1964), 341-358.

— Relative simplicial approximation. **Proc. Camb. phil. Soc.**, **10** (1964), 39-43.